JIGS AND FIXTURES

Third Edition

Jigs and Fixtures

Third Edition

P H Joshi

Consultant
Production Engineering Services
Pune

Tata McGraw Hill Education Private Limited
NEW DELHI

McGraw-Hill Offices

New Delhi New York St Louis San Franscisco Auckland Bogotá
Caracas Kuala Lumpur Lisbon Madrid Mexico City Milan Montreal
San Juan Santiago Singapore Sydney Tokyo Toronto

Published by Tata McGraw Hill Education Private Limited,
7 West Patel Nagar, New Delhi 110 008.

ISBN (13): 978-1-25-906122-6
ISBN (10): 1-25-906122-1

Vice President and Managing Director—Asia-Pacific Region: *Ajay Shukla*
Executive Publisher—Professional: *R Chandra Sekhar*
Assistant Sponsoring Editor—S & T: *Simanta Borah*
Manager—Production: *Sohan Gaur*
Manager—Sales and Marketing: *S Girish*
Deputy Marketing Manager—Science, Technology & Computing: *Rekha Dhyani*
General Manager—Production: *Rajender P Ghansela*
Assistant General Manager—Production: *B L Dogra*

Typeset at DigiConv Technologies, J-6, Street No. 3, Near Vijay Chowk, Laxmi Nagar, Delhi 110 092, and printed at Gopsons, A – 2 & 3, Sector – 64, Noida, U.P. – 201 301.

Cover Printer: Gopsons

Cover Design: Kapil Gupta

RAXZCRQZRBBAR

The McGraw·Hill Companies

To
My beloved mother
Kesar
and
The enterprising engineers of India

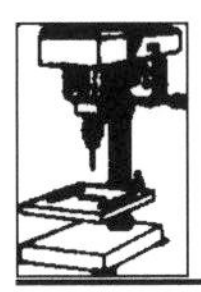

Preface to the Third Edition

The readers' response to the second edition surpassed that of the first. Also, McGraw-Hill, New York, published the US Edition titled: *Jigs and Fixtures Design Manual.*

During my training programmes for Pune Divisional Productivity Council, some attendees sought solutions to various problems they faced in their respective industries. I realised that most of the transmission, engine and vehicle manufacturers were irked by frequent breakage of small drills while drilling deep angular oil holes in components like crankshaft. Removing a broken drill jammed in a workpiece by spark erosion or throwing the crankshaft in scrap are very costly options. I have included solutions to this problem in this edition.

This edition also includes the pitfalls to be avoided while locating castings and forgings, particularly, problems posed by flash or uneven material distribution at parting lines/planes. There is also a case study on drilling scores of linear holes with equal pitch without incurring the cumulative error encountered in linear indexing jigs.

I have added a table giving overall and locating dimensions of some models of commercially available pump jigs. I have also added a graph showing the relationship between applied (screw) force (F_s) and clamping force (F_w) for various lever-to-heel contact lengths of standard hook-bolt clamps. Also included are additional entries in standard for the clamps. The chapter Shop Setups has been enhanced by adding a variety of elements such as universal clamps, stepped heels and compound tables.

Inclusion of slitless, hydraulically actuated collets and expanding mandrels with standard sizes will add to the utility of the treatise. This edition also includes hydraulic force multiplier (intensifier), which does not require a power pack.

The third edition also comprises construction details of large jigs, light materials for reducing jig weight and special knurled bushes used for enhancing interference with the softer housing. Another unique addition is the receiver gauges for checking the centrality of keyways in shafts and housings.

Figures have been improved, in general, by adding recommended ranges of wedge/cam/taper angles. I have also added workpiece drawings to all illustrations of jigs and fixtures to facilitate better comprehension.

Numerically Controlled (NC) and Computerised Numerical Control (CNC) machines have now become affordable to most medium-scale industries. Usage of these can save substantial amount of time and money in manufacture of tooling. I have added a chapter on modern developments in the field. It details the salient features and requisites of jigs and fixtures for usage on NC and CNC machines. It also cites the modifications necessary for usage of conventional jigs and fixtures on NC/CNC machines.

Availability of standardised parts—even precision sub-assemblies, such as toggle clamps, indexing modules and machined base plates and columns—commercially has reduced the investment and invaluable time required for building jigs and fixtures considerably. The section on modular construction in the chapter Developments in Jigs and Fixtures should enlighten readers on the topic.

I welcome problems faced by professionals. The fourth edition will contain solutions to these new problems. The second edition was published 13 years after the first and the third edition eight years after the second. At 74, I hope the fourth edition is published sooner.

Acknowledgement

I am thankful to my daughter Mrs Sunanda Suresh Bohra for her assistance in writing and illustrating the third edition.

PRAKASH HIRALAL JOSHI

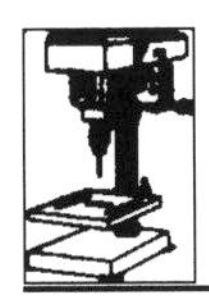

Preface to the First Edition

After working for 25 years as a tool designer and industrial engineer, I taught jigs and fixtures to production engineering students for some years. This book is a product of the experience gained during that tenure.

Being an experienced professional, I noticed some shortcomings in the existing books available to students. I have attempted to overcome those shortcomings in this book.

I have included a large number of drawings of workpieces from which the necessary jigs and fixtures can be independently designed. The book meets most of the syllabi requirements of students of production engineering. It would also serve as a useful reference manual for practising engineers.

I had been involved with English literature for 20 years before I ventured into technical writing. I have strived to impart brevity, clarity and order, essential in this type of literature. It is for the readers to judge how far I have succeeded in my endeavour.

Acknowledgement

I am thankful to Mr P A Keni for his valuable help in illustrating this book.

Prakash Hiralal Joshi

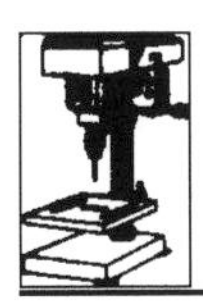

Contents

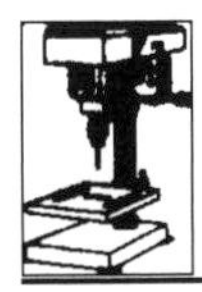

CHAPTER 1

Introduction

Mass production aims at high productivity to reduce unit cost and interchangeability to facilitate easy assembly. This necessitates production devices to increase the rate of manufacturing and inspection devices to speed-up inspection procedure.

Production Devices

Production devices are generally workholders with/without tool guiding/setting arrangement. These are called jigs and fixtures.

Jigs are provided with tool guiding elements such as drill bushes. These direct the tool to the correct position on the workpiece. Jigs are rarely clamped on the machine table because it is necessary to move the jig on the table to align the various bushes in the jig with the machine spindle.

Fixtures hold the workpiece securely in the correct position with respect to the machine/cutter during operation. There is sometimes a provision in the fixture for setting the tool with respect to the workpiece/fixture, but the tool is not guided as in a jig. Fixtures are often clamped to the machine table.

Elements of Jigs and Fixtures

Generally, all the jigs and fixtures consist of:

1. ***Locating Elements*** These position the workpiece accurately with respect to the tool guiding or setting elements in the fixture.
2. ***Clamping Elements*** These hold the workpiece securely in the located position during operation.

3. ***Tool Guiding and Setting Elements*** These aid guiding or setting of the tools in correct position with respect to the workpiece. Drill bushes guide the drills accurately to the workpiece. Milling fixtures use setting pieces for correct positioning of milling cutters with respect to the workpiece.

Advantages of Jigs and Fixtures

1. ***Productivity*** Jigs and fixtures eliminate individual marking, positioning and frequent checking. This reduces operation time and increases productivity.
2. ***Interchangeability*** Jigs and fixtures facilitate uniform quality in manufacture. There is no need for selective assembly. Any part of the machine would fit properly in assembly, and all similar components are interchangeable.
3. ***Skill Reduction*** Jigs and fixtures simplify locating and clamping of the workpieces. Tool guiding elements ensure correct positioning of the tools with respect to the workpieces. There is no need for skillful setting of the work piece or tool. Any average person can be trained to use jigs and fixtures. The replacement of a skilled workman with unskilled labour can effect substantial saving in labour cost.
4. ***Cost Reduction*** Higher production, reduction in scrap, easy assembly and savings in labour costs result in substantial reduction in the cost of workpieces produced with jigs and fixtures.

Inspection Devices

Inspection devices facilitate interchangeability. It calls for uniformity which must be limited, taking into account the machine's capability. Certain variations in the size of shaft (or hole) should be allowed for economic reasons.

Limits and Fits

The largest and the smallest dimensions of the shaft (or hole) are called the high and low limit, respectively. The difference between these limits, i.e. the permissible variation, is called tolerance. If tolerance is allowed only on one side of the nominal dimension, it is called unilateral. For example, $20.00^{+0.02}_{-0.00}$ has got unilateral tolerance. If tolerance is allowed on both sides of the nominal dimension $\left(20.00^{+0.01}_{-0.01}\right)$, it is called bilateral.

Classification of Fits Tolerance and its direction depend upon the functional requirements of the assembled parts. The following four classes of fits cover most of the functional requisites of engineering assemblies.

1. ***Running Fit (Fig. 1.1a)*** This provides for easy rotation as well as axial movement of shaft (male part) in the hole (female part). It is used for bearing diameters of rotating shafts. Locators in production devices are made running fit with respect to the workpiece to facilitate quick loading and unloading.
2. ***Push Fit*** This fit requires light hand pressure or tapping for assembly of the mating parts. It is used mainly for precise assembly of replaceable locators in jigs and fixtures.
3. ***Press Fit (Fig. 1.1a)*** The mating parts are assembled by hammering or with a press. There is a positive interference between the hole and the shaft. This prevents rotary as well as axial movement between the assembled parts. Hence, press fit is used widely for assembly of drill bushes (outside diameter) and locators, which are rarely replaced.
4. ***Force Fit*** This is used for permanent assemblies, such as wheels and hubs, on shaft. Force fit parts require heavy pressure for assembly.

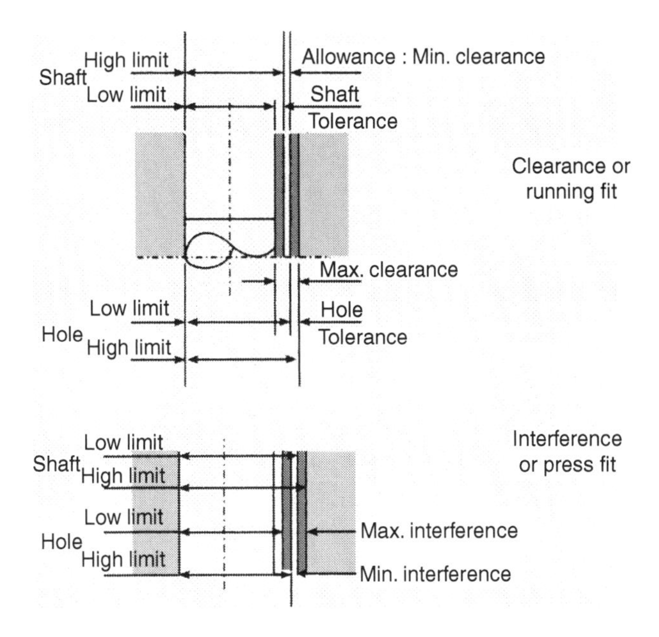

Fig. 1.1a *Limits and fits*

The clearance or interference provided for obtaining the various fits is called allowance. In shaft basis of fits, the diameter of the shaft is kept constant while that of the hole is varied. In hole basis, the hole size is kept constant and the shaft size is varied to obtain the various fits. As most of the holes are made by fixed diameter tools (drills, reamers, etc.), the hole basis is used widely in modern industry to keep the investment in cutting tools low.

The International Standards Organisation has standardised 27 types of fits and 18 grades of tolerances, which have been adopted by many countries. The tolerance depends upon the mating diameter sizes. The distribution of the tolerance is specified by alphabets. Holes are specified by capital letters *A*, *B*, *C*, *D*, etc. whereas shafts are specified by small letters *a*, *b*, *c*, *d*, etc. The alphabets are suffixed by digits 1, 2, 3, 4, 5...16 showing the grade of accuracy. Digit 1 signifies the highest accuracy and digit 16 the least (Fig. 1.1 b).

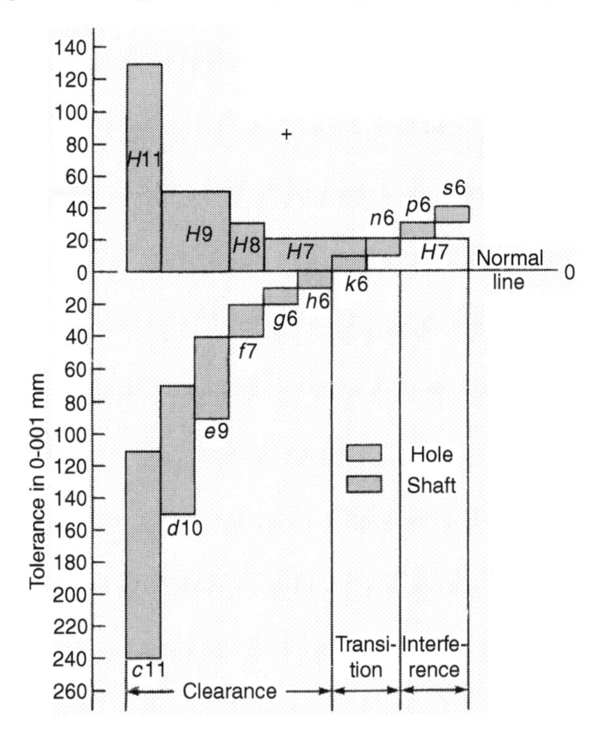

Fig. 1.1b *Limits and fits*

In toolmaking, accuracy grades 7–11 have been found to be the most convenient. Generally, unilateral *H* type tolerance distribution is preferred. Most of the accurate holes are made to *H*7 limits, which can be obtained by careful reaming. For mass production, the less accurate *H*8 holes are used. Simple drilling produces a hole within *H*11 tolerance. Figure 15.1 shows the limits for the grades of holes used widely. A 200 hole falling in range 18–30 mm has got the following tolerances for the various grades:

$$20\phi H7 \_\_ 20^{+0.21}_{+0}$$

$$20\phi H8 \_\_ 20^{+0.033}_{+0}$$

$$20\phi H11 \_\_ 20^{+0.13}_{+0}$$

Shaft sizes are varied to obtain the required fits with the desired degree of precision. The following combinations are widely used in toolmaking:

	High Precision Hole/Shaft	*Accurate Hole/Shaft*
1. Running Fit	*H7/f6*	*H8/f7*
2. Push Fit	*H7/h6*	*H8/h7*
3. Press Fit .	*H7/p6*	*H8/p7*
4. Force Fit	*H7/s6*	*H8/s7*

For example, for a 200 H7 hole, the shaft should be:

$20\phi f6$, i.e. $20.00^{-0.016}_{-.034}$ for precision running

$20\phi h6$, i.e. $20.00^{-0}_{-.017}$ for Pusn fit

$20\phi p6$, i.e. $20.00^{+.022}_{+.035}$ for press fit

$20\phi s6$, i.e. $20.00^{+.035}_{+.048}$ for force fit

Thus, by controlling the hole and shaft sizes within certain tolerances, we can obtain the desired fit with interchangeability in various assemblies.

The workpieces are inspected at every stage to ensure that the dimensions are within the tolerance. The checking is speeded up by using inspection devices such as gauges and fixtures. These simplify inspection so that unskilled/semiskilled labour can be used to keep down the inspection costs.

Materials Used in Jigs and Fixtures

Jigs and fixtures are made from a variety of materials, some of which can be hardened to resist wear. It is sometimes necessary to use nonferrous metals like phospher bronze to reduce wear of the mating parts or nylons or fibre to prevent damage to the workpiece. Given below are the materials often used in jigs, fixtures, press tools, collets, etc.

1. ***High Speed Steels (HSS)*** These contain 18% (or 22%) tungsten for toughness and cutting strength, 4.3% chromium for better

hardenability and wear resistance and 1% vandadium for retention of hardness at high temperature (red hardness) and impact resistance. HSS can be air- or oil-hardened to RC 64–65 and are suitable for cutting tools such as drills, reamers and cutters.

2. ***Die Steels*** These are also called high carbon (1.5–2.3%) high chromium (12%) (HCHC) cold working steels and are used for cutting press tools and thread forming rolls. Hot die steels with lesser carbon (0.35%) and chromium (5%) but alloyed with molybdenum (1%) and vanadium (0.3–1%) for retention of hardness at high temperature are used for high-temperature work like forging, casting and extrusion.
3. ***Carbon Steels*** These contain 0.85–1.18% carbon and can be oil hardened to RC62–63. These can be used for tools for cutting softer materials like woodwork, agriculture, etc. and also for hand tools such as files, chisels and razors. The parts of jigs and fixtures like bushes and locators, which are subjected to heavy wear can also be made from carbon steels and hardened.
4. ***Collet Steels (Spring Steels)*** These contain about 1% carbon and 0.5% Manganese. Spring steels are usually tempered to RC 47 hardness.
5. ***Oil Hardening Non-Shrinking Tool Steels (OHNS)*** These contain 0.9–1.1% carbon, 0.5–2% tungsten and 0.45–1% carbon. These are used for fine parts such as taps, hand reamers, milling cutters, engraving tools and intricate press tools, which cannot be ground after hardening (RC 62).
6. ***Case Hardening Steels*** These can be carburised and case hardened to provide 0.6–1.5 thick, hard (RC 59–63) exterior. 17 Mn1Cr95 steel with 1% manganese and 0.95% chromium is widely used. 15 Ni2Cr1Mo25 steel with additional nickel (2%) reduces thermal expansion up to 100°C. Case hardening steels are suitable for parts which require only local hardness on small wearing surfaces where costlier, difficult to machine, full hardening tool steels are not warranted.
7. ***High Tensile Steels*** These can be classified into medium carbon steels with 0.45%–0.65% carbon (En8-9) and alloy steels like 40 Ni2Cr1Mo28 (En24). The tensile strength can be increased up to 125 kg/mm^2 (RC 40) by tempering.

   Medium carbon steels are used widely for fasteners and structural work while alloy steels are used for high stress applications like press rams.

8. ***Mild Steel*** It is the cheapest and most widely used material in jigs and fixtures. It contains less than 0.3% carbon. It is economical

to make parts that are not subjected to much wear and are not highly stressed from mild steel.

9. ***Cast Iron*** It contains 2–2.5% carbon. As it can withstand vibrations well, it is used widely in milling fixtures. Self-lubricating properties make cast iron suitable for machine slides and guideways. The ingenious shaping of a casting and the pattern can save a lot of machining time. Although the strength of cast iron is only half the strength of mild steel, a wide variety of grades have been developed. Nodular cast iron is as strong as mild steel, while mechanite castings have heat, wear and corrosion resistant grades.
10. ***Steel Castings*** These combine the strength of steel and shapability of a casting.
11. ***Nylon and Fibre*** These are usually used as soft lining for clamps to prevent denting or damage to the workpiece under high clamping force. Nylon or fibre pads are screwed or stuck to mild steel clamps.

    Fibre is also used to reduce weight of Jig/Fixture. I have seen a 1.1 m × 0.7 m German jig made of fibre reinforced by a steel angle iron frame. Fibre weighs only $1/6^{th}$ of steel. So two person can load/unload the jig manually onto a larger workpiece (Also see topic titled: *Jigs for Large Workpieces* in Chapter 5 on Drill Jigs).
12. ***Phospher Bronze*** It is widely used for replaceable nuts in screw operated feeding and clamping systems. Generally, screw making process is time consuming and costly. So, their wear is minimised by using softer, shorter phospher bronze mating nuts. These can be replaced periodically.

    Phospher bronze is also used in applications calling for corrosion resistance, like boiler valves.

Presentation of Workpiece

A jig or fixture drawing shows the workpiece in position with the jig/fixture. However, the workpiece should be easily discernible from the jig/fixture. To accomplish this, the workpiece is drawn in a chaindotted line, preferably in colour (red, green or blue), which can be easily distinguished from the black linework of the fixture/jig drawing.

The workpiece drawn in a fixture/jig drawing is considered transparent. As a result, locators, studs or other parts of the fixture passing through the workpiece are drawn in full lines instead of dotted (Fig. 1.2). Similarly, the parts of the fixture placed behind the workpiece are drawn full instead of dotted. As the workpiece in transparent, it would not obstruct or block the view of any part of the jig or fixture.

The workpiece is drawn mainly to facilitate drawing of the jig/fixture. In fact, the designer first draws the workpiece in coloured chaindotted line and then draws the jig/fixture around it. He can thus position the locators, clamps and bushes quickly and correctly with respect to the workpiece. Tool room, methods and manufacturing engineers studying a jig/fixture drawing can distinguish the workpiece from the chaindotted linework and see how it is placed in the jig/fixture. Thus, delineation of workpiece facilitates drawing of jig/fixture. It also helps the manufacturer and user of the jig/fixture to understand disposition of the workpiece with respect to jig/fixture.

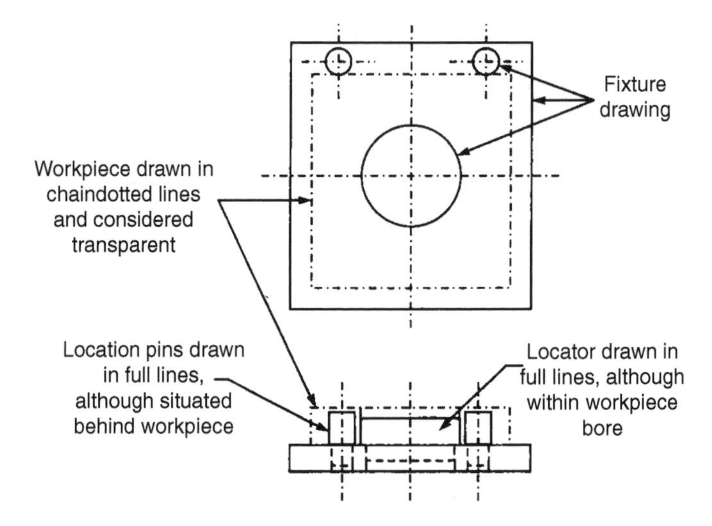

Fig. 1.2 *Presentation of workpiece*

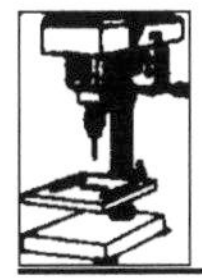

CHAPTER 2

Location

Principles

Workpiece Requisites

The location has to meet dimensional requirements of the workpiece stated on the component drawing. For example, in the workpiece illustrated in Fig. 2.1, the drawing clearly states that hole C should be at distance *D* from face A. Consequently, we must use face A as a datum for locating the work-piece while drilling hole C. This would ensure that hole C is at distance *D* from face A. If we use face B as a stopper, the variation in length *L* would cause inaccuracies in the position of hole C. If length *L* is oversize by 1 mm, hole C will be at $(D + 1)$ mm from face A. If length *L* is underrsize the hole would shift towards face A and would be nearer than distance *D* from face A.

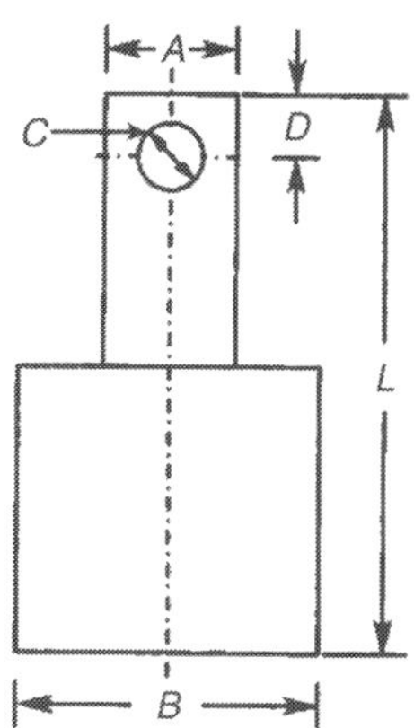

Fig. 2.1 *Location and workpiece dimensions*

If we locate on face A the hole would always be at distance *D* from face A irrespective of the variation in length *L*.

Accuracy

Location should be done on the most accurate surface of the workpiece. A machined surface is preferable to an unmachined one. When more than one machined surfaces are available, locate from the most accurate surface. For example, the centre of the turned part in Fig. 2.2 can be located from outside diameters 110 or 80 or from central 40ϕ bore. 80ϕ has the minimum tolerance of 0.05, so the workpiece can be located most accurately from outside diameter 80. Location from 40ϕ bore would be less accurate than location from 80ϕ but more precise than location from outside diameter 110ϕ, which has a much wider tolerance of 1 mm (±0.5 mm).

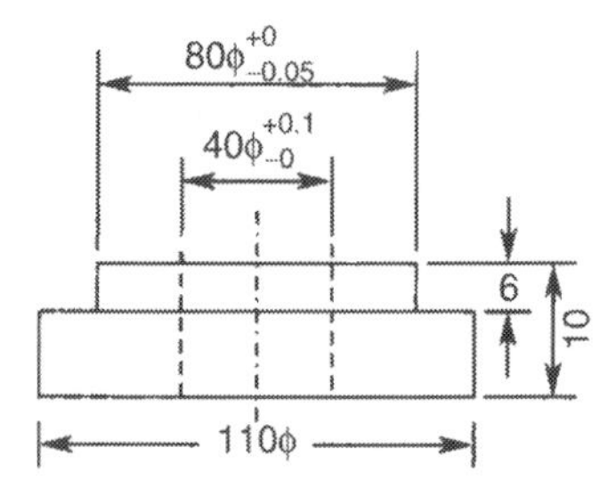

Fig. 2.2 *Accuracy of location surfaces*

Constraints

Location should prevent linear and rotary motion of the workpiece along and around the three major axes X, Y and Z.

The plate shown in Fig. 2.3 can move along the three axes X, Y and Z and can also rotate around these axes. The location system should prevent all these motions positively.

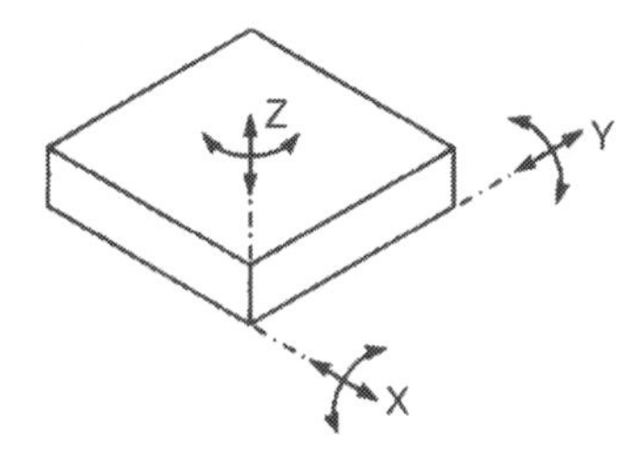

Fig. 2.3 *Six degrees of freedom*

Motion Economy

Location system should facilitate easy and quick loading of the workpiece in the fixture. It should effect motion economy. For example, there are two ways of drilling holes B and C in the turned component illustrated in Fig. 2.4a. We can drill either of the holes B and C first by locating on the machined bore A and then, locate on the drilled hole to drill the other hole.

If we drill hole C first and use it for location we would have to use two locators at right angles to each other and the workpiece needs to be loaded on the locator for bore A first.

It would be necessary to use another *removable* locator for hole C (Fig. 2.4b). Otherwise it would not be possible to load or unload the work-piece on the locator in bore A. Also, location on hole C would involve two motions—first, loading on locator A then inserting a removable pin in hole C which must be removed before the workpiece can be slid off axially from locator in bore A for unloading.

On the other hand, if we drill hole B first and use it for location while drilling hole C, it is possible to load the workpiece on both the locators in hole A and B in one motion as both the locators would be parallel (Fig. 2.4c). Thus, parallel locators are preferable to those placed at right angles.

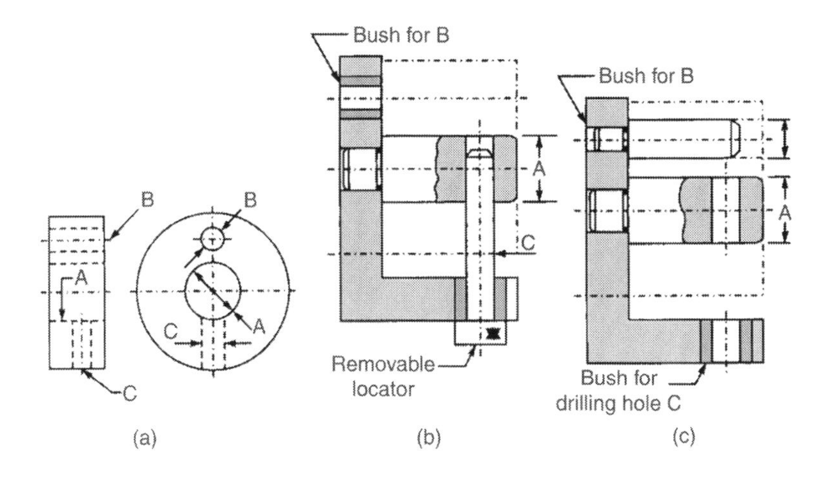

Fig. 2.4 *Motion economy in location*

Redundant Locators

Redundant locators should be avoided. In case of the workpiece depicted in Fig. 2.5, we can only locate effectively on surface A or B. For, although both the surfaces had been machined during previous operations, the distance between them would vary according to the process capability. If a fixed surface similar to A is provided to locate the surface at B as well, it would act as a redundant location since the job can be located from either A or B only. If the distance between surfaces A and B of the workpiece is more, there would be clearance between the locator and surface B. When clamped, the workpiece would bend as shown in Fig. 2.5b. When the clamp is released, the distorted part would spring back to its original position causing dimensional as well as form (flatness) errors. If the step in the component is less than the height of the locator, the component would not seat properly either on surface A or B (Fig. 2.6). The clamping force would distort the workpiece. This would cause errors, as the distorted part would spring back to its original position when the workpiece is unclamped.

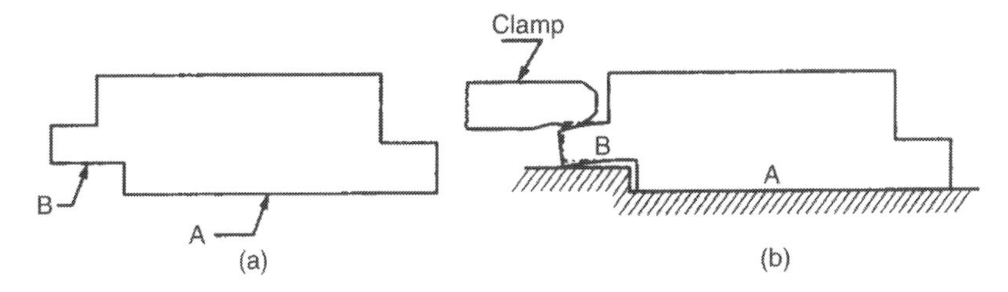

Fig. 2.5 *Redundant location*

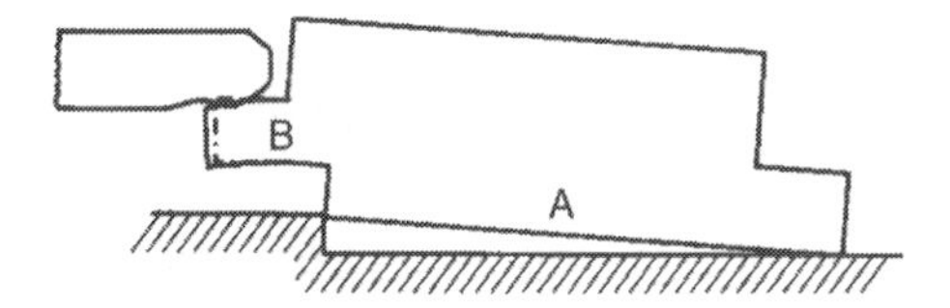

Fig. 2.6 *Workpiece distortion due to redundant location*

Under such circumstances, the redundant location at surface B should be replaced by an adjustable support illustrated in Fig. 2.7.

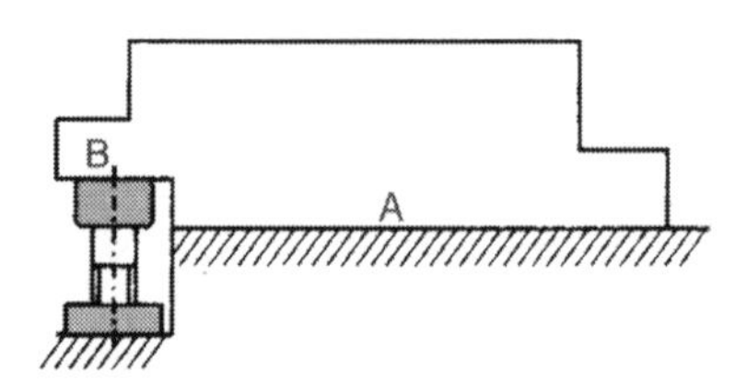

Fig. 2.7 *Adjustable support*

Foolproofing

The location system should positively prevent wrong loading of the workpiece in a fixture by foolproofing. The workpiece shown in Fig. 2.8 is to be located from holes A and C. As holes B and C are equidistant from A and their size is also the same, there is a risk of the workpiece being loaded wrongly as shown by the chain-dotted line. This wrong loading can be prevented by providing a foolproofing pin, which would obstruct the path of the workpiece if it is loaded wrongly. It would be impossible to load the workpiece wrongly due to the foolproofing pin.

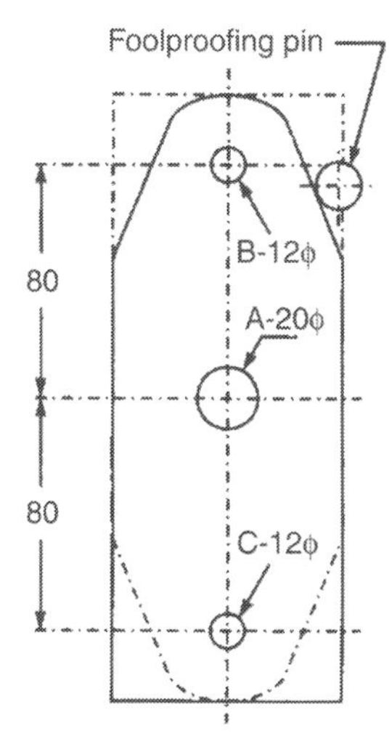

Fig. 2.8 *Foolproofing*

Locating Methods

A workpiece can be located from:

1. Plane surface
2. Profile
3. Cylindrical surface

Location from Plane Surface

A plane surface can be located with three points on the surface. A rough unmachined surface can be located with three location pads having point contact. This can be done by providing three location pins having spherical surfaces at the locating points as shown in Fig. 2.9. The pins should be spaced as widely as possible for more accurate location. The height of the collar of the pins should be equal so that the located surface is parallel to the baseplate resting on the machine table. Although the three pins can define a plane, they cannot provide adequate support to the workpiece during machining operation such as milling. Additional adjustable supports are necessary to prevent distortion and vibrations in the workpiece during clamping and machining. The number of adjustable supports would depend upon the shape, strength and size of the workpiece.

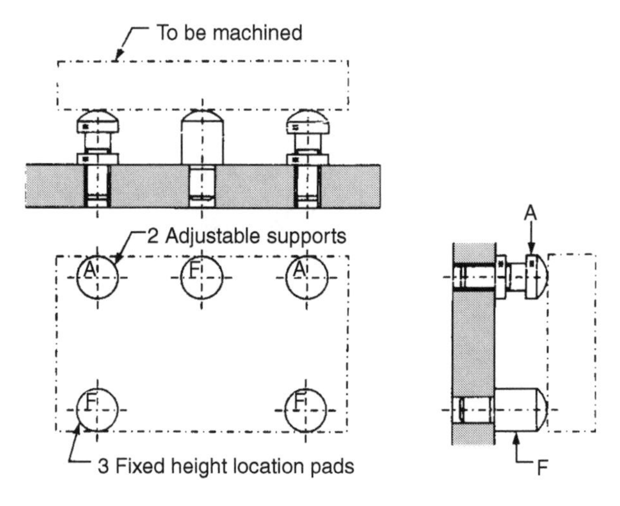

Fig. 2.9 *Adjustable support for rectangular workpieces*

Figure 2.10 illustrates a threaded adjustable support with the locking nut. Care should be taken that the adjustable supports do not dislocate the workpiece from the locating (resting) pins. This can be done by limiting the force used for adjusting the support. The screw illustrated in Fig. 2.10 is adjusted by rotating the knurled collar by using one's fingers so that the adjusting force would not dislocate (lift) the workpiece from the fixed locating pads (Fig. 2.9).

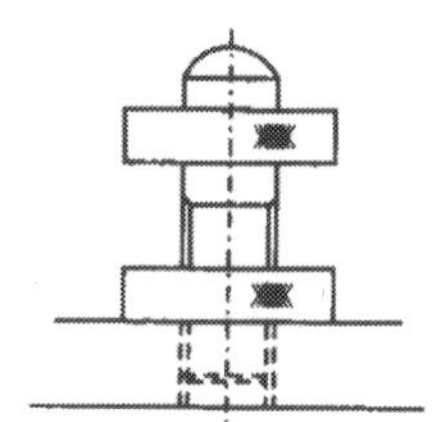

Fig. 2.10 *Adjustable support*

Surfaces that are reasonably plane (flat), such as hot or cold rolled plates, can be located by fixed locating pads and adjustable supports.

For locating very rough, uneven surfaces, it is necessary to use adjustable locating pads. Casting and forging can be located by adjustable screw pads as illustrated in Fig. 2.11.

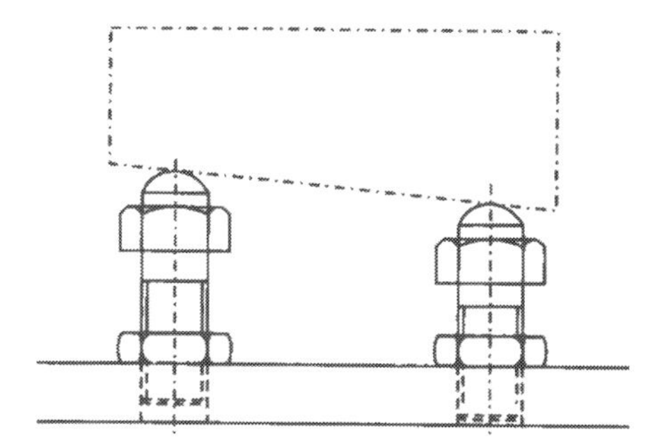

Fig. 2.11 *Adjustable locators*

During the first operation, it is often necessary to level the surface to be machined with a marking block by adjusting the locating pads. Even in the case shown in Fig. 2.11, there should only be three locators, and the workpiece should be supported at other points by adjustable supports having knurled collar. A hexagonal head screw rotated by a spanner can easily act as a screw jack and dislocate the workpiece from the locating pads. Sometimes, it is difficult to reach a support which is in recess or is distant from the operator. Under such circumstances, it is necessary to provide an elaborate adjustable support as shown in Fig. 2.12a.

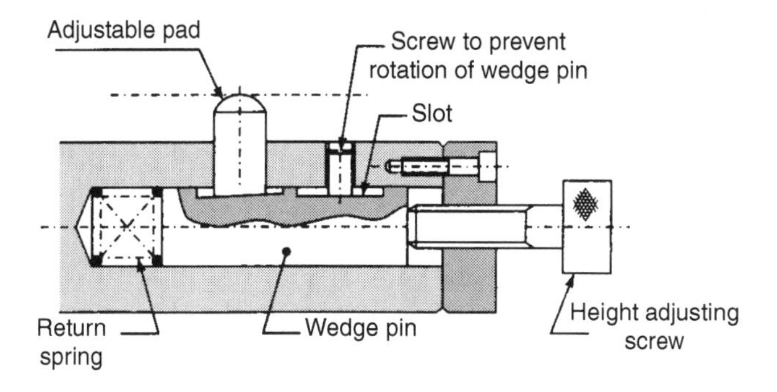

Fig. 2.12a *Adjustable support at inaccessible place*

The inclined surface on the wedge pin raises the pad when the wedge pin is pushed forward by the height adjusting screw. When the adjusting screw is withdrawn, the return spring pushes the wedge pin towards the right and the pad slides down by gravity.

Wedge angle is usually 10 °. Figure 2.12b shows the forces configuration. The wedge is usually moved by a screw. Page 43 (Chapter 4) gives the formula for calculating the force (F_s) generated by a screw. The force transmitted at the top face of the vertical supporting pin is proportional to the applied force F_s, the wedge angle (A) and coefficient s of friction between wedge pin and its housing bore, between the wedge pin and the supporting pin at the angular face, and between the supporting pin and its housing bore. Generally, the coefficient of friction between two dry machined faces ranges from 0.1 to 0.15. For the wedge angle (A) of 10° and the coefficient of friction 0.15, F_W = 1.96 Fs. For lesser coefficient of friction (0.10), $F_W = 2.55\ F_s$. For other wedge angles (A) and coefficients of friction.

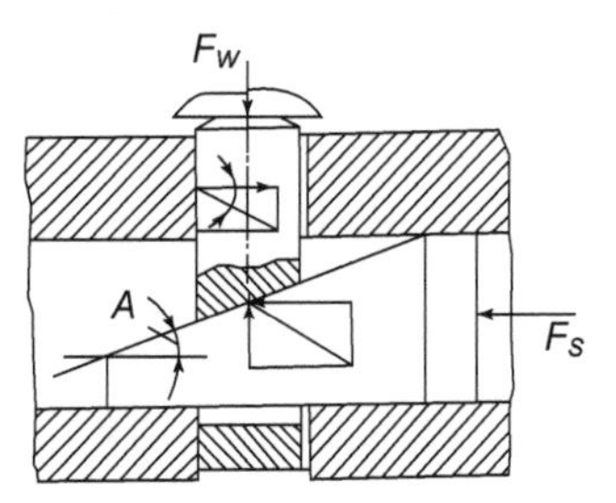

Fig. 2.12b *Forces in wedge action*

$$F_w = \frac{F_s[1 - \tan(A + f_1)\tan(f_3)]}{\tan(A + f_1) + \tan(f_2)}$$

F_s = Force developed by screw (page 47)
A = Wedge angle
$f_1 = \tan^{-1}$ [Coefficient of friction between wedge pin and supporting pin]
$f_2 = \tan^{-1}$ [Coefficient of friction between wedge pin and its housing]
$f_3 = \tan^{-1}$ [Coefficient of friction between supporting pin and its housing]

Figure 2.13 shows another arrangement in which the pad is spring-loaded so that it adjusts itself against the workpiece surface with limited spring force. The pad is locked in position by the clamping screw. The retaining screw prevents the pad from being pushed out of the housing by the spring.

Square or rectangular workpieces can be located better by replacing one of the locating pads by an equalising rocker as shown in Fig. 2.14a.

The rocker provides support at two points R. It pivots itself to suit the surface to be located. It provides contact at four points without contradict-

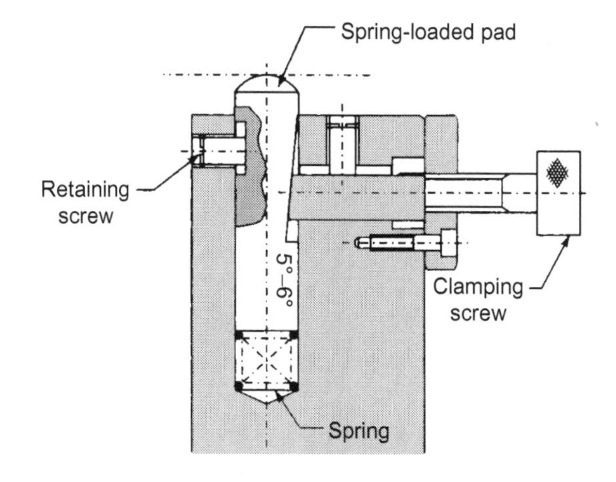

Fig. 2.13 *Spring-loaded pad*

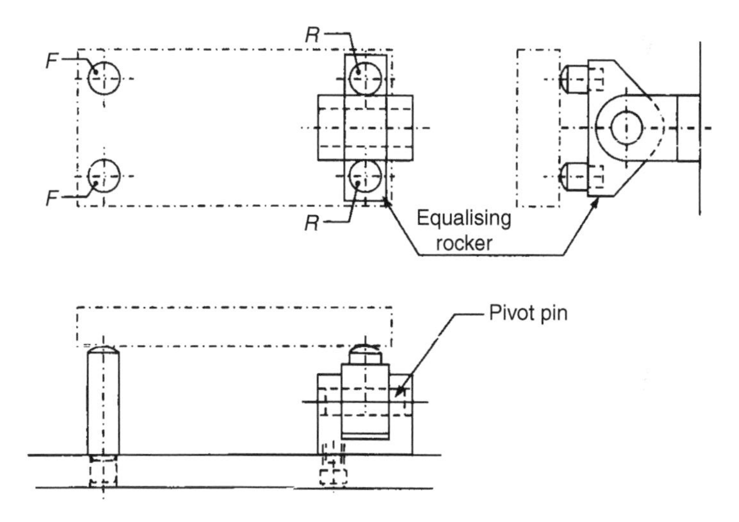

Fig. 2.14a *Equalising rocker location*

ing the three-point location of the plane. The pivot pin of the rocker acts as a single point complementing the other two points *F* in defining the plane.

Linear Self-adjusting Support Pins

Figure 2.14b shows three linear, self-adjusting, supporting pins. The pins are pushed upwards by light springs through the conical pins placed right below the supporting pins. The springs should push the conical pins and the support pins upwards to ensure contact between the workpiece and the

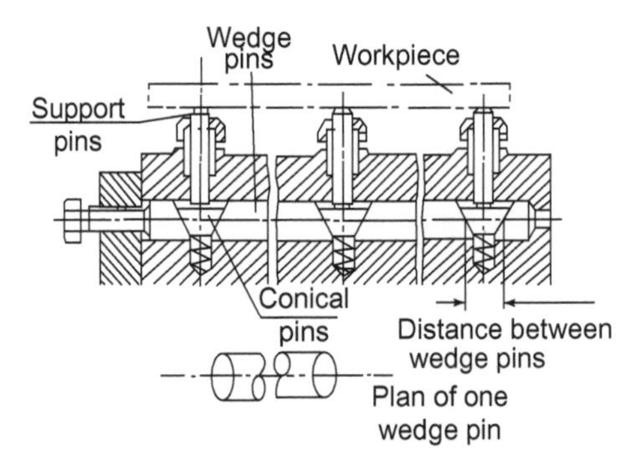

Fig. 2.14b *Three linear self-adjusting, supporting pins*

support pins; but they should not lift it off the locators (rest pads). The cones angles of the pins match with angular surface machined on wedge pins. These can be moved axially by a screw with a hexagonal head. Turning the adjustment screw clockwise reduces the distance between the angular faces of the wedge pins.. The wedge pins move axially, assume suitable positions, till all the three conical pins touch the angular faces of the wedge pins to provide a positive support instead of spring support. Light tightening of the hexagonal headed bolt secures the pins in the position by clamping the conical pins against the angular faces of the wedge pins. The Hex. Head bolt can be replaced by a tommy bar screw to limit the clamping force, lest the workpiece is lifted off the locators (rest pads).

A machined surface can be located better by pads having a flat surface. For large components, the pads can be screwed to the body of the fixture as shown in Fig. 2.15. This saves machining time as only seats for the pads need to be machined instead of the entire body of the large fixture. Moreover, the locating pads can be levelled easily by grinding them individually after removing them from the fixture body. Errors in the machine of pad seats can be easily corrected by providing compensation in the pads.

For small workpieces, no location pads are necessary. The fixture body itself can be machined suitably to provide the locating surfaces. Ample recess should be provided in the corners so that burr on the workpiece corners, or dirt or swarf do not obstruct proper location through positive contact of the workpiece with the locating surface (Fig. 2.16).

Location pads in large fixtures automatically provide similar recess.

Six-point Location Figure 2.17 illustrates six-point location of a cubical workpiece. The workpiece is clamped against pads 1, 2 and 3. This prevents its linear movement along Y axis and rotation about axes X and Z. Pads 4 and 5 prevent linear motion along Z axis and rotation about Y axis. Pad 6 prevents linear motion along X axis. Thus, linear motion along the three axes as well as rotation around them is prevented.

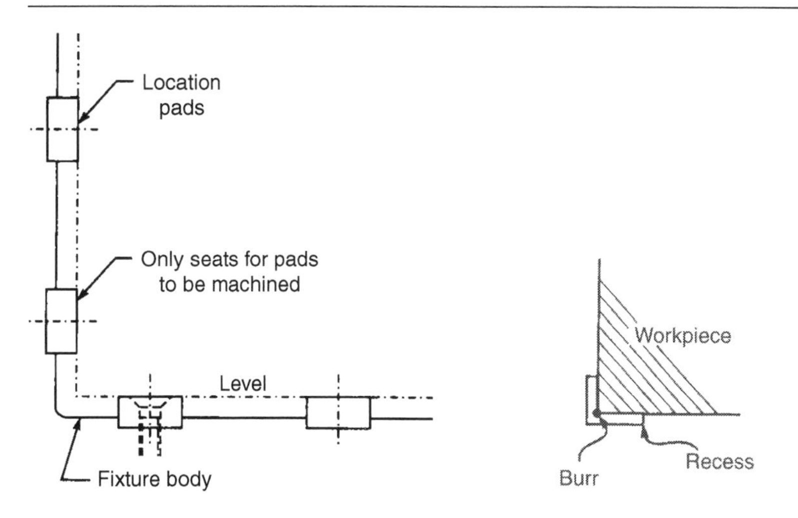

Fig. 2.15 *Location pads for large fixtures*

Fig. 2.16 *Recess for burr and dirt*

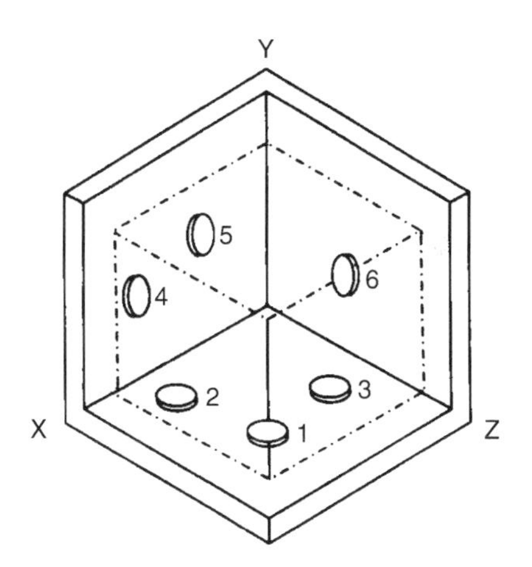

Fig. 2.17 *Six-point location*

Location from Profile

For simple components where appearance is important, a sighting plate can be provided. It is slightly bigger than the workpiece. The workpiece can be positioned on the sighting plate in such a way that there is equal margin on all the sides, as shown in Fig. 2.18.

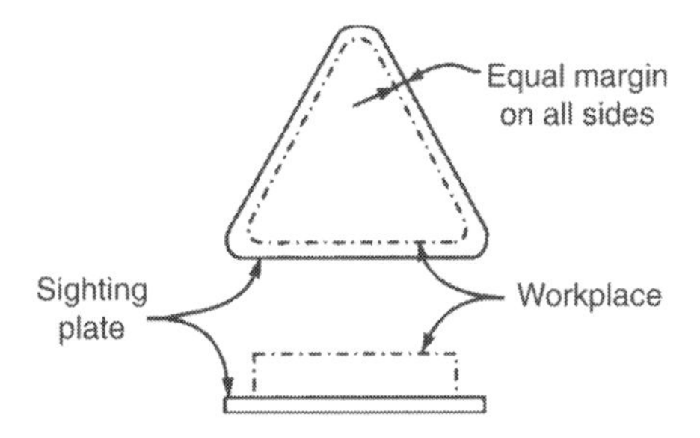

Fig. 2.18 *Sighting location*

The profile of a workpiece can also be located by confining the profile with cylindrical locating pins (Fig. 2.19).

When there is considerable variation in workpiece dimensions from batch to batch, an eccentric locator can be used (Fig. 2.20). The eccentricity of the locator can be varied by rotating it to suit the workpieces in the batch. The workpiece shown in Fig. 2.21 has got a milled flat on the collar. Dim F of the flat would be almost be the same for all the workpieces milled in a single batch. So, the eccentricity of the locator can be set to suit one of the workpieces from the milled batch and the eccentric locator would locate accurately all the workpieces in the batch.

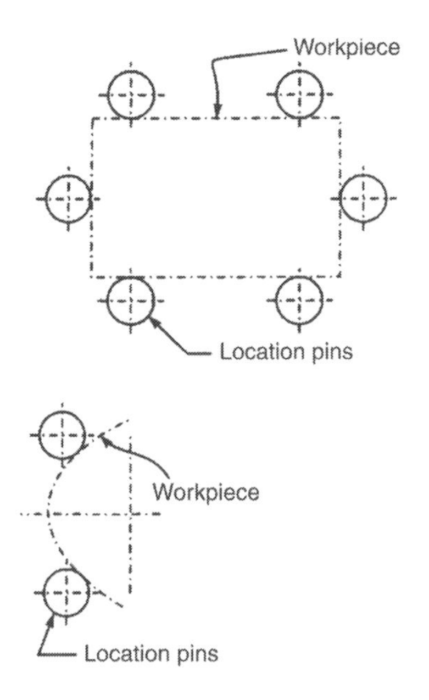

Fig. 2.19 *Profile location by pins*

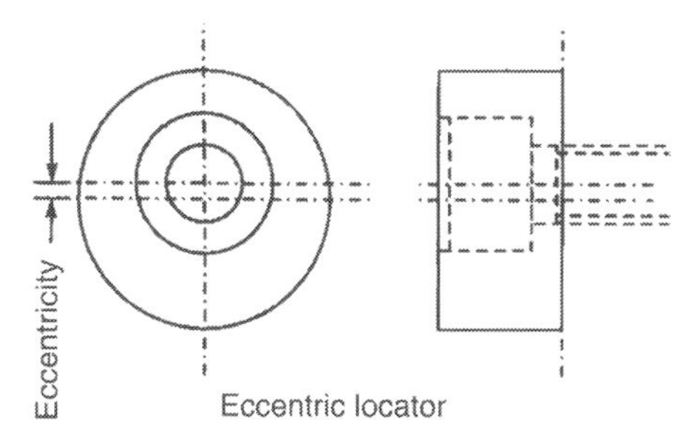

Fig. 2. 20 *Eccentric locator*

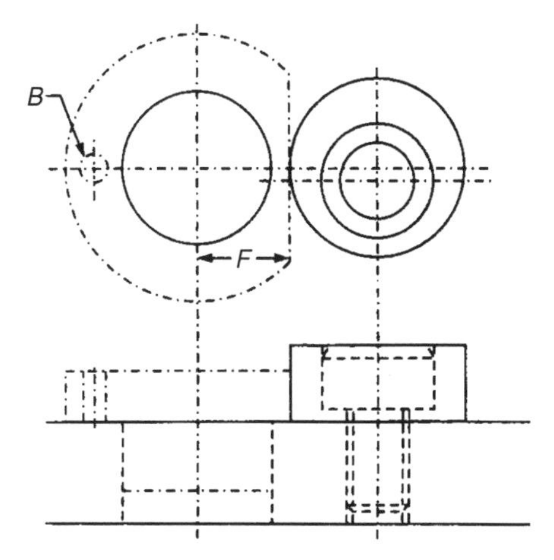

Fig. 2.21 *Application of eccentric locator*

The profile of a workpiece can be located by providing a pocket or nest around the profile of the workpiece (Fig. 2.22). The inside profile of the nest matches with the outside of the workpiece. The height of the nest should be lesser than the workpiece to permit grip over the workpiece for unloading. For thin sheet metal workpieces, finger slots or ejection arrangement should be provided for unloading the workpiece. Alternatively, a partial nest can be used.

Sheet metal blanks from the same die or die cast components from the same mould are almost identical. Such workpieces with little variation can be located precisely by a close fitting nest.

Location from Cylinder

Location from a cylinder is the most common and convenient form of location. For, when a cylinder is located on its axis and base, it can only

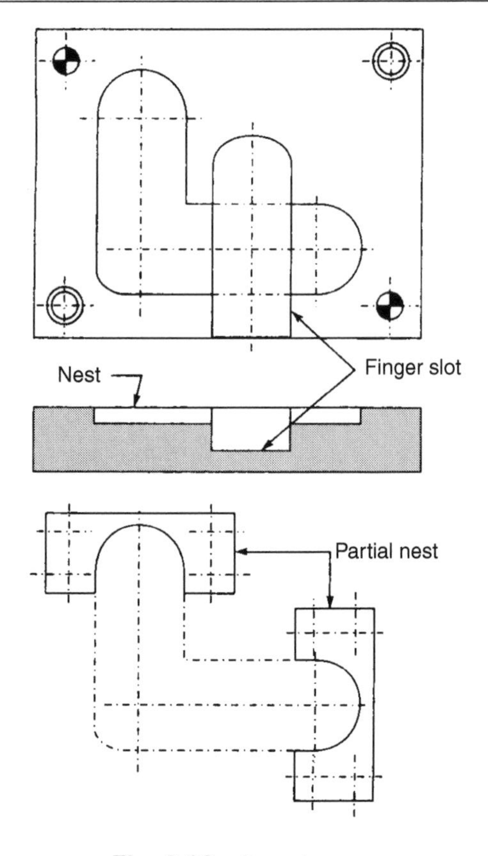

Fig. 2.22 *Location nests*

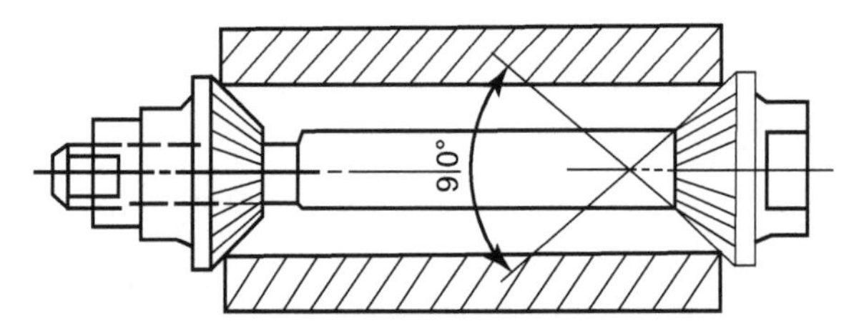

Fig. 2.23a *Conical locators for rough bores*

rotate about its axis. All other motions are constrained. Un-machined bores of castings or forgings can be located by two knurled conical locators (Fig. 2.23a) with 90° included angle. Un-machined external cylindrical surfaces like bosses in castings and forgings can be located by conical bores (Fig. 2.31). If the cylinder shown in Fig. 2.23a is located on a spigot having axis *Y–Y*, it can neither move linearly nor rotate around axes *X–X* or *Z–Z*.

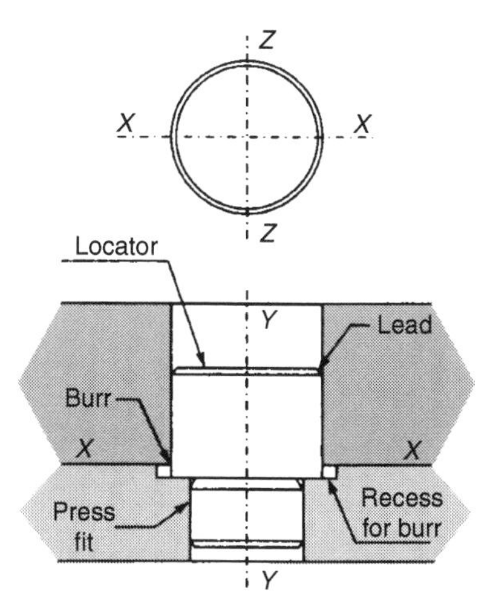

Fig. 2.23b *Cylindrical locators*

Clamping from top prevents linear motion along axis *Y–Y*. The seating surface for the locator should be recessed to provide space for dirt or workpiece burr. This ensures proper seating of the workpiece on the locating face. There should be ample chamfer or radius at the entry point so that the components can be loaded quickly. The chamfer is called lead. It centralises the workpiece quickly with the locator. The locator itself is located in the fixture by a concentric diameter generally made press fit in the fixture body.

Locating posts are often used for anchoring clamping studs (Fig. 2.24). The posts used for clamping should be secured by a retainer nut or a grub screw to prevent it from coming out of the fixture body when the clamp is tightened.

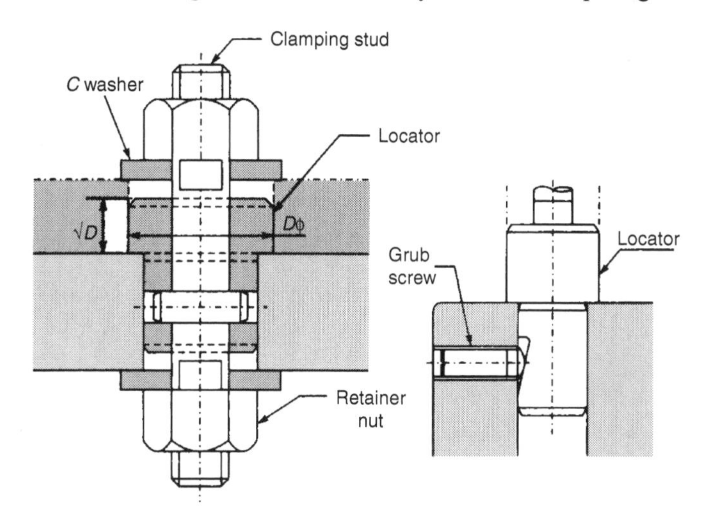

Fig. 2.24 *Locators subjected to axial pull*

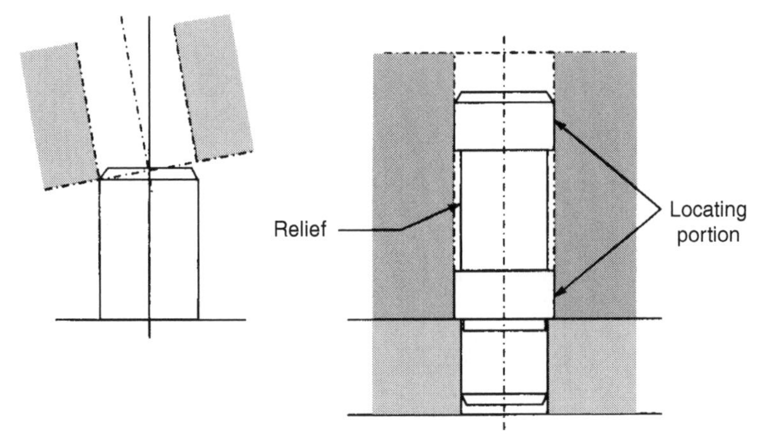

Fig. 2.25 *Prevention of jamming*

The length (L) of the locator should be short to minimise the loading/unloading time. Short length also reduces the possibility of workpiece jamming on the locator during loading/unloading. The optimum length (L) depends upon the minimum locator diameter (D), the distance (L_1) of the nearest edge from the hole centre and the minimum clearance (c) between the locator and the hole (Fig. 2.26a).

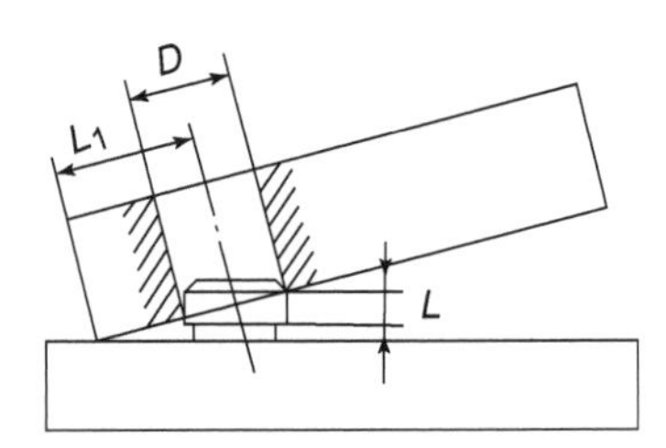

Fig. 2.26a *Removal of work-piece from* a *single pin*

$$\text{Locator Length}(L) = \frac{L_1 + 0.5D}{D}\,(\sqrt{2D_c})$$

While locating on two holes the centre distance (L_2) between them must be reckoned (Fig. 2.26b).

$$\text{Locator Length}(L) = \frac{L_1 + L_2 + 0.5D}{L_2 + \text{D}}\ \sqrt{2\text{c}\{L_2 + D\}}$$

We have also to reckon that the locator is also subjected to various forces developed during operation. The locator provides support to the workpiece during operation. Hence, it is necessary to use long location posts when the workpiece is fragile. Under such circumstances, there should be ample lead at the entry point and the locator should be relieved, i.e. made underrsize in the central portion.

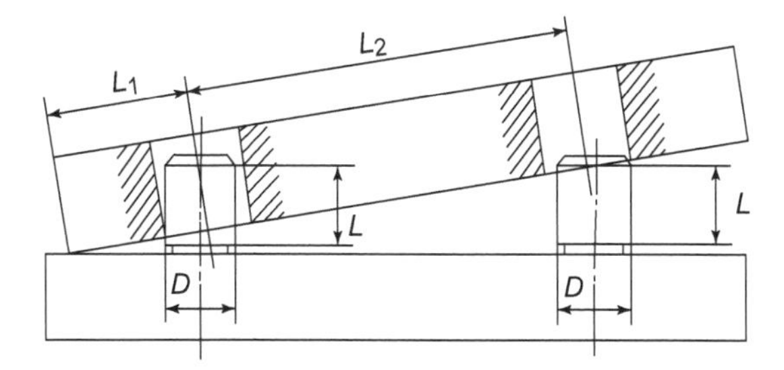

Fig. 2.26b *Removal of workpiece from two pins*

For locating a cylinder on the outside diameter, it is necessary to use a bush, which is called location pot. They should have generous lead at the entry point, and the central portion should be relieved in case of long pots (Fig. 2.27).

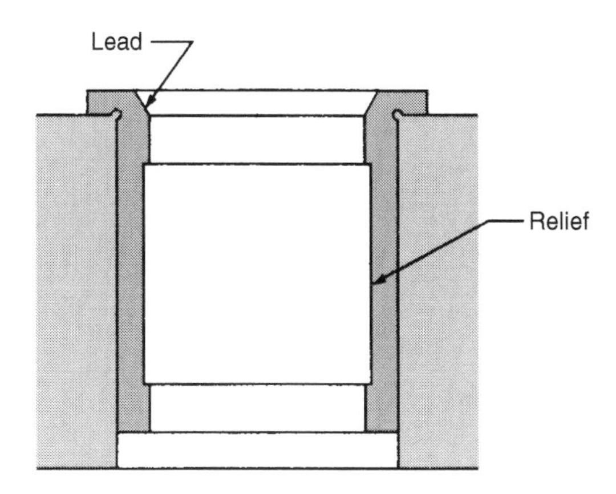

Fig. 2.27 *Female locators*

A single cylindrical locator cannot prevent rotation of the workpiece around the axis of the locator. For this, it is necessary to provide a second locator. For example, it is necessary to use two dowel pins to ensure that the piece is completely constrained.

If we want to fix plate B on base A we must use at least two dowel pins P and Q as shown in Fig. 2.28. If we use only one dowel pin P, plate B can pivot around P. The provision for dowel Q would prevent plate B from pivoting around P. The dowels P and Q should be placed as far as possible.

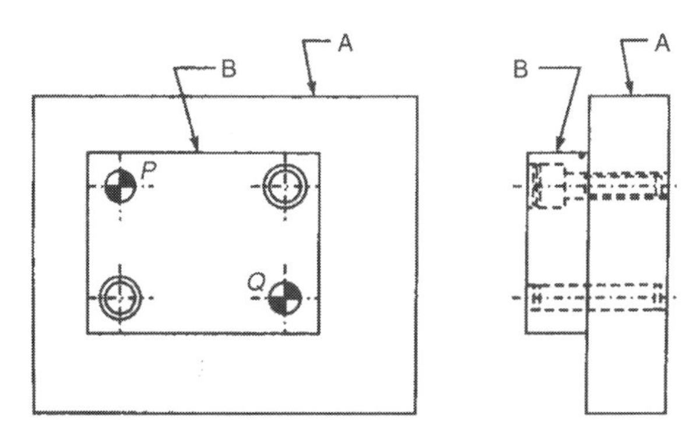

Fig. 2.28 *Use of dowels*

The dowels are used for permanent assembly of two parts. The holes in base *A* should be located from plate B so that there is no question of variation of centre distance between dowel holes P and Q.

When we have to use two holes in a workpiece for location, we must take into account the variation in the centre distance of the two holes due to the wear of the guide bushes for cutting tools.

This variation can be taken care of by making one of the two location pins diamond shaped as shown in Fig. 2.29.

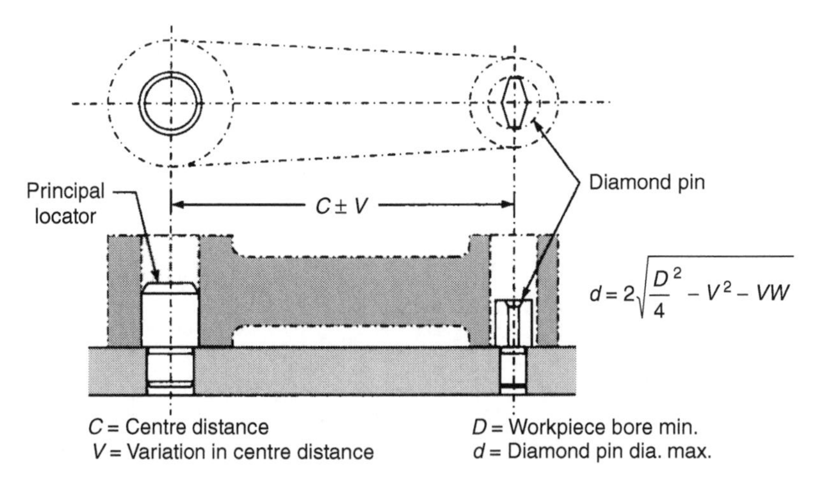

Fig. 2.29a *Diamond pin application*

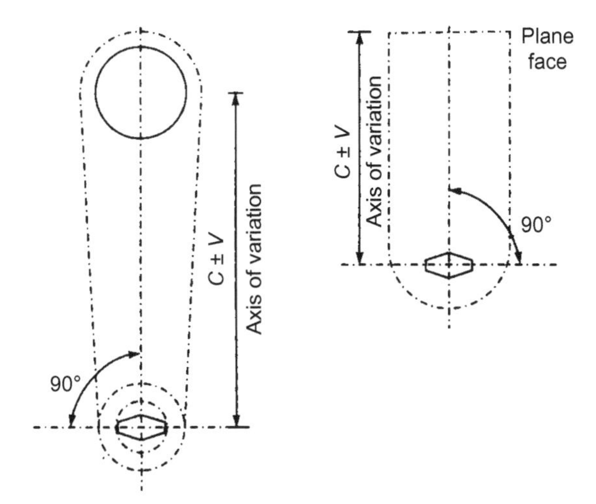

Fig. 2.29b *Positioning diamond pin correctly*

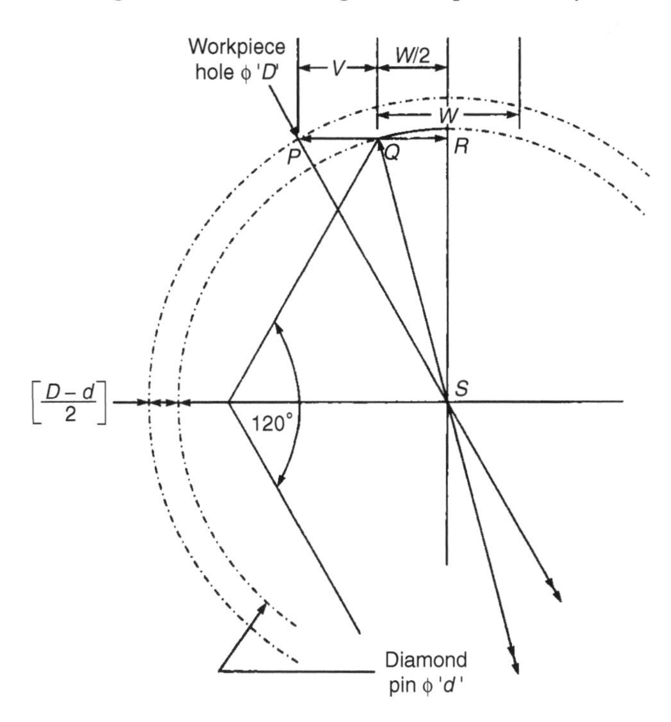

Fig. 2.29c *Principle of diamond pin*

Out of the two holes, the important and accurate one should be used for principal cylindrical location with a full pin. The diamond shaped pin should be used to constrain pivoting of the workpiece around the principal locator.

The principal locator should be longer than the diamond pin so that the workpiece can be located and pivoted around it before engaging with the diamond pin (Fig. 2.29a). This simplifies and speeds up loading of the workpiece.

Diamond pin can also be used for accommodating the variation in the distance of a hole from a plane surface (Fig. 2.29b).

Figure 2.29c illustrates the principle of a diamond pin. The locating surface of a diamond pin is usually less than 12% of a full cylindrical pin. This provides more clearance at location points. Clearance V at corner Q is much more than radial clearance ($D - D/2$) between the workpiece hole and the diamond pin. Referring to Fig. 2.29c, in triangle PRS:

$$\therefore \quad PS^2 = PS^2 + RS^2$$

$$= (PQ + QR)^2 + (QS^2 - QR^2)$$

$$\left(\frac{D}{2}\right)^2 = \left(V + \frac{W}{2}\right)^2 + \left(\frac{d}{2}\right)^2 - \left(\frac{W}{2}\right)^2$$

$$\frac{D^2}{4} = V^2 + VW + \frac{W^2}{4} + \frac{d^2}{4} - \frac{W^2}{4}$$

$$\therefore \quad d = 2\sqrt{\frac{D^2}{4} - VW - V^2} \qquad (2.1)$$

Example 2.1 Calculate the diameter of a diamond pin placed at 45 ± 0.15 distance from a plane surface if the locating hole in the workpiece D is 55.55/55.596 and engagement width W of the pin is 2 (Fig. 2.29b).

Solution: Minimum ϕ of workpiece hole = D

$$D = 55.55$$

$$\text{Variation, } V = 0.15$$

$$W = 2$$

$$\therefore \text{Diamond pin } \phi = d$$

$$d = 2\sqrt{\frac{55.55^2}{4} - 0.15 \times 2 - 0.15^2}$$

$$= 2\sqrt{771.45 - 0.3 - 0.0225}$$

$$= 2\sqrt{771.1275}$$

$$= 55.538$$

Radial clearance $(D - d)/2$ is only 0.006. But the clearance at location corner Q is 0.15, i.e. 25 times the radial clearance. The pin should be made further underrsize to provide precision running fit ($H7/f6$) with the workpiece.

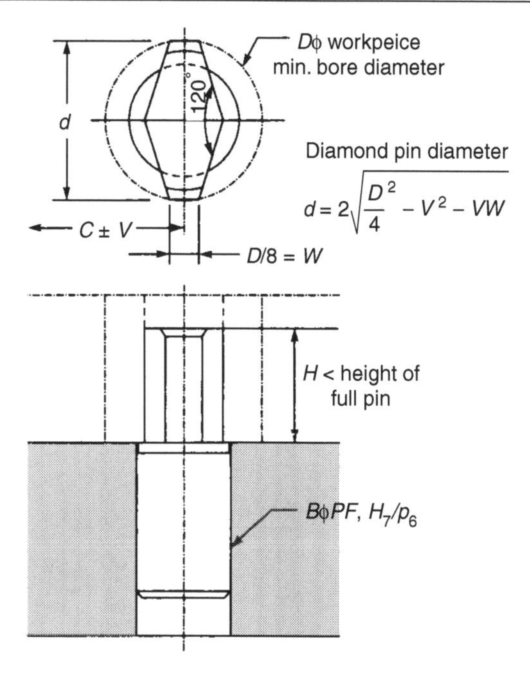

Fig. 2.30 *Diamond pin design*

$$\text{Diamond pin } \phi = d = 55.538\text{f6}$$
$$= 55.538^{-0.03}_{-0.049}$$

Width W of the diamond pin is usually kept one-eighth of the workpiece hole ϕD (Fig. 2.30). It can, however, be varied suitably to accomodate variation V in centre distance C in the workpiece and the desired fit between the diamond pin and the hole.

Example 2.2 Determine permissible variation V in centre distance 45 in example 2.1, if width W is increased to 7. While pin d remains same, i.e. 55.538f6.

$$d = 2\sqrt{\frac{D^2}{4} - VW - V^2}$$
$$55.538 = 2\sqrt{771.45 - 7V - V^2}$$

or $\quad V^2 + 7V - 0.33264 = 0$

$$V = \pm 0.0472$$

Angular accuracy required in location is the ultimate criterion for the radial clearance permissible between the diamond pin and the workpiece hole.

Example 2.3 Determine the angular accuracy of location if a diamond pin with 4 mm land is used for locating axis of 2 – ϕ32 *H7* holes and centre distances between the holes (Fig. 2.29a) is 200 ± 0.2.

Solution: $D = 32$; $W = 4$; $V = 0.2$

$$\therefore \quad d = 2\sqrt{\frac{D^2}{4} - VW - V^2}$$

$$= 2\sqrt{\frac{32^2}{4} - 0.2\times 4 - 0.2^2}$$

$$= 31.947$$

$$\therefore \text{ Pin } \phi = 31.947 \text{ f6 } = 31.947^{-0.03}_{-0.049}$$

$$\text{Angular accuracy } = \tan^{-1}\left[\frac{D-d}{2C}\right]$$

$$= \tan^{-1}\left[\frac{32-31.897}{2\times 200}\right]$$

$$= 0.01475° \quad = 0°0'53.11''$$

Location land W of diamond pin should be square to the axis along which variation V occurs. When a diamond pin is used to locate the axis of two cylindrical holes (Fig. 2.29a), the land should be square to the axis joining the centres of the holes. While locating a plane surface and a hole (Fig. 2.29b), the centre line of land W should be parallel to the plane surface.

Conical Location Conical locators are used mainly to locate rough unmachined cylinders in castings and forgings. Cored holes and bosses are centralised by conical locators (Fig. 2.31). Conical locators generally have axial adjustment with a screw, which is also used to clamp the located work-

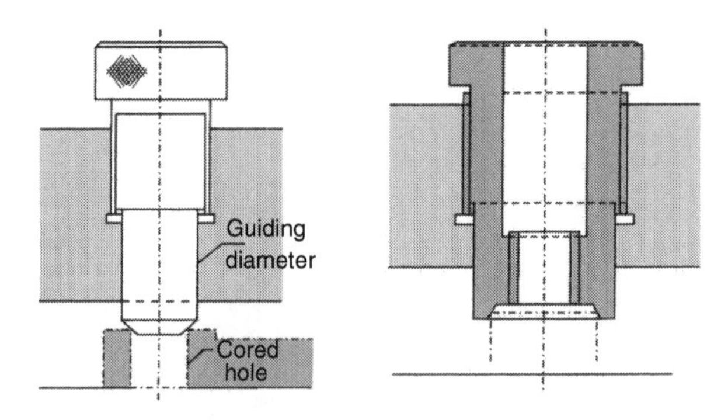

Fig. 2.31 *Conical locators*

piece in position. When a casting has a single boss which is to be drilled, a bush is made integral with the locator to facilitate drilling of the workpiece in the located position.

Vee Location Vee locators are used extensively to locate cylindrical surfaces from outside. Fixed V blocks are used for approximate location. These are generally fixed by screws to the fixture body and dowelled to prevent shifting during operation (Fig. 2.32).

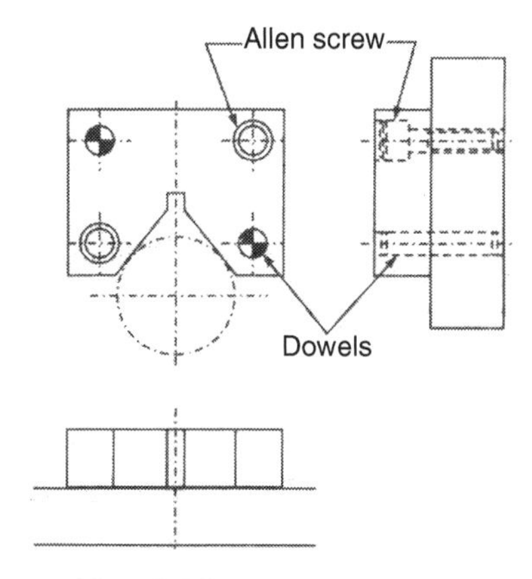

Fig. 2.32 *Fixed V locator*

For more accurate location, it is necessary to make V locator adjustable along the axis of V. The position of V block is adjusted by a screw to take care of the variation in the size of the workpiece (Fig. 2.34).

An adjustable V locator should be guided by a guide plate to constrain its movement along the axis of V. The guides must be dowelled to prevent shifting during operation. The side of the V face is sometimes inclined slightly to provide downward clamping force (Fig. 2.33).

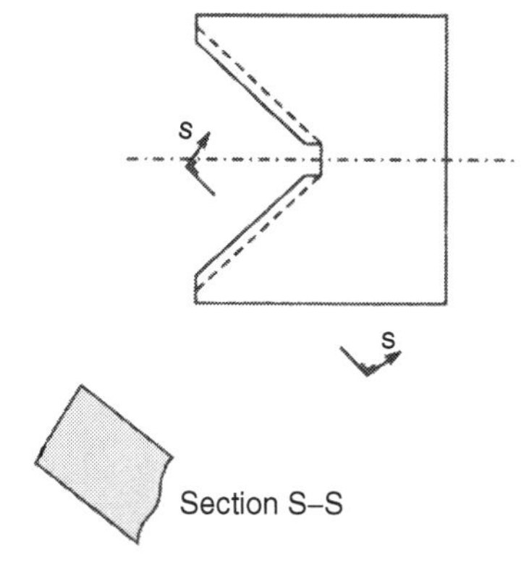

Fig. 2.33 *Inclined V*

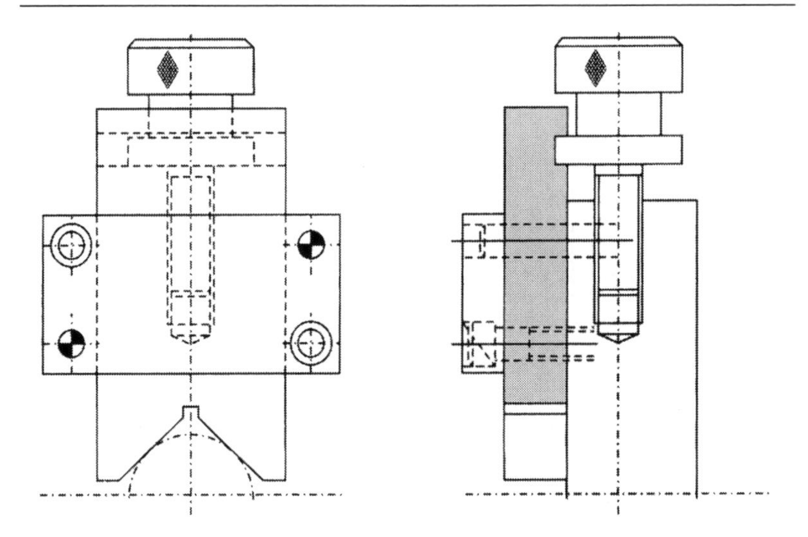

Fig. 2.34 *Screw adjusted V locator*

A Vee locator can be adjusted quickly by using a cam for adjustment (Fig. 2.35).

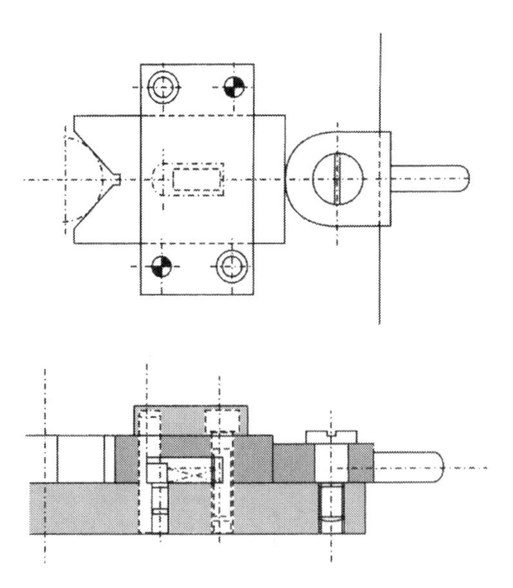

Fig. 2.35 *Cam-operated V locator*

It is necessary to provide a return spring for bringing back the V location to its original position when a cam is used.

When the V plate has to be withdrawn quickly for a considerable distances, a swinging eyebolt is used. A slotted thrust plate must be provided as a seating face for the V adjusting nut. (Fig. 2.36).

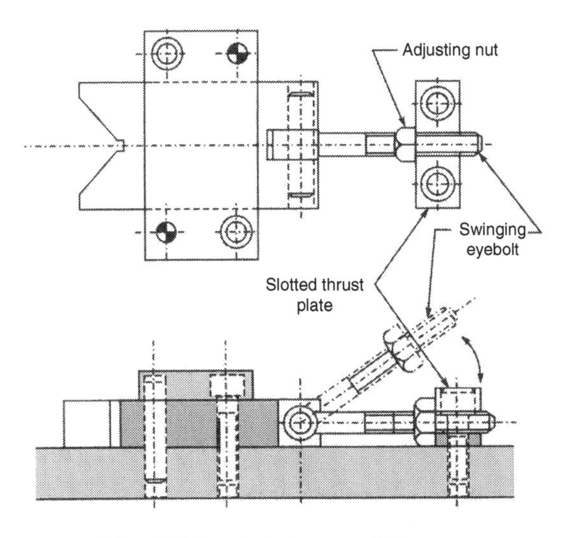

Fig. 2.36 *Quick action V locator*

When a cylindrical workpiece is located by the V block, the position of its centre would depend on its diameter. However, the centre would always lie on the centre line of V. So, for drilling central holes in round bars, the V block should be placed in such a way that its centre line is vertical. Even if the size of the workpiece varies, the drilled hole would always be at its centre (Fig. 2.37).

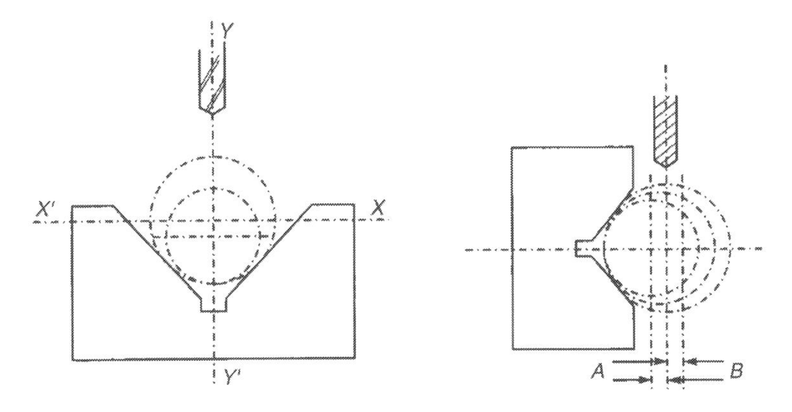

Fig. 2.37 *Correct position of V* **Fig. 2.38** *Correct position of V*

On the other hand, if the V block axis is horizontal, the variation in the diameter of the workpiece would lead to errors. As shown in Fig. 2.38, the hole in underrsize bar would be eccentric by length A, whereas in case of an oversized bar, the hole would be offset by length B.

Locating Castings, Forgings and Mouldings

Most dies and moulds have two halves to facilitate removal of the formed workpiece. Excess raw material overflows (spills) at the interface between the die halves (Fig. 2.39). This projection at the joint is called flash. The flash is rarely uniform around the die cavity. Location on flash will give very erratic results. It should be avoided. This can be done by providing a clear groove in the flash area encountered by the locator. Fig. 2.40 shows a groove in a vee locator used for locating a cast boss. The groove accommodates the uneven flash ensuring that the workpiece is located on a better surface. Fig. 2.41 shows a locator for a flat surface. It locates above the flash. It has got a downward angle in the location area. The angle matches the draft angle (usually 5°) provided in the die (or pattern) for easy removal of workpiece after casting. The angle presses the workpiece downward onto the locating (resting) surface.

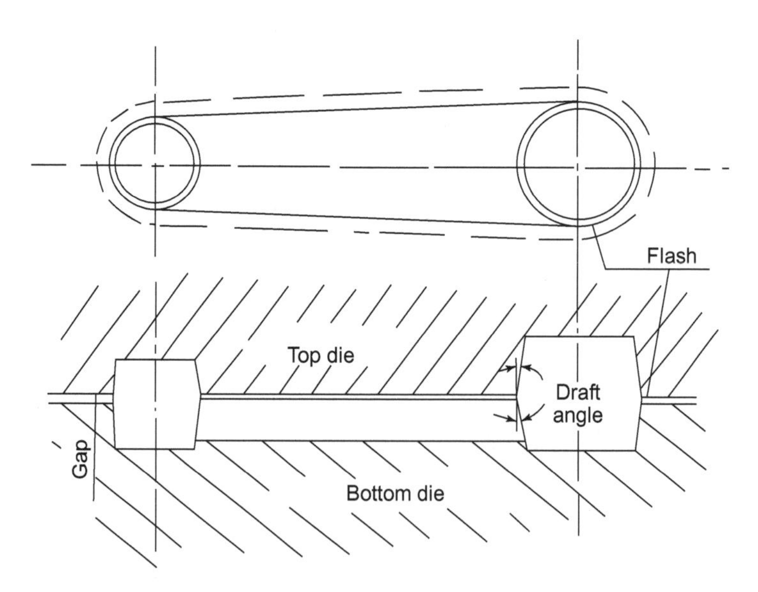

Fig. 2.39a *Flash projection in forgings and mouldings*

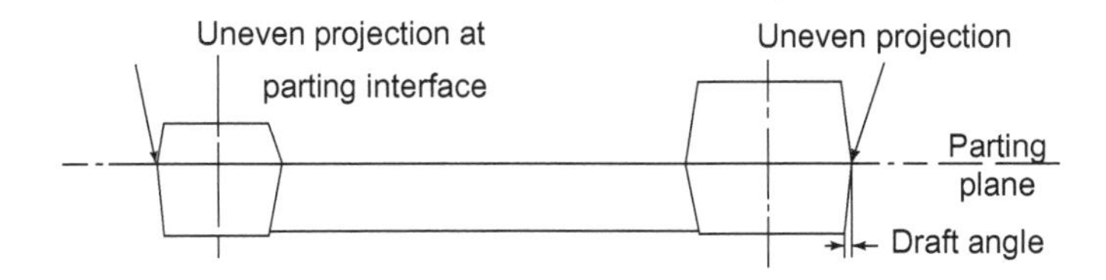

Fig. 2.39b *Uneven projection at parting plane*

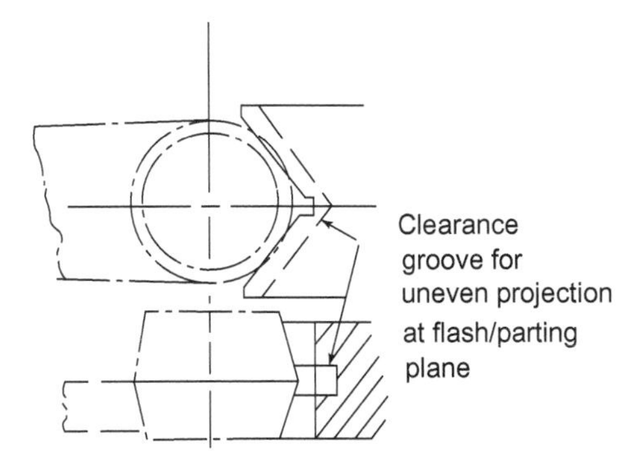

Fig. 2.40 *'V' locator grooved at Flash/parting plane*

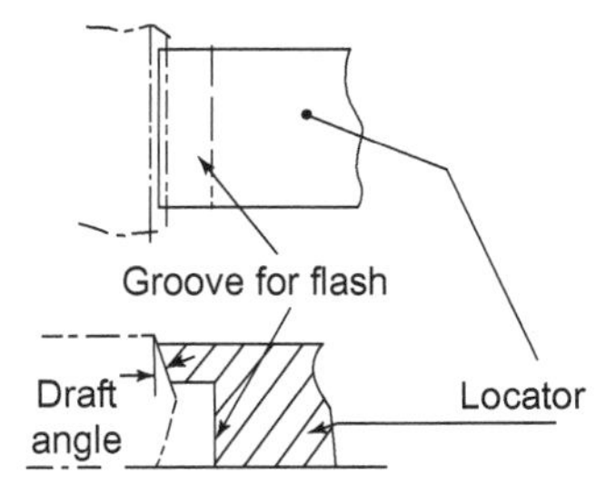

Fig. 2.41 *Flash clearance grooves for flat locators*

Summary

Principles of Location

1. Location must be related to the dimensional requirements stated on the component/workpiece drawing.
2. It is preferable to use a more accurately machined surface than a less accurate surface for location.

3. The workpiece should be prevented from moving along and rotat ing around the X, Y and Z axes.
4. Location system should facilitate easy and quick loading and unloading of the workpiece and aim at motion economy.
5. Redundant locators must be avoided.
6. Location system should positively prevent wrong loading of the workpiece by foolproofing.

Locating Methods

Plane Surfaces

1. A reasonably flat surface can be located by three pins of equal height having spherical surfaces at the location points.
2. A rough, uneven or tapered plane surface should be located by three adjustable location pins having spherical ends.
3. Additional adjustable supports are necessary to prevent vibrations or distortion of the workpiece during machining operation. The force for adjusting the supports should be kept minimum so that the workpiece does not get dislocated or lifted from the location pins.
4. A machined surface can be located by pads having flat surface.
5. There should be ample clearance for burr or dirt to ensure proper seating of the workpiece surfaces.
6. A cube can be prevented from linear movement and rotation around axes X,Y and Z by six location pads.

Profile

1. A profile can be located approximately by aligning it with a slightly bigger sighting plate.
2. Locating pins can also be used to locate a profile or cylindrical workpieces.
3. Variations in workpiece sizes from batch to batch can be taken care of by using eccentric locators whose eccentricity can be set to suit the batch.
4. Workpieces with little variation can be located precisely with nesting plates with suitable provision for unloading or ejection.

Cylinder

1. Spigots used for locating bores should have ample lead for easy entry, and their length should be short to prevent jamming of the workpiece.
2. Long locators for fragile workpieces should be relieved at the centre.
3. Location posts, which are also used for clamping, should be retained by a nut or a grub screw.
4. When two location pins are used, the less important one should be made diamond-shaped. The important full pin should be longer than the diamond pin in order to facilitate easy loading of the workpiece.
5. Rough cored holes and bosses are located by conical locators, which often have integral clamping arrangement and drill bush.
6. Fixed V blocks are used to locate approximately the outside surface of a cylinder.
7. For precise location, an adjustable guided V block is necessary. The V block can be adjusted by a screw or a cam. It can be with drawn quickly by using a swinging eyebolt.
8. V blocks should be positioned in such a way that the variation in the workpiece would not affect the location for the operation. For drilling central holes, the centre line of V should be vertical.
9. Clearance grooves should be provided at flash line of cast, forged and moulded workpieces.

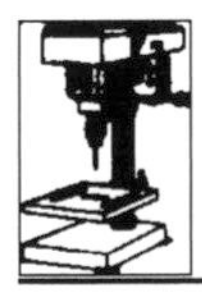

CHAPTER 3

Clamping

Clamping elements hold the workpiece firmly engaged with the locating elements during operation. The clamping system should be strong enough to withstand forces developed during operation. At the same time, the clamping force should not dent or damage the workpiece. Speed of operation, operator fatigue and strategic positioning are other important considerations for contriving a clamping system.

Principles of Clamping

Position

Clamping should be positioned to direct the clamping force on a strong, supported part of the workpiece. Clamping on unsupported part bends slender workpieces, as shown in Fig. 3.1. This affects the accuracy of the operation. A vertical hole drilled in the bent workpiece would become angular when the unclamped workpiece springs back to its original shape, as shown by the chairdotted lines in Fig. 3.1.

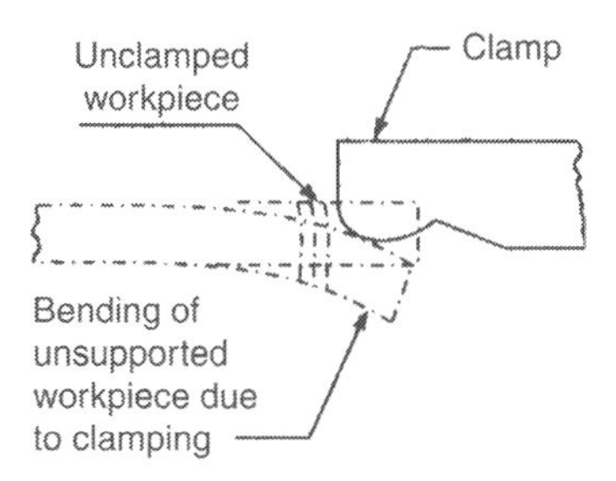

Fig. 3.1 *Distortion of unsupported workpiece*

The clamping system should not obstruct the path of loading and unloading of the workpiece. The clamps in the path of loading should be retractable (Fig. 3.9) or swinging type (Fig. 3.10a), so that the clamps can be withdrawn or swung clear of the path of loading and unloading of the workpiece.

Clamps should not obstruct the path of the cutting tool. They should not get drilled, milled or welded during operation.

Strength

The clamping system should be capable of holding the workpiece securely against the forces developed during operation. The clamping force should not dent or damage the workpiece with excessive pressure. For clamping weak or fragile workpieces, the clamping force should be distributed over a wider area of the workpiece. While clamping soft workpieces, clamps should be fitted with pads of softer materials, such as nylon or fibre to prevent damage and denting of the workpiece.

Productivity

Clamping time should be minimised by using hand knobs, tommy bars, knurled screws, handwheels and handles (Fig. 3.2), so that the clamp can be tightened or loosened manually without using spanners, as a spanner further adds motions of picking, aligning and laying it down.

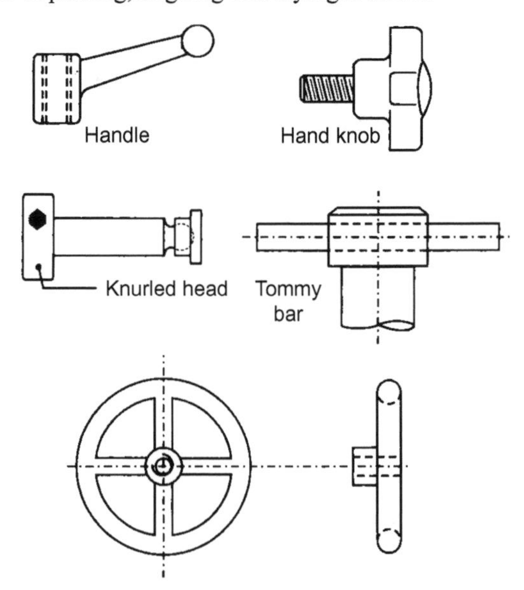

Fig. 3.2 *Hand operated clamping devices*

Operator Fatigue

Operator fatigue should be taken into account. If a considerable number of clamps are to be tightened and loosened repeatedly, it is better to use pneumatic or hydraulic clamping which, in addition to reducing operator fatigue, saves clamping time. Power clamping facilitates tightening or loosening of many clamps simultaneously.

Workpiece Variation

The clamping points should be provided with ample radius to make the clamp operable even if there is variation in the workpiece. Heel pin pressure surface should also be made spherical to permit some tilting of the clamp (Fig. 3.3a).

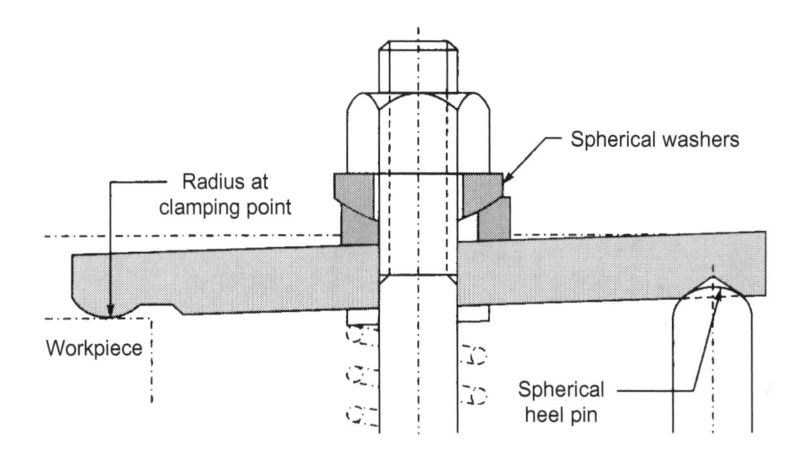

Fig. 3.3a *Clamping variable workpieces*

Misalignment between the clamp surface and the clamping nut due to tilting of the clamp can be countered by use of spherical washers between the clamp and the nut. As washers are used in pairs, the two washers have matching male and female spherical seats. The spherical bearing allows the washers to tilt with respect to each other. The lower female washer tilts with the clamp while the upper male washer below the nut remains square to the nut. The spherical seat transmits the clamping pressure from the nut to the clamp. Figure 3.3b shows a clamp with a cylindrical washer.

In multiple clamping, a pivoted equaliser is used for clamping two unequal workpieces simultaneously. The equaliser clamp pivots around the

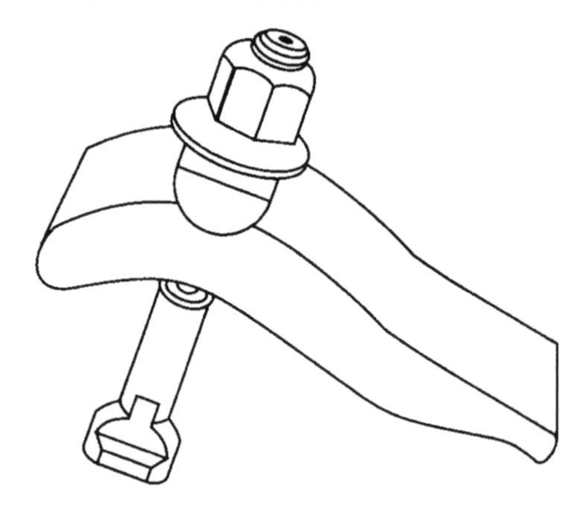

Fig. 3.3b *Universal clamp with cylindrical washer*

pin to suit the workpieces (Fig. 3.4). The equaliser principle can be extended to facilitate clamping of many even number of workpieces simultaneously by a single clamp (Fig. 3.5).

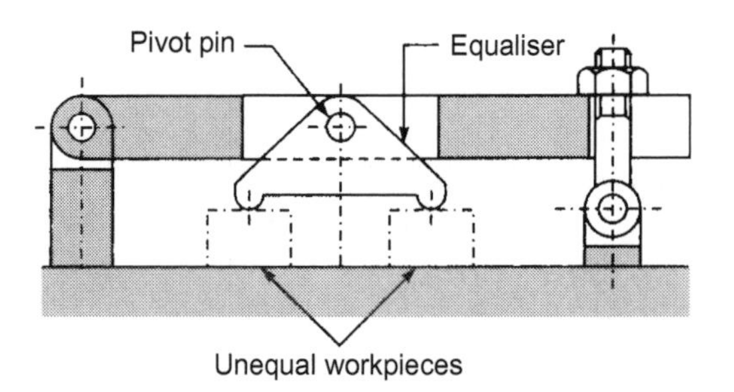

Fig. 3.4 *Equaliser for two workpieces*

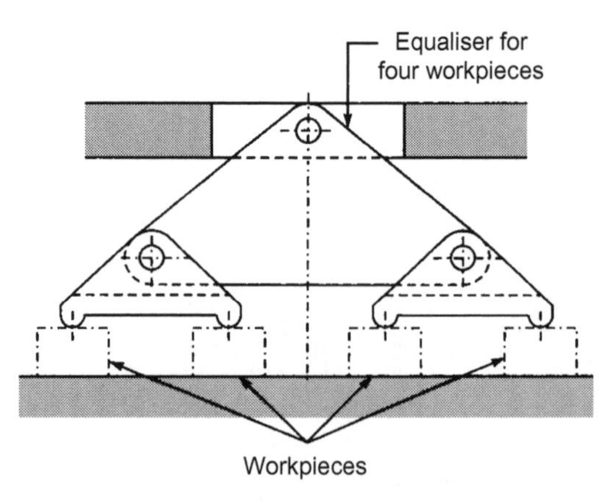

Fig. 3.5 *Equaliser for four workpieces*

Types of Clamps

Clamps can be broadly classified into screw clamps, strap clamps, pivoted clamps, hinged clamps, swinging clamps, quick action clamps, multiple clamps, power clamps and non-conventional clamps.

Screw Clamps

Screw clamps are threaded devices with knurled collar, hand knob, tommy bar or spanner flats for rotating and tightening the screw (Fig. 3.6).

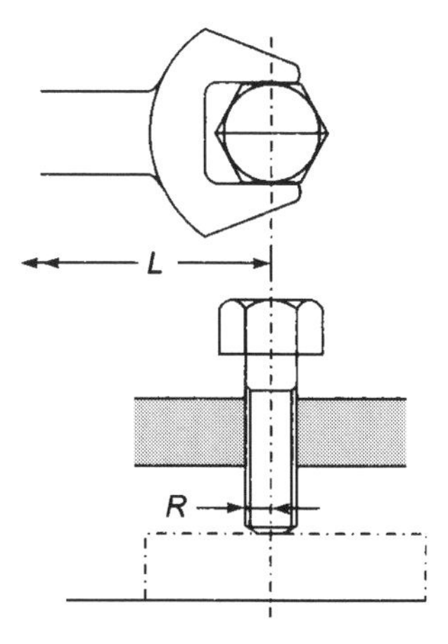

Fig. 3.6 *Screw clamp*

The Clamping area of a screw clamp can be increased by a provision for a pad (Fig. 3.7a). The clamping pad is free to rotate on the pivot. This eliminates friction between the workpiece and the pad. The clamping pad remains stationery on the workpiece while the screw rotates and rubs on the conical seat of the pad.

A swivel-type clamping pad provides a spherical joint between the clamping pad and the clamping screw (Fig. 3.7a). This allows the clamping pad to swivel around the clamping screw. The swivelling pad adjusts itself to suit the inaccuracies in the clamping face of the workpiece. The cross pin pulls the pad backwards when the screw is retracted. Figure 3.7b shows another type of floating pad.

The force developed by the screw can be calculated with the following formula:

$$F_s = \frac{F_h L}{R \tan(\alpha + \phi)}$$

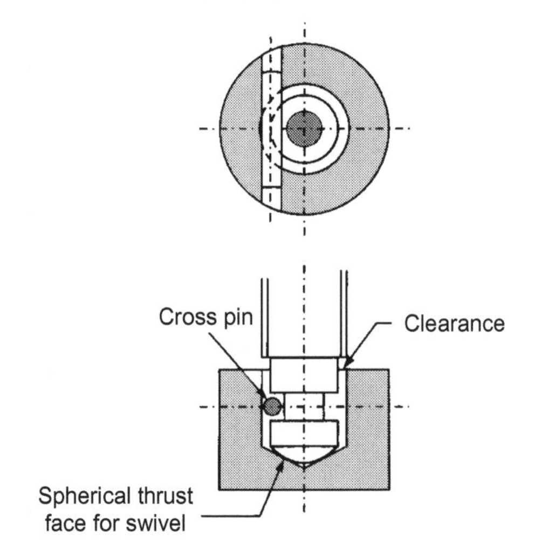

Fig. 3.7a *Floating pad*

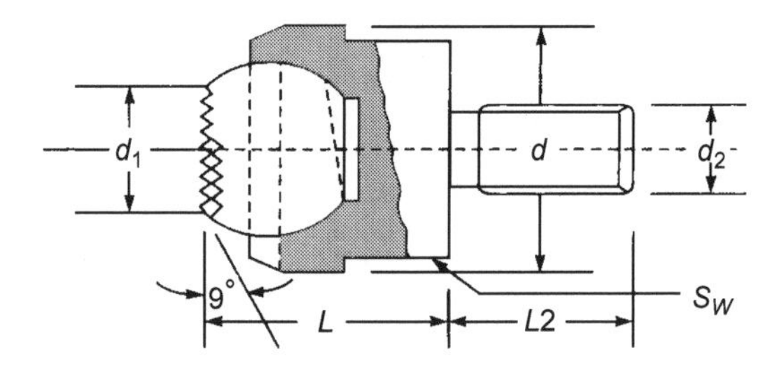

Fig. 3.7b *Another type of floating pad*

F_s = Force developed by screw
F_h = Pull or push applied to spanner
R = Pitch radius of screw thread
α = Helix angle of thread
ϕ = Friction angle of thread
L = Length of spanner or lever

A 12 mm hexagonal headed bolt with 100-mm-long wrench and a 10 kg manual pull can develop 700 kg clamping force along the axis of the screw.

Strap or Plate Clamps

These are made of rectangular plates and act like levers. In its simplest form, the clamp is tightened by rotating a hexagonal nut on a clamping screw (Fig. 3.8). One end of the clamp presses against the workpiece and the other on the heel pin, thus, loading the clamp like a simply supported beam. The clamping face of the clamp is curved and the pressure face of the heel pin is made spherical to take care of any variations in the workpiece.

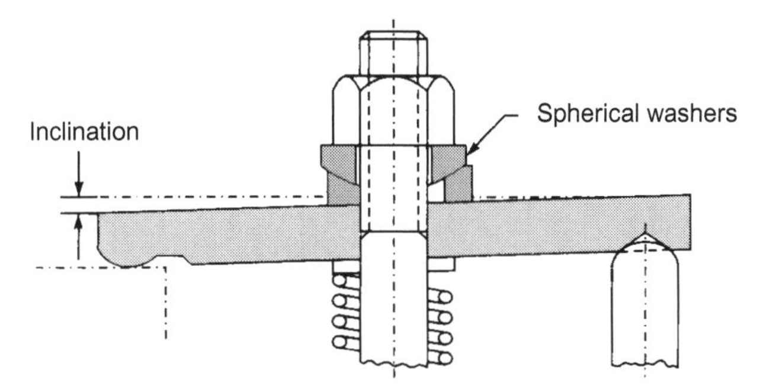

Fig. 3.8 *Simple plate clamp*

The provision for spherical washers between the clamp and the hexagonal nut provides a spherical joint which permits the clamp to tilt with respect to the screw and the nut. Thus, the clamp operates satisfactorily even if there is considerable variation in the workpiece height.

Generally, strap clamps are provided with a washer and a spring below the clamp. The spring lifts the clamp as the nut is loosened. The workpiece becomes free of even the gravitational load due to clamp weight. The spring holds the clamp in a raised position during loading and unloading of the workpiece.

Retractable Strap Clamps When clamps fall in the path of loading and unloading, they are made slotted to permit linear withdrawal (Fig. 3.9a). The clamp is retracted to the position shown by the chaindotted line during loading and unloading of the workpiece. Figure 3.9b shows a *U* clamp that can be removed altogether.

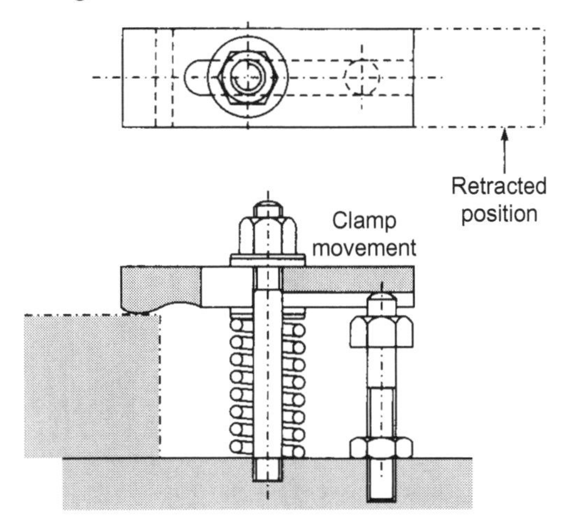

Fig. 3.9a *Slotted strap clamp*

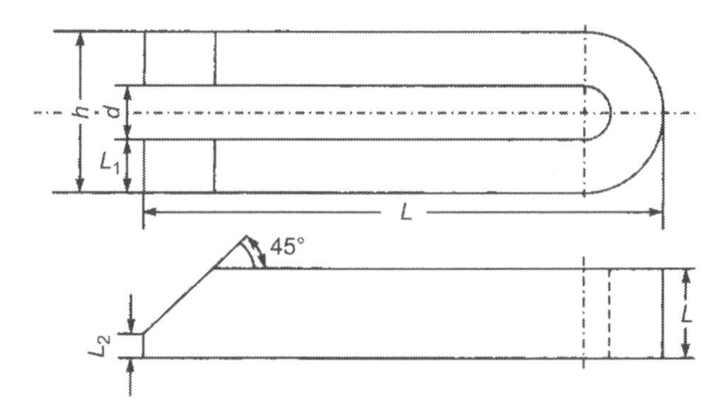

Fig. 3.9b *U clamp with open slot*

Swinging Strap Clamps In another design, the clamp is rotated by 90° to clear the passage for loading/unloading the workpiece (Fig. 3.10a). The clamp is swung to the position shown by the chaindotted line during loading and unloading of the workpiece.

Figure 3.10b shows a 45° swinging diagonal clamp developed by the author for clamping a jig for terminal box holes in the workpiece. As it is shaped to suit the square opening in the terminal box, the ends of the clamp are chamfered to enable loading and unloading of the clamp. The auxiliary view of the diagonal loading/unloading position of the clamp is in chaindotted lines.

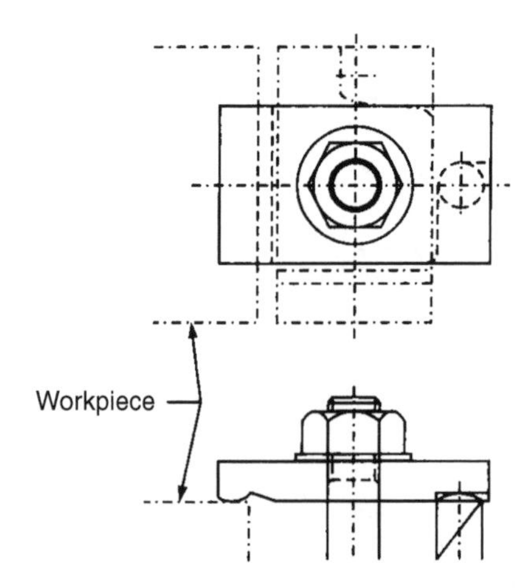

Fig. 3.10a *Swinging strap clamp*

The clamp is swung by 45° to bring the chamfered ends below the terminal box in the clamping position. The stop pins fitted in the jig plate facilitate bringing the clamp blindly in the clamping and loading/unloading

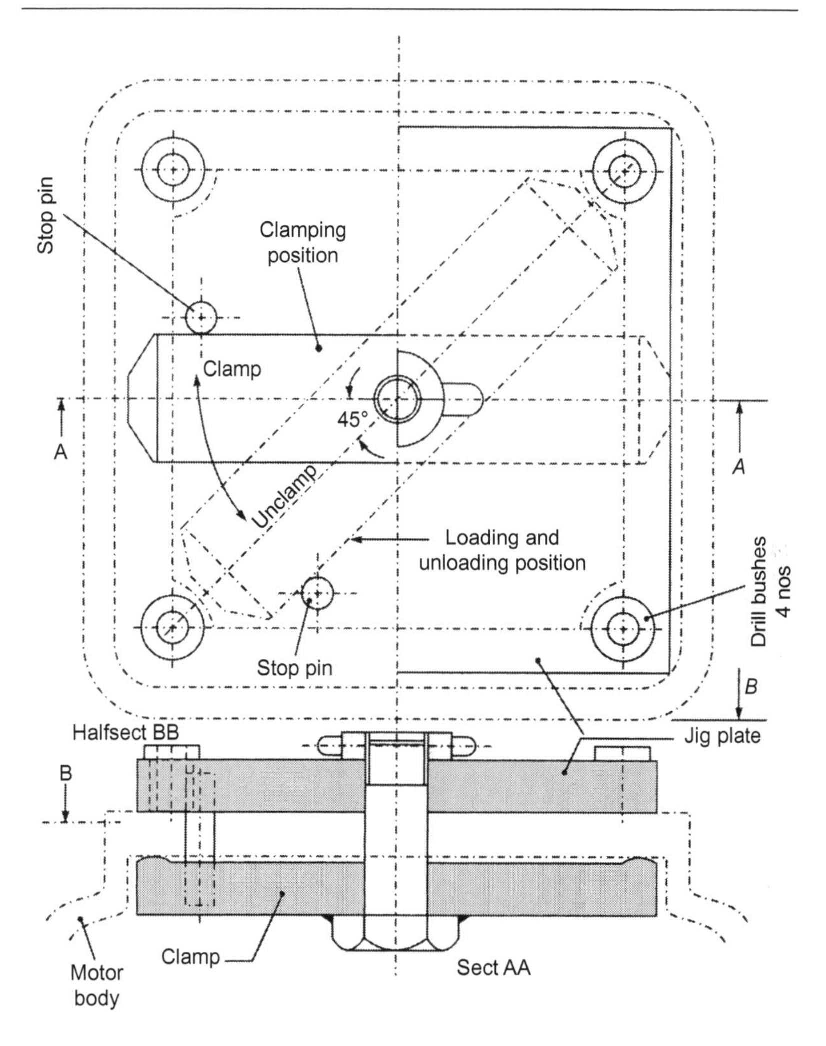

Fig. 3.10b *Special swing clamp for drill jig for terminal box holes in electrical motor body*

positions. The clamping bolt is welded to the clamp to simplify swinging of the clamp along with the bolt. The clamp is kept in the diagonal position while loading/unloading the jig. The clamp is lowered or raised through the opening in the terminal box. Clamping is effected by sandwiching the terminal box rim between the jig plate and the clamp.

After drilling is finished, the clamp is swung to the chaindotted diagonal position to permit withdrawal through the terminal box opening.

Edge Clamps Strap clamps are used extensively for clamping workpieces on the edges during facing operations. Figure 3.11 shows a simple edge clamp. The tightening of the hexagonal nut wedges the clamp between the workpiece and the angular heel surface. This clamps the workpiece. Figure 3.12a shows another edge clamp. It slides down the inclined heel as the hexagonal nut is tightened. This pushes the jaw against the workpiece to clamp its edge. Figure 3.12b shows a pivoted edge clamp.

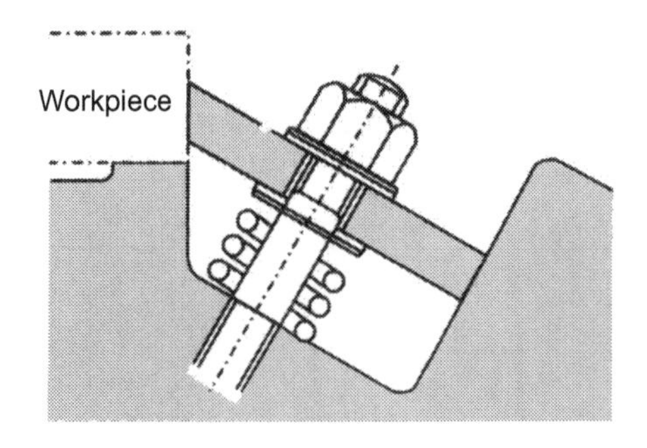

Fig. 3.11 *Edge strap clamp*

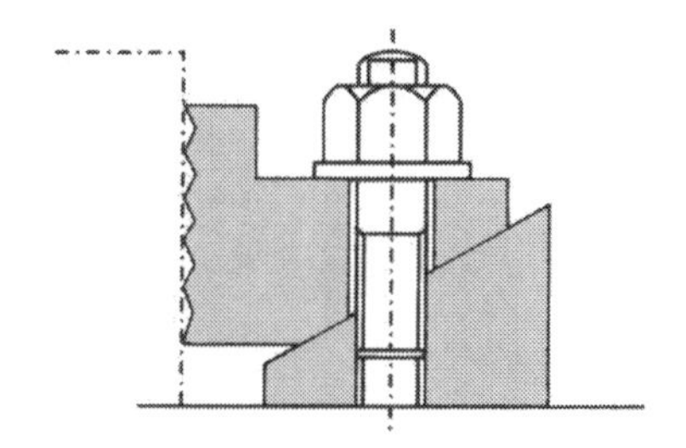

Fig. 3.12a *Edge jaw clamp*

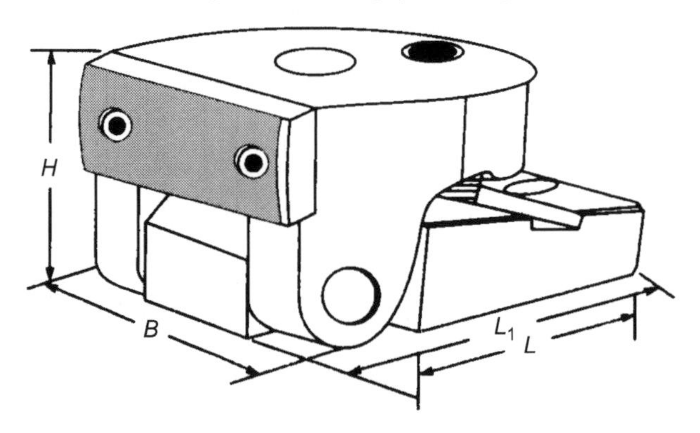

Fig. 3.12b *Hinged edge clamp*

Special Strap Clamps The clamp shape can be changed to suit the workpiece and the operation. In milling fixtures, clamps are often slotted at the centre to permit passage of the cutter (Fig. 3.13a). Circular and symmetrical workpieces can be clamped well with a spider clamp having three clamping points (Fig. 3.13b). As the clamp acts as a sort of rigid washer, no heel pin is necessary.

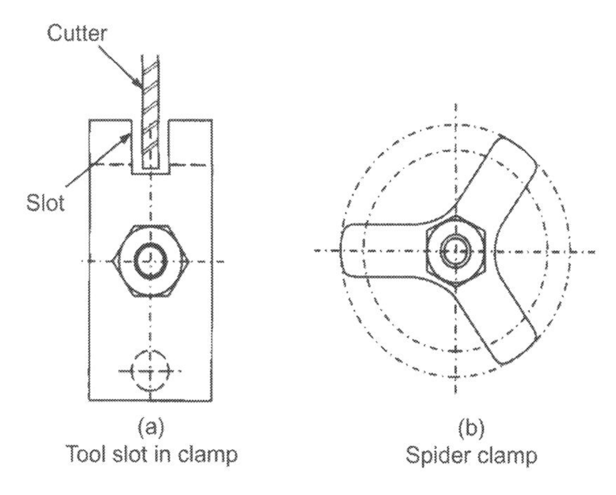

Fig. 3.13 *Special clamps*

Pivoted Clamps Clamps are often pivoted at the centre to simplify their operation. Figure 3.14 shows a pivoted strap clamp. It is tightened and loosened by the knurled head screw. The clamp pivots around the central pin during operation.

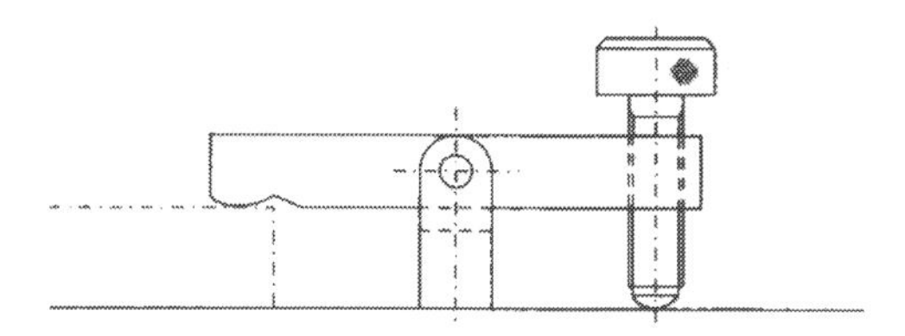

Fig. 3.14 *Pivoted strap clamp*

Figure 3.15 shows a couple of pivoted edge clamps. The point of operation should be noted, i.e. the screw has been shifted from the centre to the end opposite the clamping point. This places the clamp screw well below the path of cutter for facing workpiece top.

Pivot action can be used for two-way clamping of the workpiece (Fig. 3.16). The tightening of the knurled screw first pushes the workpiece till it touches the locator. Further tightening of the screw pivots the clamp anticlockwise till the curved face of the clamp touches downward on the workpiece. Still further tightening of the screw clamps the workpiece vertically

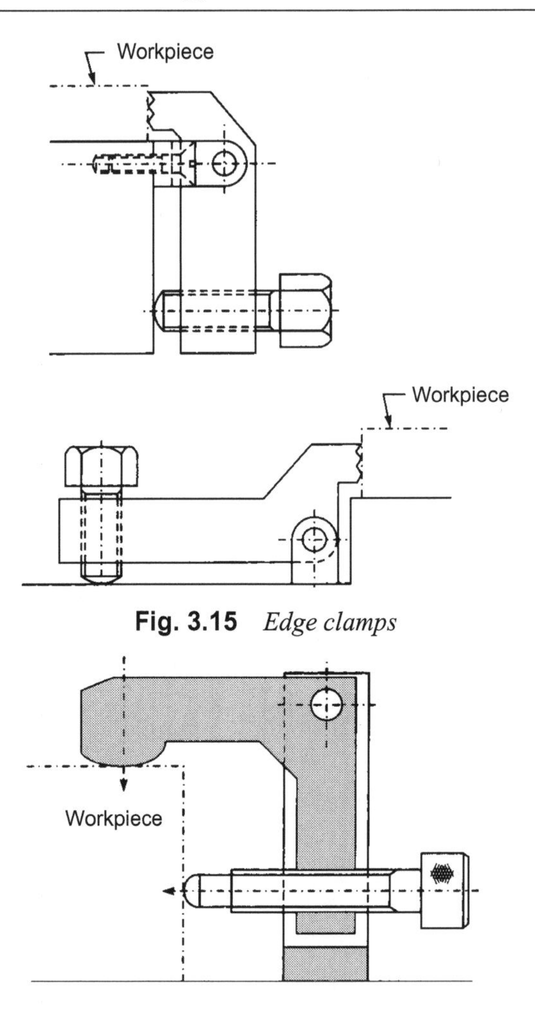

Fig. 3.15 *Edge clamps*

Fig. 3.16 *Pivoted two-way clamp*

and horizontally with the curved surface and the end of the knurled head screw. Thus, a two way-pivoted clamp pushes the workpiece against two locators before it clamps the workpiece simultaneously in two directions.

Hinged Clamps Hinged clamps provide rapid clearance of the loading and unloading passage. It is generally clamped with a swinging eyebolt. The clamp has an open slot through which the eyebolt can be swung into position as shown in Fig. 3.17(b). The tightening of the hexagonal nut clamps the workpiece. For loading and unloading the workpiece the hexagonal nut is loosened half-a-turn and the eyebolt is swung out of the open slot to free the hinged plate as shown in Fig. 3.17a. The hinged plate is swung aside during loading and unloading.

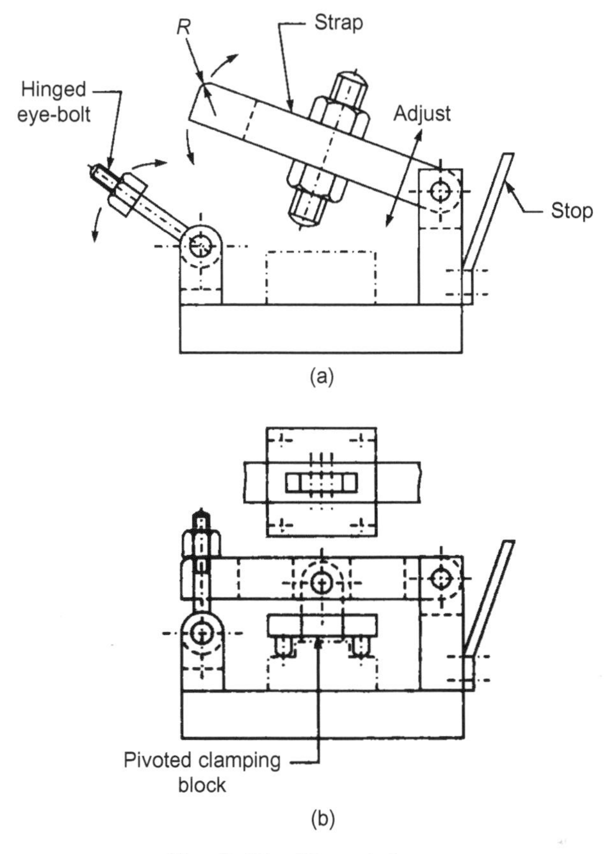

Fig. 3.17 *Hinged clamp*

A hinged clamp can also be used for two-way clamping (Fig. 3.18). The workpiece is pushed against the location pins by the pivoted edge clamp, which also houses the swinging eyebolt. The tightening of the knurled nut against the hinge clamp first pushes the workpiece against the location pins. After that, further tightening of the knurled nut pushes the clamping pad towards the workpiece, which is clamped simultaneously in two directions by the edge clamp and the pad in the hinge. The knurled nut is loosened only by half-a-turn before swinging the eyebolt and the hinge plate aside for loading and unloading the workpiece.

Swinging Clamps Like hinged clamps, swing clamps must be swung to the working position. However, in swinging clamps, the axis of rotation is square to the clamping plate face. Consequently, the swing clamps rotate in the planes of their plates. Figure 3.19 depicts a simple swinging clamp which is pivoted about the shoulder screw. The workpiece

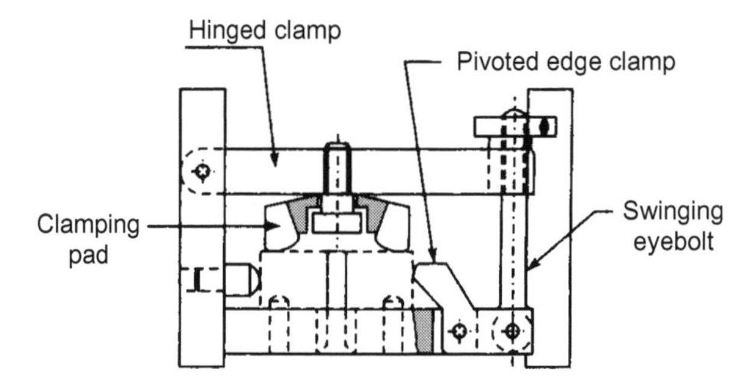

Fig. 3.18 *Hinged two-way clamp*

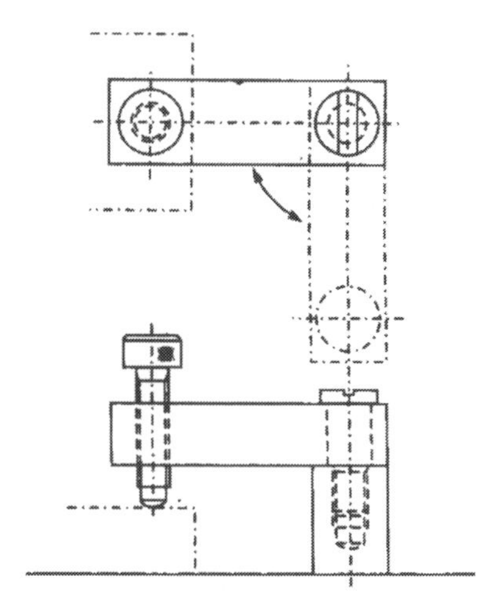

Fig. 3.19 *Swinging strap clamp*

is clamped by the knurled head screw as shown in full lines. For loading and unloading the workpiece, the clamp is swung aside as shown by the chaindotted line.

Turning fixtures use compact and sturdy swinging hook bolt clamps (Figs 3.20 and 14.6). The clamp is shaped like a short cantilever with a turned outside diameter which slides in a housing.

The housing is milled with two steps which are at right angles to each other. These act as stoppers for the working and unloading position of the clamp. A spring raises the clamp clear above the workpiece as the clamp is loosened. For securing the workpiece, the clamp is turned through right angle to touch the stopper face in the housing. It holds the clamp in position as it is tightened by the hexagonal nut. The length of the clamping lever (G) should not be more than three fourth of the mating length (J) with the housing.

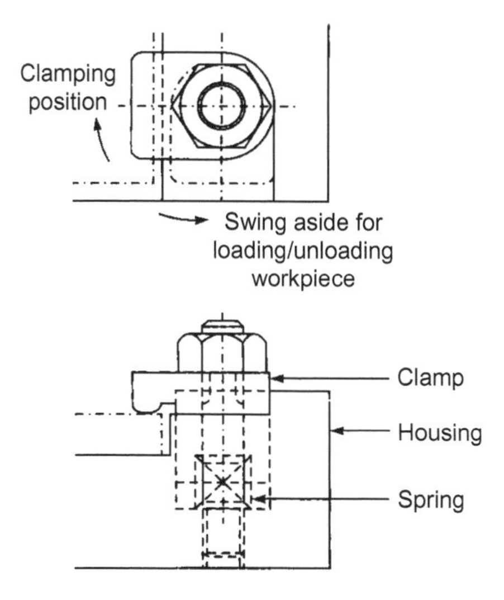

Fig. 3.20 *Swinging hook clamp*

Figure15.6a gives the dimensions of the standard hook bolt clamps while Fig.15 .6b gives the relationship between the screw and clamping forces (F_w/F_s) for various G/J ratios.

Figure 3.21a shows a swinging latch with an open slot at one end. The latch is swung around pivot *P* at the other end. Shoulder screw *S* enters the open slot during operation. The workpiece is clamped by a knurled head screw. Collars of shoulder screws *P* and *S* provide reaction backing during clamping. For unloading and replenishment of the workpiece, the clamping screw is loosened slightly and the latch is swung aside to the position shown by the chaindotted line.

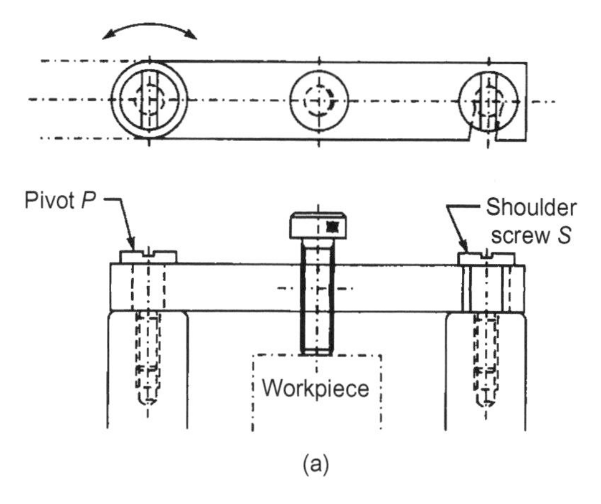

Fig. 3.21a *Swinging latch*

Figure 3.21b shows three other types of latches and their methods of operation. The chaindotted lines show the latches in clear loading and unloading position, whereas the full lines show the latches in the clamping position.

Shoulder screws are often used as pivots for thrust pads in jigs and fixtures. The shoulder diameter must be bigger than the thread diameter so that the shoulder face acts as a stop when the screw is tightened. The thickness of the pivoted part should be less than the shoulder length to provide clearance for trouble-free operation of the pivoted joint.

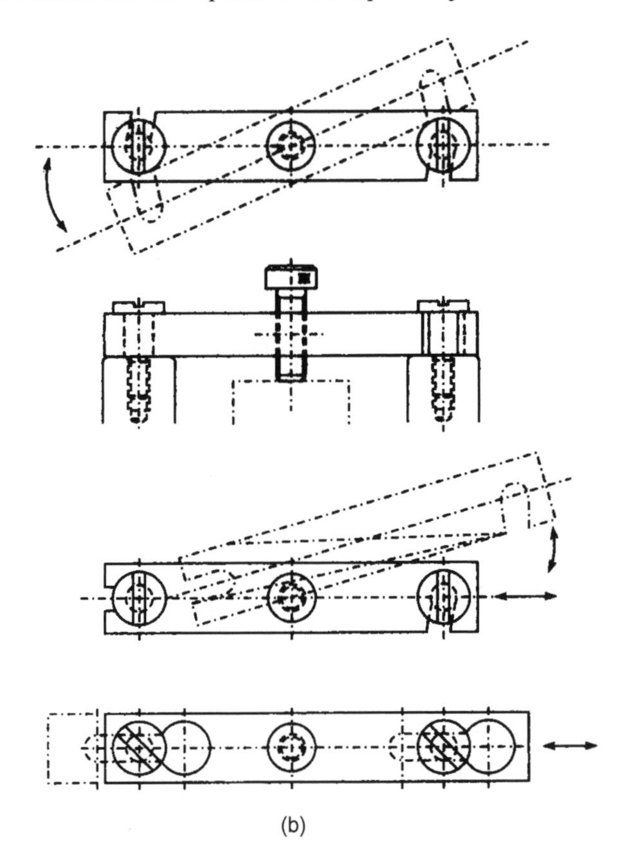

Fig. 3.21b *Various types of latches*

C Washer The C washer is a strap clamp with an open slot (Fig. 3.22) and is simple and quick in operation. The slot permits removal of C washer after a slight loosening of the hexagonal nut. The distance across corners of the hexagonal nut should be less than the bore of the workpiece to permit passage of the nut through the bore during loading and unloading. The loss of washer can be prevented by chaining it to the fixture or pivoting it around a shoulder screw. The pivot shoulder screw makes the C washer captive.

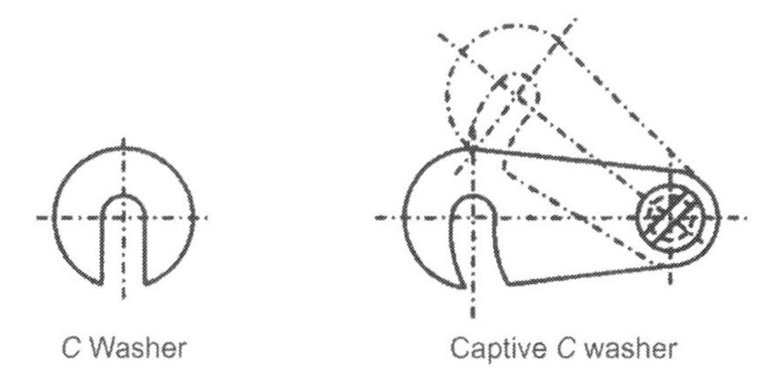

Fig. 3.22 *C washers*

Quick Action Clamps

The advent of mass production has resulted in the development of several ingenious quick action clamping gadgets. Some of these are described below.

Cams They are popular as quick action clamps. Cams tend to shift their mating faces. There is a risk of the cam clamp getting loose due to vibrations. The coefficient of friction between the cam and the mating surface must be taken into account while determining the eccentricity of the cam.

Eccentric cams are the easiest to manufacture. Eccentric pivoting of a cylinder converts it to a cam (Fig. 3.23). The eccentricity of the cam should be more than 1.5 times the variation in the workpiece. The outside diameter of the eccentric depend upon the co-efficient of friction between the eccentric and the mating surface. If the co-efficient of friction is more than 0.1, the outside diameter should be more than 20 times the eccentricity to

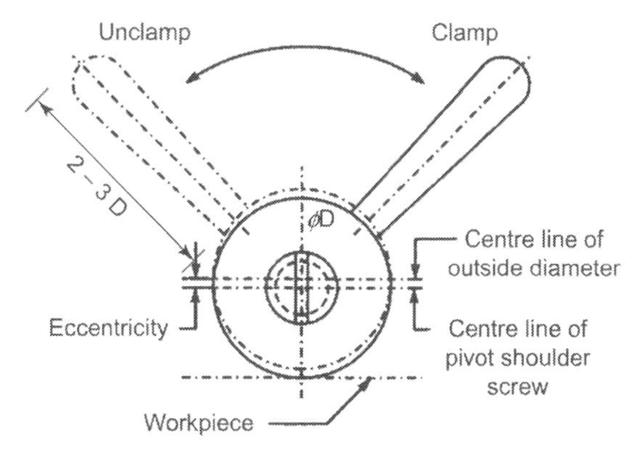

Fig. 3.23 *Eccentric cam clamp*

prevent loosening due to vibrations: The handle length should be 2–3 times the cam diameter 'D'.

The eccentric cam can replace the hexagonal nut in a strap clamp (Fig. 3.24) or a heel pin in a strap clamp (Fig. 3.25a). A female cylindrical surface can be used as a hook clamp (Fig. 3.26). Figure 3.25b shows a cam operated edge clamp.

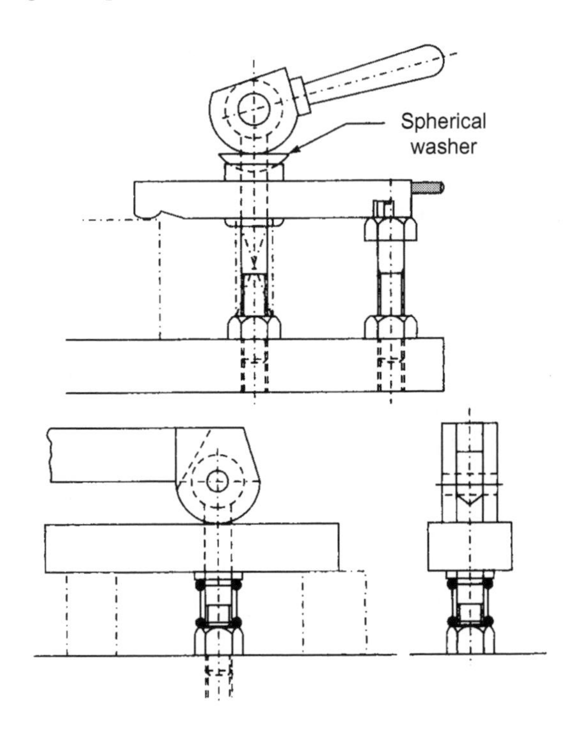

Fig. 3.24 *Replacing nut by cam*

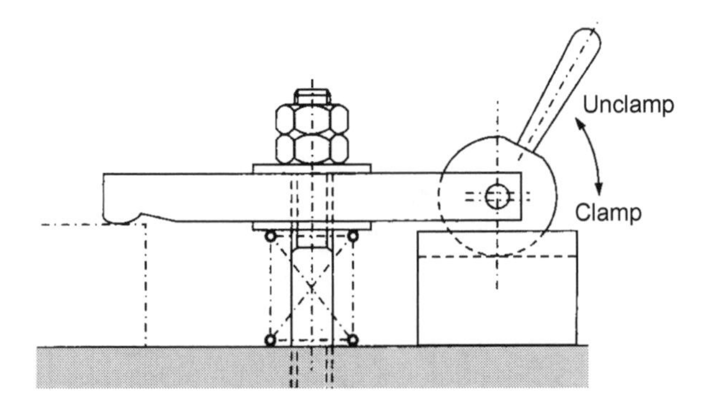

Fig. 3.25a *Replacing heel by cam*

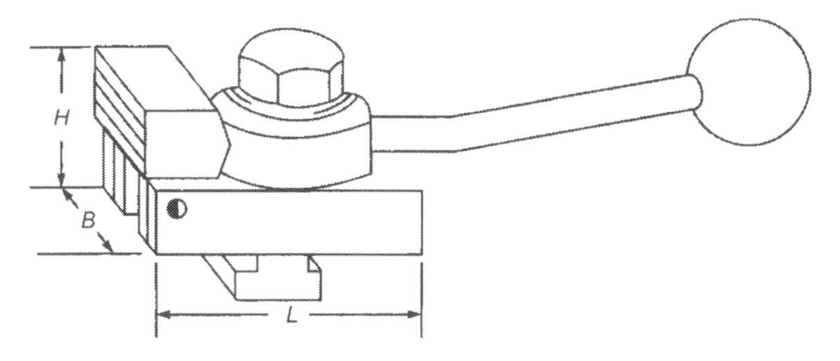

Fig. 3.25b *Cam operated edge clamp*

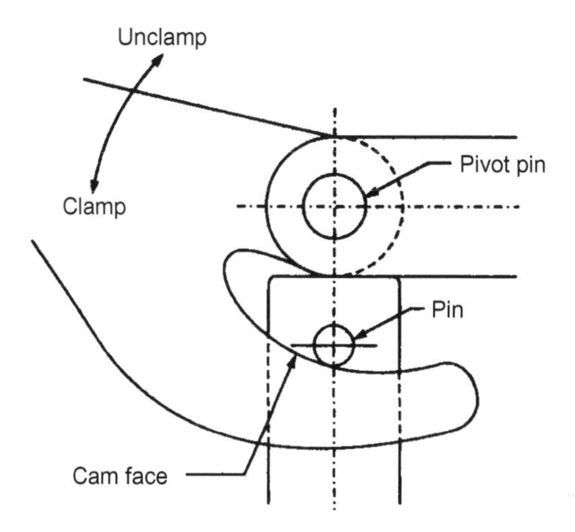

Fig. 3.26 *Hook cam clamp*

An eccentric shaft has been used for sandwich-type clamping in Fig. 3.27. The rotation of the eccentric shaft with a pinned handle raises and lowers the jig plate fixed to the two connecting rods. The jig plate is clamped against the workpiece face during drilling. For loading and unloading the workpiece, the jig plate is raised by rotating the handle in the opposite direction.

Bayonet Clamp This is a cylindrical cam with a part thread serving as a cam (Fig. 3.28). The motion of the bayonet is guided by the spherical-ended screw mating in the groove in the bayonet. A part of the bayonet groove is straight. The bayonet can be pulled back straight axially through the straight slot to provide ample clearance during loading and loading of the workpiece. For clamping the workpiece, the bayonet is first pushed forward through the straight groove to close the distance between the workpiece and the bayonet face. At the end of its straight portion, the bayonet is turned

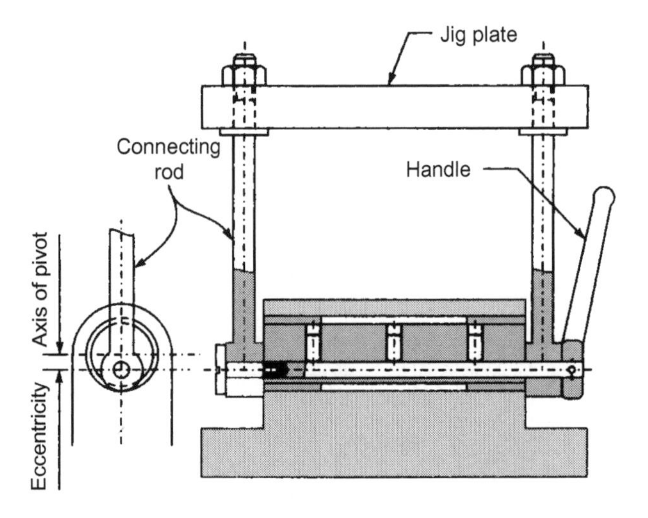

Fig. 3.27 *Eccentric shaft clamping*

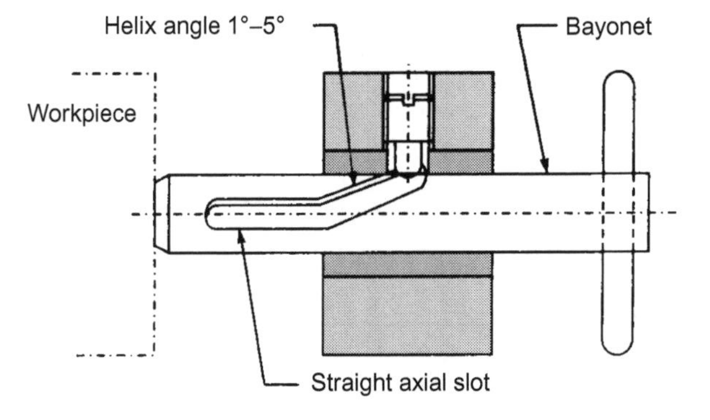

Fig. 3.28 *Bayonet clamp*

clockwise. The inclined groove in the bayonet acts like a part of a thread. The spherical-end screw pushes the rotating bayonet towards the workpiece to clamp it. To prevent the clamp from loosening due to vibrations the thread or helix angle of the inclined groove should be between 1° and 7°.

Toggle Clamps These are quick action clamps which can be withdrawn by a considerable distance for loading and unloading of the workpiece. Figure 3.29 shows two types of toggle clamps. The C frame clamp can be swung to the chaindotted position during loading and unloading. The pusher-type toggle clamp withdraws backwards during unclamping. Toggle clamps are vulnerable to workpiece variations. Most of the toggle clamps are, therefore, provided with adjustable clamping screws.

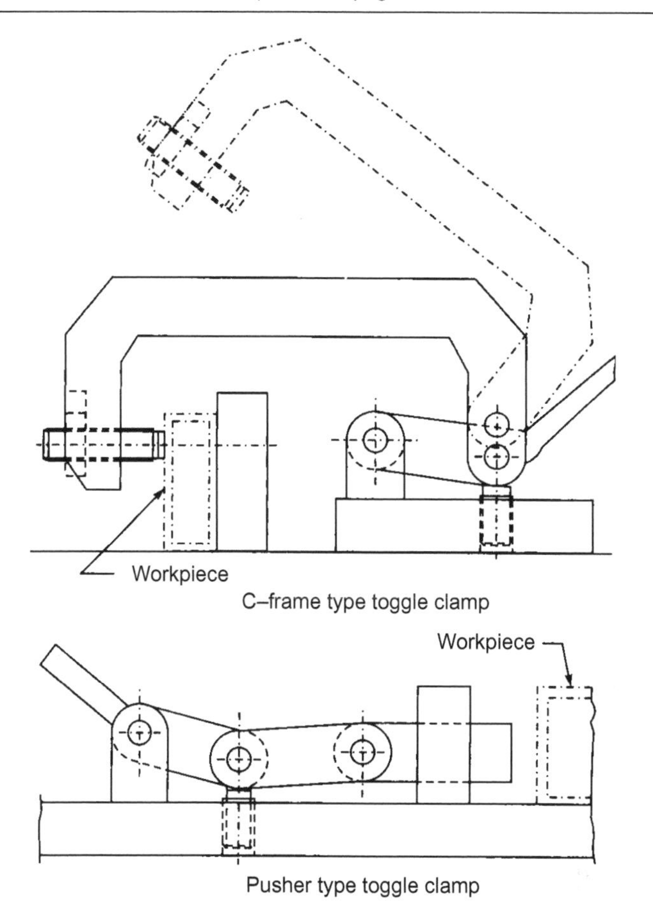

Fig. 3.29 *Toggle clamps*

Quarter-Turn Screw *(Fig. 3.30)* It is also called thumb screw and is used to clamp and unclamp hinged jig plates and latches within a quarter turn. In the unclamped position, the head of the thumb screw can pass through the slot provided in the jig/latch plate. The plate can be swung clear of the thumb screw head to the required position. For clamping the jig/latch plate, the thumb screw is turned through 90°, so that its head is at right angles to the slot in the plate. In this position, the thumb screw clamps the plate in the working position. For proper clamping, the mating faces of the thumb screw head must be filed to suit the thickness of the plate.

Quarter-turn screws are suitable for light loads only. For heavy loads, it is better to use a swinging eyebolt and nut knob-combination (Figs 3.17 and 5.17b).

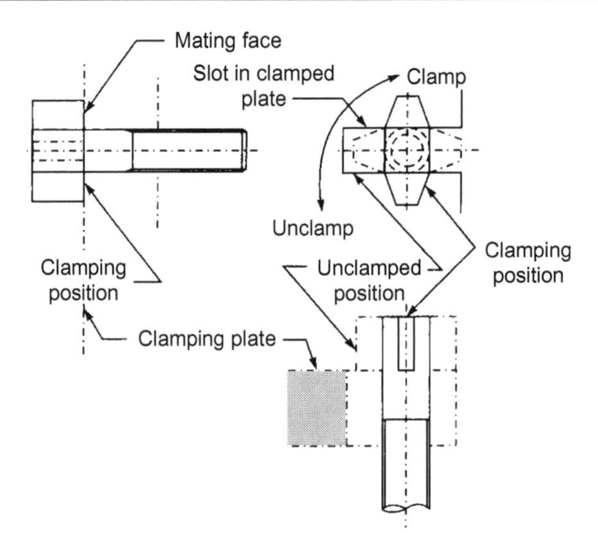

Fig. 3.30 *Quarter-turn screw*

Multiple Clamping

Double Clamping Two workpieces with limited variation can be clamped by a single strap clamp (Fig. 3.31a). Swivelable spherical washers between the nut and the clamp allow the clamp to tilt slightly to suit the variation in the two workpieces.

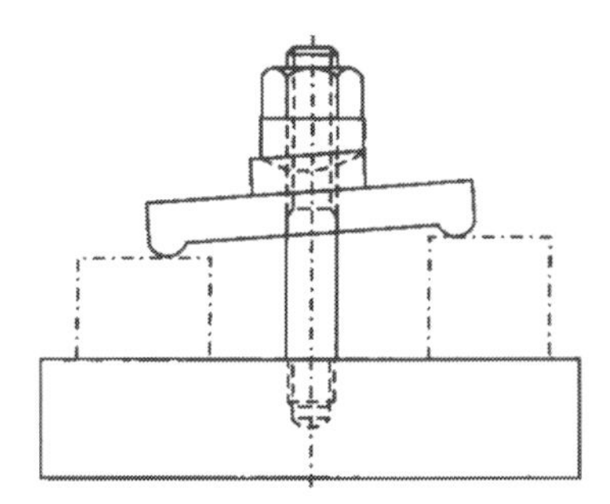

Fig. 3.31a *Double clamping*

Figure 3.31b shows a method for actuating two clamps by rotating a single handle. Furthermore horizontal cam-pin can assume suitable position to take care of the variation in thickness of flanges in the casting. Rotating the handle clockwise pushes the heel pin downwards. The angular face of the heel pin pushes the horizontal cam-pin towards the opposite clamp, raising its heel pin to clamp the workpiece at two places simultaneously.

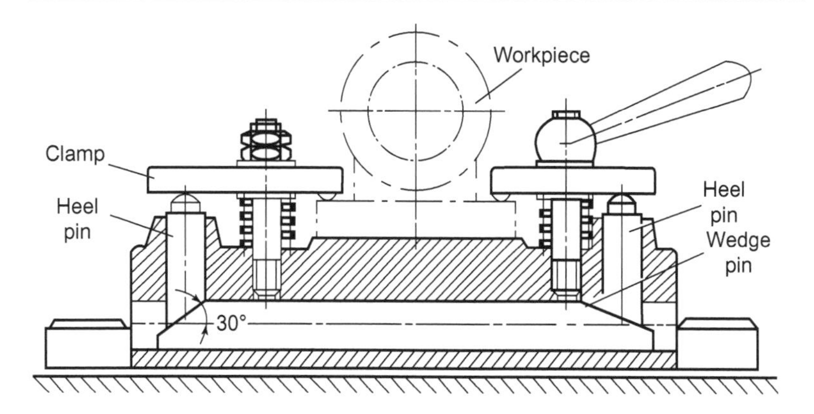

Fig. 3.31b *Tightening two clamps by a single handle*

Equaliser This method of compensating variation in two workpiece pivots the clamp around a pin (Fig. 3.4). The equaliser clamp pivots to suit the variation in the workpieces. The equaliser principle can be extended to clamp more than two workpieces. Figure 3.5 shows an equaliser arrangement for clamping four workpieces simultaneously with a single clamp.

Naturally only an even number of workpieces can be clamped by an equaliser.

Stacking Often, workpieces can be stacked together and the entire stack can be secured by a single clamp (Fig. 3.32). Alternatively, workpiece can be sandwiched between locators, and the multilayered sandwich can be secured by a single clamp. In the string milling fixtures shown in Fig. 6.12, round workpieces are sandwiched between *V* locators. All the workpieces are clamped simulateously by the hexagonal head bolt at one end of the fixure.

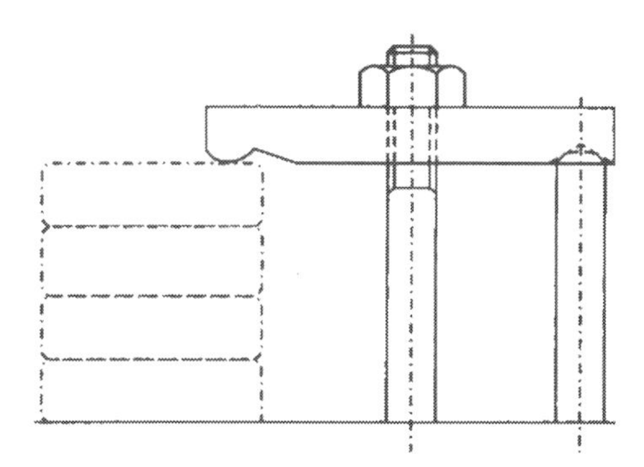

Fig. 3.32a *Stack clamping*

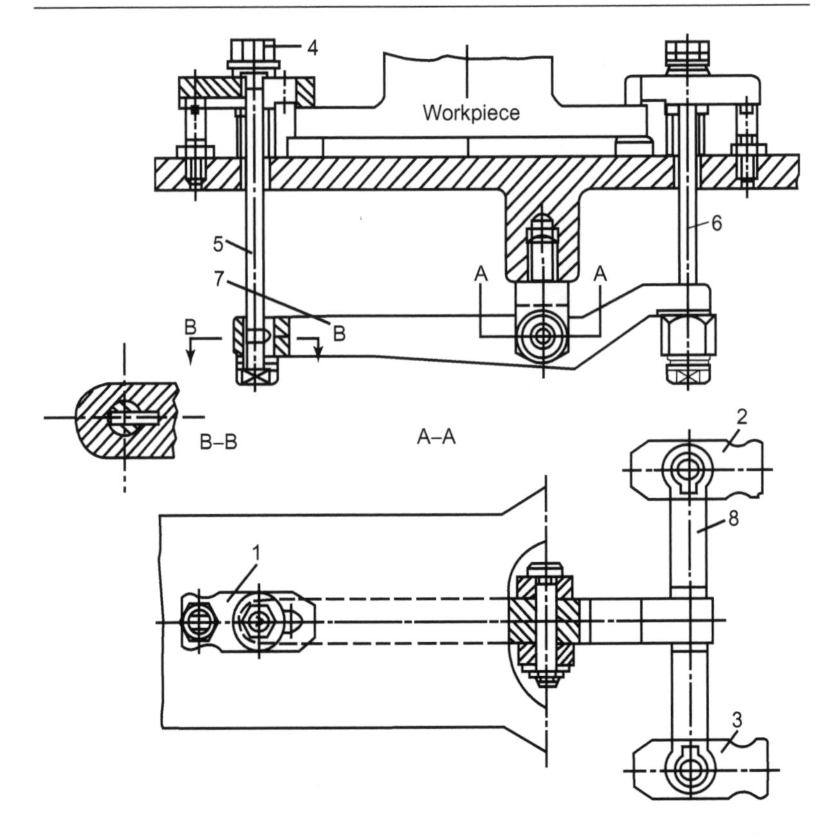

Fig. 3.32b *Actuating three clamps by tightening a single handle*

Power Clamping A number of clamps can be operated simultaneously by power clamping. Power clamping can be broadly divided into the following categories:

1. Fluid power clamping
   (a) Pneumatic clamping
   (b) Hydraulic clamping
2. Vacuum clamping
3. Magnetic clamping
4. Electrostatic clamping

1. ***Fluid Power Clamping*** Fluid power clamps are generally actuated by cylinders. Figure 3.33 shows a clamping fixture with the clamping nut attached to the cylinder ram. The feeding of pressurised fluid through the port pulls the ram downwards and presses the clamp against the workpiece. For unclamping, the port is connected to an unpressurised discharge line. The force of the spring under the clamp pushes the clamp and ram upwards. In

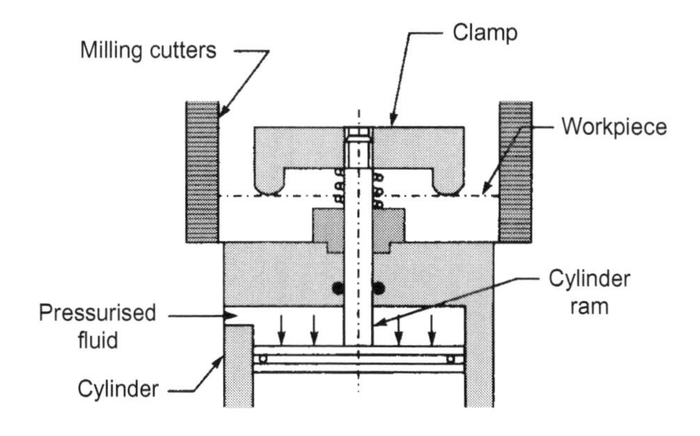

Fig. 3.33 *Fluid power clamping*

addition to unclamping the workpiece, the rising piston also drives the fluid out of the cylinder through the port.

For connecting the port alternately to pressure and discharge lines for clamping and unclamping, it is necessary to use a three-way direction control valve. Lever, pedal or electrical operation of the direction-control valve clamps or unclamps the workpiece.

The operation of a single-direction control valve can actuate a number of clamps through a number of cylinders. The valve simultaneously connects all the cylinders to pressure or discharge line. Figure 3.34 shows a fixture with four clamps and cylinders, which can be actuated by a single valve.

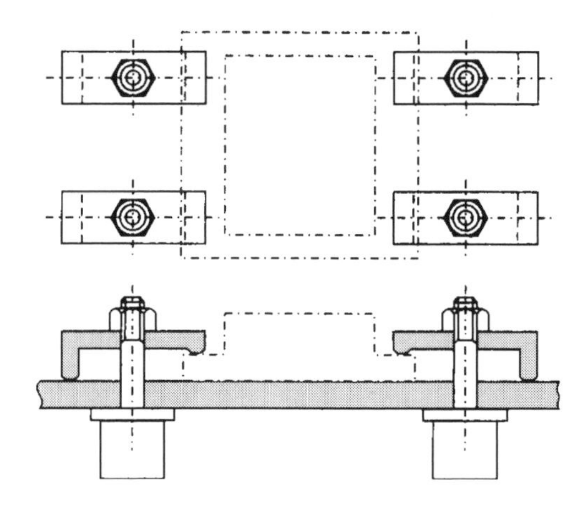

Fig. 3.34 *Multiple clamping by fluid power*

Moreover, the clamping pressures of all the clamps would be equal. The clamping pressure can be varied by regulating the pressure of the fluid.

Higher pressure can be used for heavy roughing cut. The pressure can be reduced considerably during light finishing cut.

There is a risk of sudden pressure drop in the event of a power failure. This can be countered by provision of a non-return valve in the pressure supply line. If the power fails, the non-return valve automatically closes the passage between the pressure line and the cylinder. This entraps pressurised fluid between the cylinder piston and the non-return valve. It prevents unclamping due to depressurisation of the supply source.

Some designers prefer to use positive rack and pinion nonreturn mechanism between the clamp and the cylinder (Fig. 3.35). The fluid power cylinder is used only to move the clamp into the position. The clamp would stay in position even if the cylinder is depressurised due to a power failure.

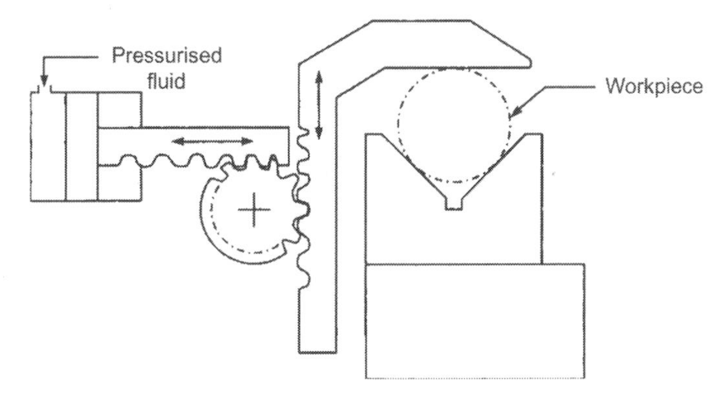

Fig. 3.35 *Rack and pinion actuated fluid power clamping*

Figure 3.36 shows a variety of cylinder mounting styles.

a. ***Pneumatic clamping*** In pneumatic clamping compressed air is used as the fluid for power transmission and application. The air is pressurised to 5–6 atmospheres (5–6 kg/cm^2) to energise it. Depressurised exhaust is discharged directly into the atmosphere through direction-control valve. Generally, a large centralised compressor supplies pressurised air to the entire shop—all the pneumatic drives and fixtures in the work place.

   Although very rapid in operation, air-operated devices are vulnerable to variations in the load they move. If the load resistance increases, the speed of the pneumatic device drops and vice versa. Consequently, pneumatic devices are unsuitable for applications in which speed variations are unacceptable. Moreover, due to ageing, joints of old distribution pipes start leaking. This causes a drop in the pressure and wastage of energy. In humid climates, moisture in

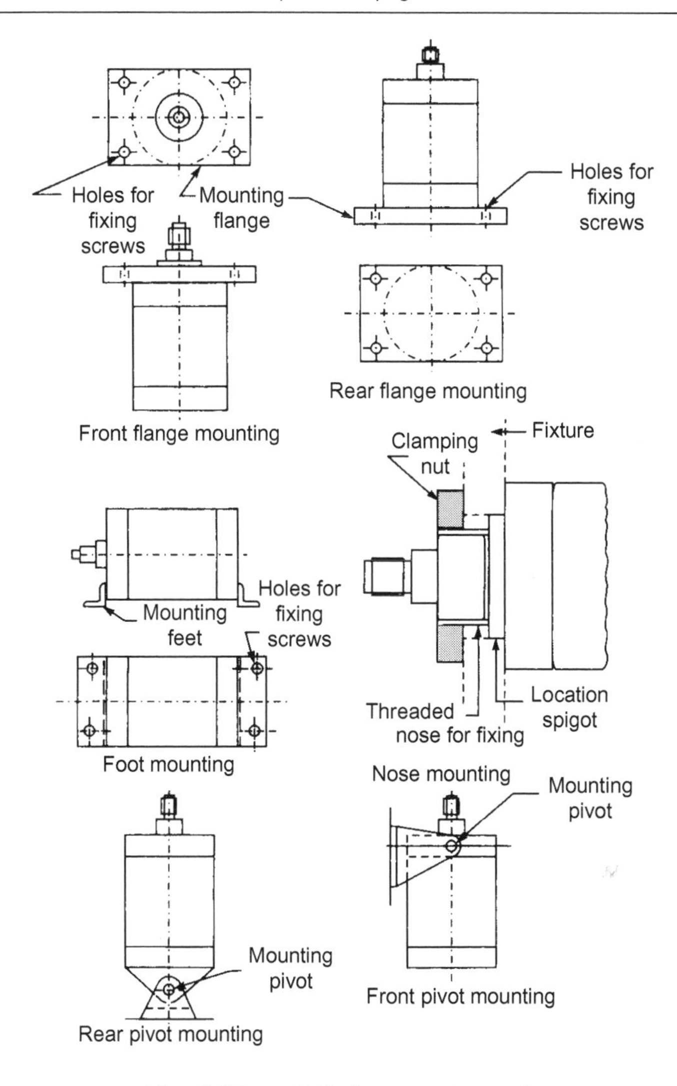

Fig. 3.36a *Cylinder mounting styles*

the air causes rusting of pneumatic cylinders and valves. This can be minimised by filtering out the moisture in the air before it enters the pneumatic fixture. It is necessary to use a lubricator also because it impregnates the air with oil mist, which is carried into the cylinders and valves to lubricate them. If it is necessary to vary the system pressure, a pressure regulator is also used.

b. ***Hydraulic clamping*** Unlike air, hydraulic oils are almost incompressible. Consequently, variation in load does not cause much speed variation in hydraulic systems. Speed variation can be minimised further to almost negligible by using pressure compensated flow control valve. The operating pressure of a hydraulic system ranges from 7 to 250 atmospheres. High pressure permits use of small compact cylinders to develop high force. However, hydraulic cylinders are slow in operation in comparison with pneumatic actuators. Oil is re-circulated in the system through a reservoir. Generally, every machine or fixture would have its own individual hydraulic reservoir and power unit. Large centralised power units are rarely used. The hydraulic operation of a mechanism generally requires substantial investment for hydraulic power pack and cylinders.

Hydraulic Power Multiplier Figure 3.36b shows a hydraulic power multiplier. The force (F_s) exerted by the screw '1' is enhanced manifold by using the device. The small ram with diameter '*d*' is pushed by the screw to develop hydraulic pressure in the oil in the big '*D*' diameter cylinder. This pushes the bigger ram to clamp workpiece, through a pin, with much more force 'F_w'.

$$F_w = F_s \times (D/d)$$

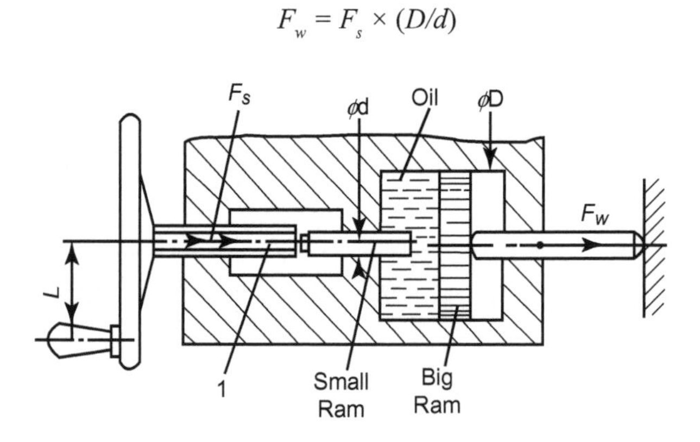

Fig. 3.36b *Hydraulic force multiplier (intensifier)*

This device does not require a costly power pack, but the small as well as the big ram must be provided with rubber seals to prevent oil leakage . The seals are not shown in the figure. Furthermore the multiplier body must be split into 2 or 3 parts to facilitate the manufacture as well as the assembly.

2. ***Vacuum clamping*** This is particularly convenient for securing thin flat sheets which are vulnerable to distortion under heavy clamping force. Vacuum clamping provides light clamping. The holding face is provided with 0.025 mm deep grooves which serve as vacuum ducts. The clamping face is circumscribed by a rubber seal groove all around. The seal in the groove segregates the clamping vacuum area from the space outside the seal. The vacuum pressure is usually limited to 1 kg/cm^2. Figure 3.37 shows a vacuum-holding fixture, distribution grooves and rubber seal.

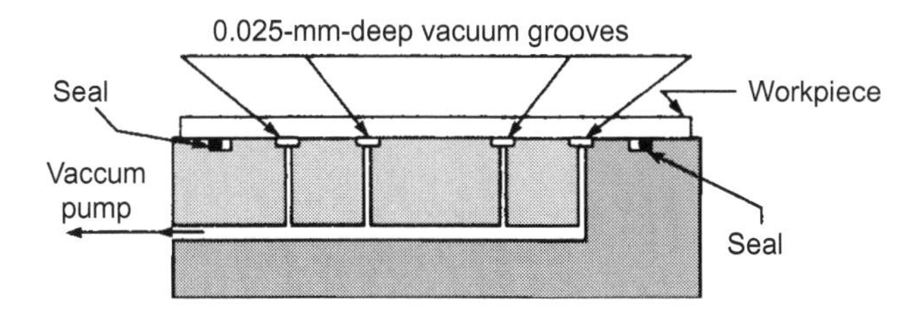

Fig. 3.37 *Vacuum clamping*

3. ***Magnetic Clamping*** Magnetic clamping force can be developed by permanent magnets or electromagnets.

a. ***Permanent magnets*** They are mounted on a sliding member, which can be moved under a non-magnetic material on a table to block magnetic flux. This releases the workpiece. For clamping the workpiece, permanent magnets are moved under the magnetic part of the table. This allows the magnetic flux to pass through the workpiece and hold it magnetically. The permanent magnets are slid in the clamping and unclamping positions by a lever.

Generally, the magnetic table area is divided into alternative strips of magnetic and non-magnetic material. The non-magnetic strips block the path of a part of the magnetic flux and force the flux to pass through the workpiece to clamp it magnetically (Fig. 3.38). Thus, the non-magnetic strips act as flux dams or barriers. In permanent magnet tables, the magnets are slid below the non-magnetic strips to completely block the magnetic flux during unclamping.

b. ***Electromagnetic clamping*** Electromagnetic tables use solenoid coils as temporary magnets. When DC current is passed through the solenoid coil, it acts like a magnet. The coils and the table is demagnetised on switching off the current and the workpiece is released. The magnetic clamping force can be varied by varying the current passing through the solenoid coil.

Magnetic clamping leaves some residual magnetism in the workpieces. This can be removed by demagnetising the workpiece.

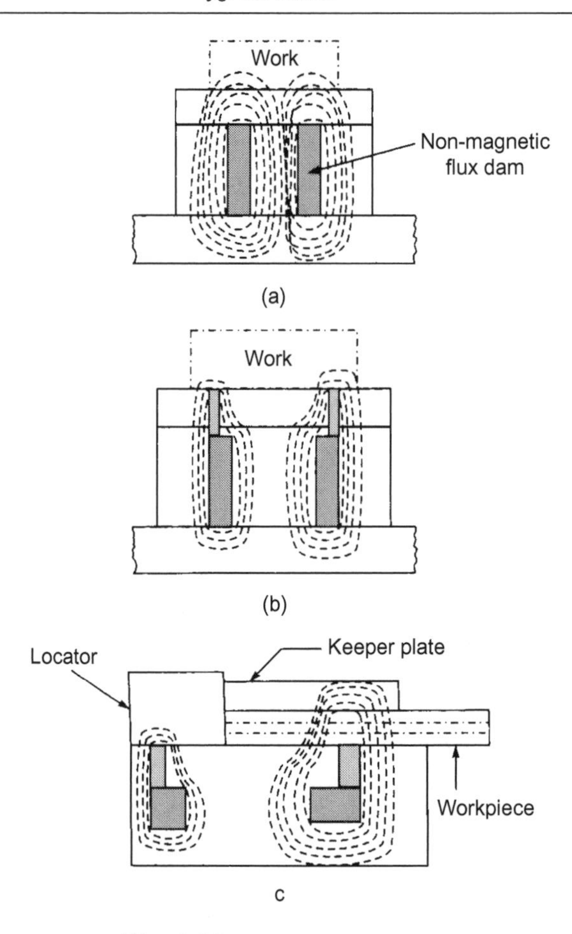

Fig. 3.38 *Magnetic clamping*

4. ***Electrostatic clamping*** In this method, the workpiece is charged with static electricity with polarity opposite to the polarity on the chuck face. The opposite attracting polarities of the workpiece and the chuck face develop the clamping force. The workpiece and the chuck are separated by insulating dielectric fluid. The clamping force can be varied by varying the static electrical charge. Even non-conducting materials can be coated with a thin metallic layer and secured by electrostatic clamping. The workpieces must be clean and dry for good electrostatic clamping.

Non-conventional Clamping

Adhesive Clamping Flat-surfaced workpieces subjected to light loads can be stuck to workholders by a thin film of compatible adhesive.

However, adhesives require some curing time for hardening. Furthermore, after completion of the operation, the workpiece has to be cleaned and the adhesive removed, which is a time-consuming operation. Consequently, adhesive clamping is used only when no other alternatives are available. Even then it can be used only for light loads.

Fusion clamping In this, the workpieces are jacketed by a cast of low melting point bismuth alloy, which is melted and poured around the workpiece. On cooling and solidification, the alloy secures the workpiece firmly. Complicated shape can be secured well by this method.

The alloy casting can be cut into two valves and machined to attach them to chuck or vice jaws. The jaws can be used for repeated clamping of the workpieces. Fusion clamping is, sometimes, the only method of clamping possible in odd-shaped difficult workpieces.

Compensating Differential Clamps

Differential clamps adjust their position themselves to suit the workpiece (Fig. 3.39). As a result, the clamps do not subject the workpiece to bending or any other distortion. They clamp the workpiece without shifting its position. The lever jaws are closed or opened by turning a screw which engages in *T* slot in the operating cam. The slot in the cam is much wider than the collar of the operating screw. This wide clearance allows the cam to slide towards any of the lever jaws. If jaw *A* touches the workpiece first the cam slides in the opposite direction towards jaw *B* till *B* also touches the workpiece. With both the jaws touching the workpiece, further tightening of the operating screw forces the jaws against the workpiece and clamps it firmly. Differential clamps are very convenient for securing a workpiece without shifting or distorting it.

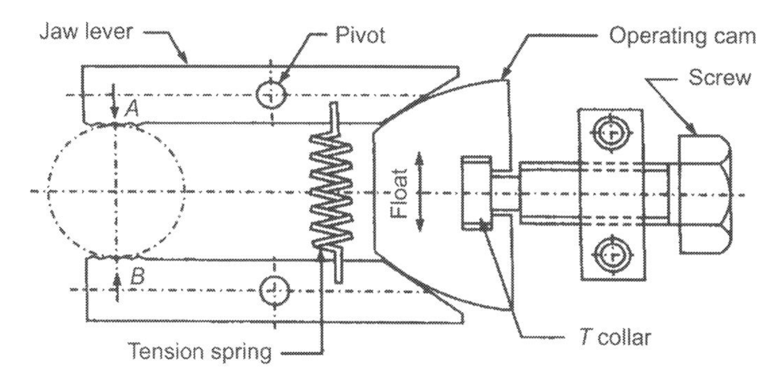

Fig. 3.39 *Differential clamp*

Figure 3.40 shows a gripper used for clamping parallel plates. The swivelling clamping pads position automatically to suit the object to be gripped as the clamping screw is turned.

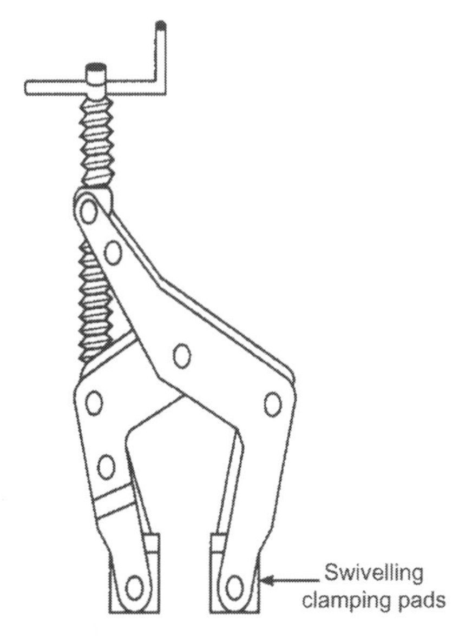

Fig. 3.40 *Differential clamp*

Summary

Principles of Clamping

1. Position clamp on a strong supported part of the workpiece, clear of the workpiece loading/unloading and cutting tool paths.
2. Clamp strength should be adequate to withstand operational forces without damaging the workpiece.
3. Quick operation without spanner (knobs, levers). Pneumatic/hydraulic operation for simultaneous actuation of numerous clamps.
4. Compensation for variation in the workpiece through radii at clamping point and on the heel pin, use of spherical washers and equalisers (in multiple clamping).

Clamps Types

1. Screw clamps with/without floating pad.
2. Plate clamps: slotted, swinging, edge clamps, pivoted two-way clamps, hinged clamps, hook clamps, latches, C washers.
3. Quick action clamps: Cam clamps, bayonet clamps, quarter-turn screw, toggle clamps.
4. Multiple clamping: double clamping, stacking workpieces, power clamping with penumatic/hydraulic actuation, magnetic clamping.
5. Non-conventional clamping using adhesives, fusion.

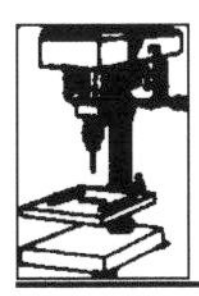

CHAPTER 4

Indexing Devices

Indexing is a process of quick, accurate location of a workpiece or fixture in a number of specific positions. Indexing involves periodic linear or rotary movement of the indexed part to the next position. An indexing plunger locates the indexed part precisely in each position.

Linear Indexing

When a number of holes with the same size and pitch are to be drilled in a workpiece (Fig. 4.1), the cost of the jig can be reduced greatly by resorting to linear indexing. Figure 4.2 depicts an indexing jig for a workpiece. The indexing pin is first inserted into hole *A* and used as a stopper for drilling the first hole through the drill bush. After drilling, the pin is removed from hole *A* and the workpiece is moved towards the right till the centre line of the drilled hole coincides with the centre line of bush *B*. The indexing pin is inserted into the drilled hole in the workpiece through bush *B*. The workpiece is, thus, indexed linearly to drill the next hole at 100 mm distance (pitch) from the hole drilled earlier. After drilling the second hole, the indexing pin is removed from the workpiece and the workpiece is moved further to the right till the hole drilled later coincides with the axis of the indexing pin

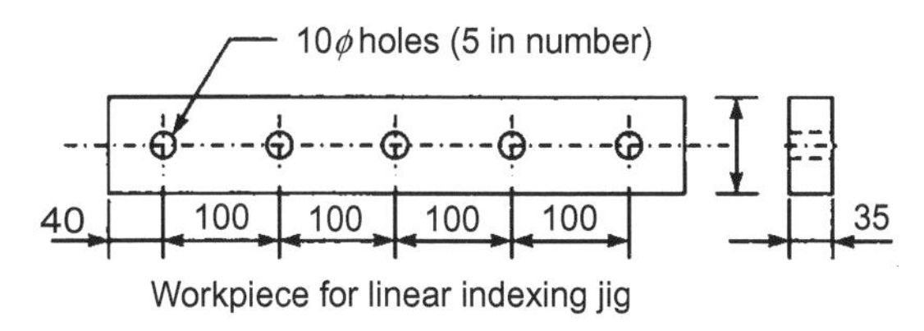

Fig. 4.1 *Workpiece for linear indexing drill jig*

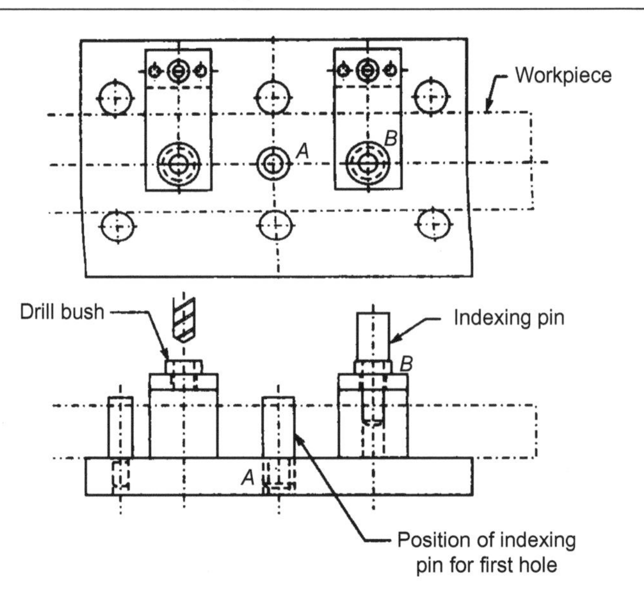

Fig. 4.2a *Linear indexing drill jig*

in bush *B*. The indexing pin is inserted through the workpiece drilled hole later to hold it in position for drilling the next hole. The procedure can be repeated to drill any number of holes at the given 100 mm pitch in similar workpieces. Thus, if there are 20 holes in the workpiece, we can eliminate 18 drill bushes by using linear indexing arrangement.

Precision Linear Indexing

A drilled hole usually measures within H11 tolerance range, more than H9 tolerance of a milled slot. For a 12 dia. hole the size will be –0/+0.11 mm. One can not locate precisely from such a widely varying hole. Even if we make the indexing pin a very close fit (g6: –.006/–.02), there can still be variation of 0.13 in the centre distance of the drilled holes. Generally, clear (+0.5) holes for fixing screws can easily accommodate this variation till the wear of the drill guiding bush reaches 0.22 (0.5 –0.13 –0.15). After that the bush must be replaced. Otherwise the excessive wandering of the drill in the worn bore will create misalignment problems in assembly.

For precise linear pitch, say + or –0.025 mm, it is necessary to provide an indexing surface which is more precise than H11—say H7. Accurate location hole facilitates precise linear motion thru accurate indexing. A 12 dia. H7/g6 combination will confine the indexing error to 0.04 (0.02 + 0.02) only 1/3 of the error in H11/g6 fit.

For accurate linear indexing, we have to provide an **indexing plate** which is firmly attached to the workpiece to be drilled, and moves along with the workpiece during indexing. Figure 4.2b shows a workpiece, and Fig. 4.2c shows the indexing plate clamped to it by two swinging clamps. There are location pins for locating the channel at the ends. Note the uni-directional dimension system (Fig. 4.2b). The maximum centre distance 920 has the same tolerance (± 0.15) as the minimum C. D. 40. There should not be any cumulative error.

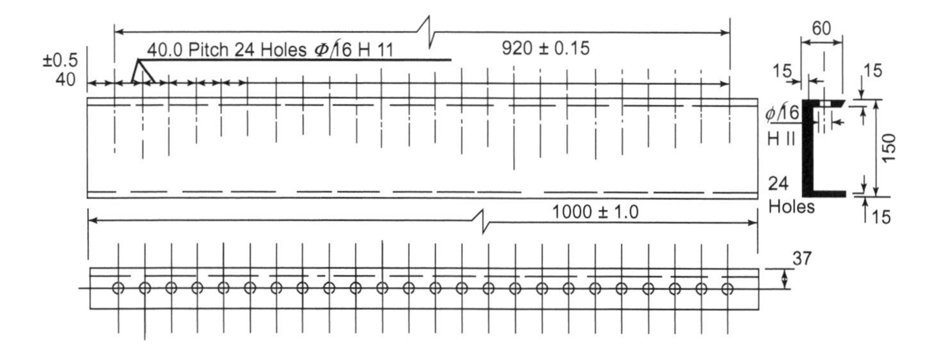

Fig. 4.2b *Spindle frame (workpiece) for indexing plate (Fig. 4.2c) and drill jig in Fig. 4.2d*

More number of holes (24) causes more wear. The bore of the drill guide bush must be checked more often, say every alternate day, by providing a plug gauge if necessary. The renewable type design allows quick replacement of worn bush—without removing the drill jig from the drilling m/c table.

Figure 4.2d shows the complete drill jig. Two pads locate the workpiece channel: one for resting, and another for centre distance (37) from the channel base. The indexing pin is housed in the angle plate of the jig body. The tapered pin engages with the tapered holes in the bushes in the indexing plate (Sect. A–A in Fig. 4.2d) to ensure precise linear indexing of the workpiece even after wear of the tapered locating surfaces. A spring ensures positive engagement of the indexing pin.

After drilling a hole the workpiece is unclamped slightly to permit moving (indexing) it for drilling the next hole. The indexing handle is pulled to compress the spring to allow withdrawal of the indexing pin from the tapered mating hole. The workpiece is moved forward for indexing .After the indexing pin crosses the tapered hole the indexing handle can be released. When the pin reaches the next tapered hole, the spring force will automatically push the pin into the mating hole.

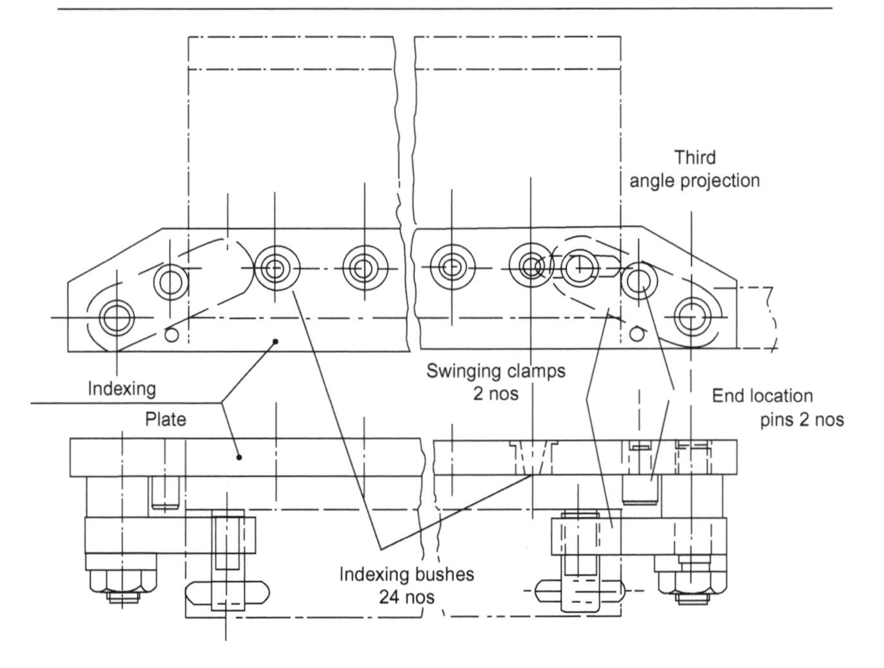

Fig. 4.2c *Indexing plate for workpiece in Fig. 4.2b*

The workpiece weighs more than 25 kg. The left and right side of the jig are fitted with angle iron fabricated frames mounted with ball bearings which serve as wheels (Fig. 4.2d plan). These reduce the fatigue resulting from moving the heavy workpiece . The left hand supporting structure must be a little longer than a metre, so that it can be used as a rest while clamping the indexing plate to the workpiece. The right hand support need not be longer than 550 mm .

A similar arrangement can be used for milling slots with equal size and pitch in a workpiece as shown in Fig. 4.3. In both instances, the indexing plunger is located on the previously machined part of the workpiece. The part must be unclamped for indexing and reclamped before the operation commences.

Rotary Indexing

Rotary indexing facilitates accurate positioning of a part around its axis. It can be used conveniently for drilling equi-spaced holes in round workpieces (Fig. 4.4a).

After drilling the first hole through bush A, the workpiece is unclamped and rotated clockwise to align the drilled hole with the axis of the indexing pin. The indexing pin is inserted in the drilled hole to index the workpiece

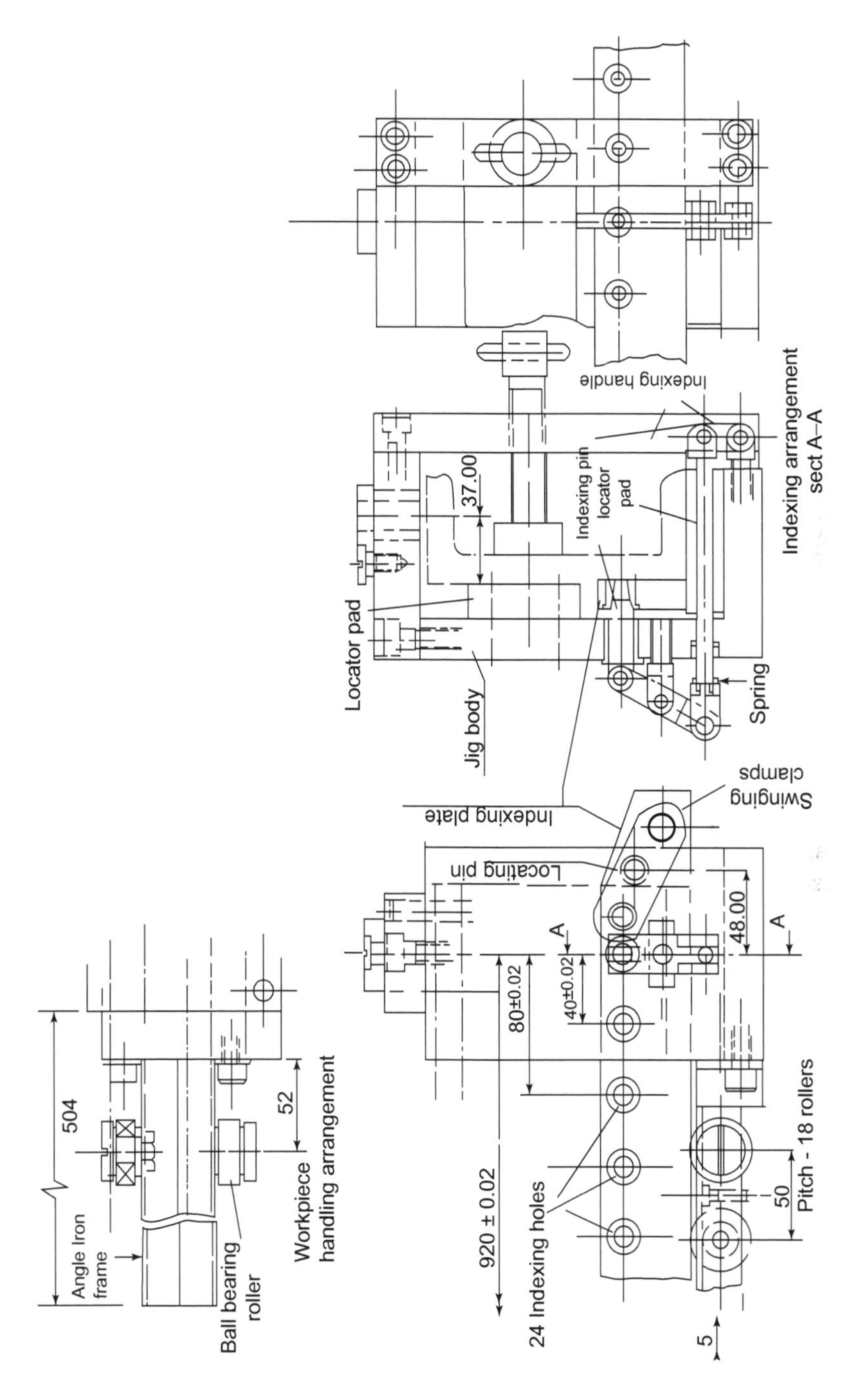

Fig. 4.2d *Drill jig for workpiece in Fig. 4.2b*

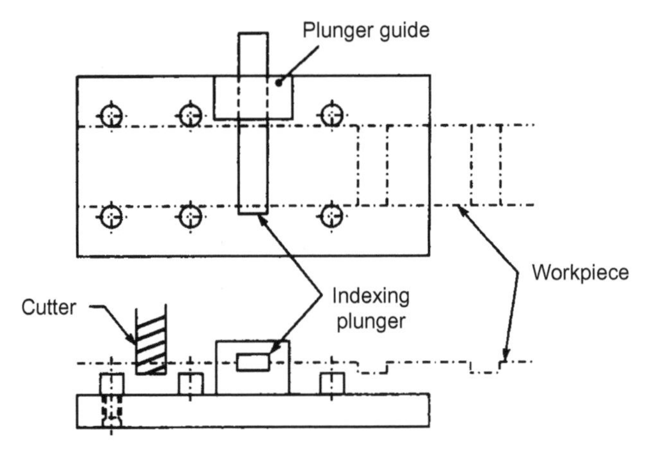

Fig. 4.3 *Linear indexing milling fixture*

for drilling the next hole. The workpiece is clamped again before drilling the next hole. Thus, rotary indexing can be used to drill any number of equi-spaced holes with only two guides bushes.

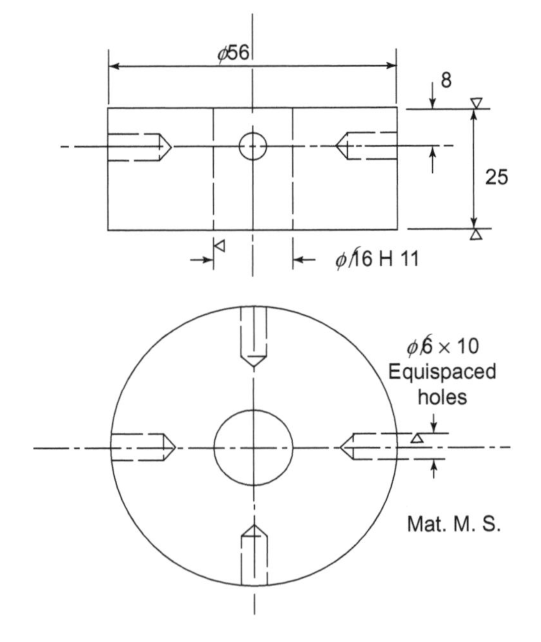

Fig. 4.4a *Workpiece for rotary indexing jig in Fig 4.4b*

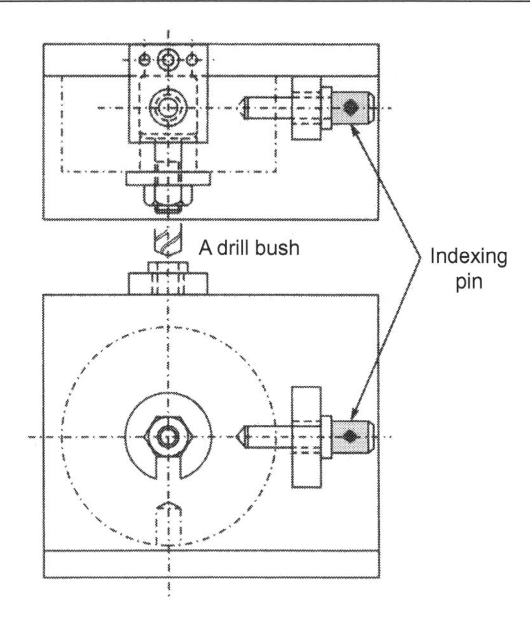

Fig. 4.4b *Rotary indexing drill jig*

Indexing Plate

For more precise indexing, the workpiece is located and clamped on an accurate indexing plate which moves along with the workpiece (Fig. 4.5). The indexing plate is provided with hardened bushes or slots to minimise wear caused by repeated operation of indexing arrangement in mass manufacture.

The indexing plate can be rotated about the central pivot and clamped in position with a hand knob. The pivoted indexing lever engages in accurately machined slots of hardened indexing plate to position the workpiece precisely.

The slots can be tapered (Fig. 4.6) to prevent inaccuracies resulting from wear. Similarly, a round bush and indexing pin can be tapered to counter the effect of wear (Fig. 4.6).

Instead of an indexing pin and bush, we can use a ball and conical dimple arrangement for indexing (Fig. 4.7). The ball is pushed against the conical dimple by a spring. When the indexing plate is rotated with some force, the ball is pressed downwards against the spring and remains there till its centre aligns with the next conical dimple in the indexing plate. As soon as the dimple aligns with the ball, the spring pushes the ball into the dimple and the indexing plate is indexed. For indexing the next position, the indexing plate must again be rotated with some force to drive the ball out of the

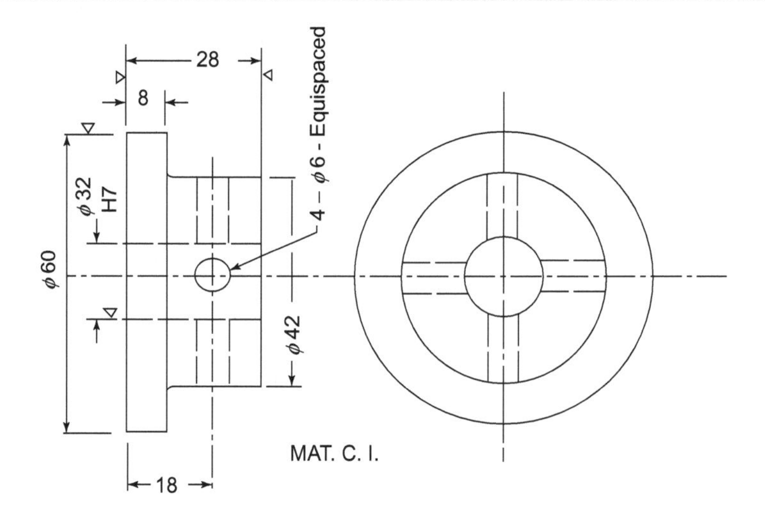

Fig. 4.5a *Workpiece for jig in Fig 4.5b*

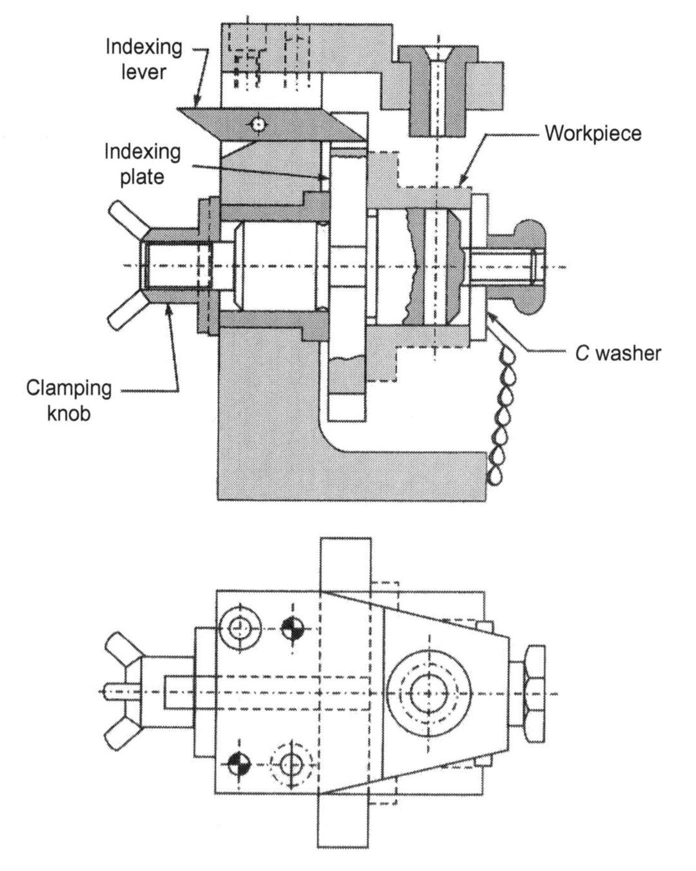

Fig. 4.5b *Drill jig with indexing plate*

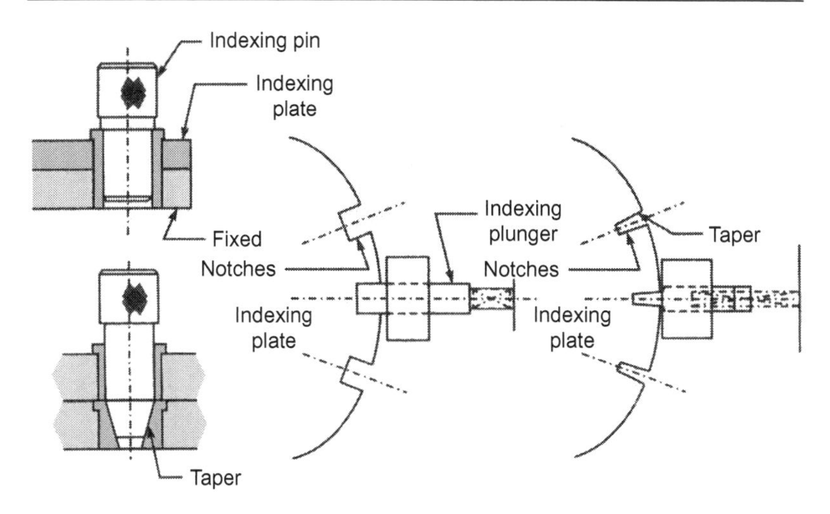

Fig. 4.6 *Indexing plungers*

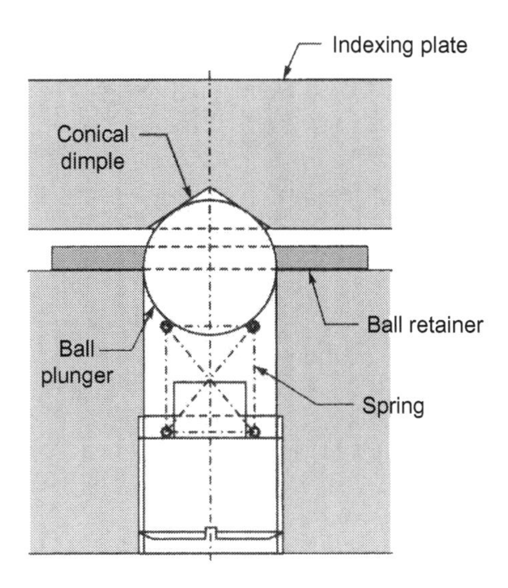

Fig. 4.7 *Indexing by a ball*

dimple against the spring. After indexing, the indexing plate must be clamped in position for the operation. It must be unclamped during indexing.

Rotary Indexing Tables

In rotary tables rack and pinion are often used for withdrawal of the indexing pin (Fig. 4.8). A pinion engages with the gear teeth of a rack in the

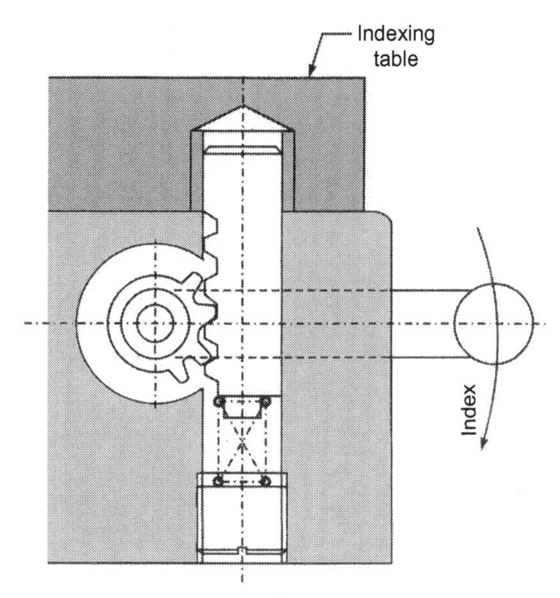

Fig. 4.8 *Indexing in rotary tables*

indexing pin. The spring below the indexing pin pushes the indexing pin into the bush in the indexing plate.

For indexing, the handle attached to the pinion is turned clockwise. This rotates the pinion clockwise and the gear teeth push the indexing pin downwards to withdraw it from the bush in the indexing plate. The indexing table can now be rotated for indexing. After rotation, the handle can be released. When the centre to the next bush in the indexing table alings with the centre of the indexing pin, the spring automatically pushes the indexing pin into the bush and the table is indexed.

Figure 4.9 shows a standard indexing table with 12 indexing positions. Figure 4.10 shows another standard indexing (dividing) fixture with a built-in-collet clamping arrangement for round parts. This fixture can be used conveniently for milling flats, squares and hexagons on round workpiece of various sizes. For different diameters of round workpieces, different collets are required. If the collet clamping arrangement is replaced by a self-centreing chuck (Chapter 7), it can clamp a wide range of round workpieces eliminating the need for a number of collets of different diameters.

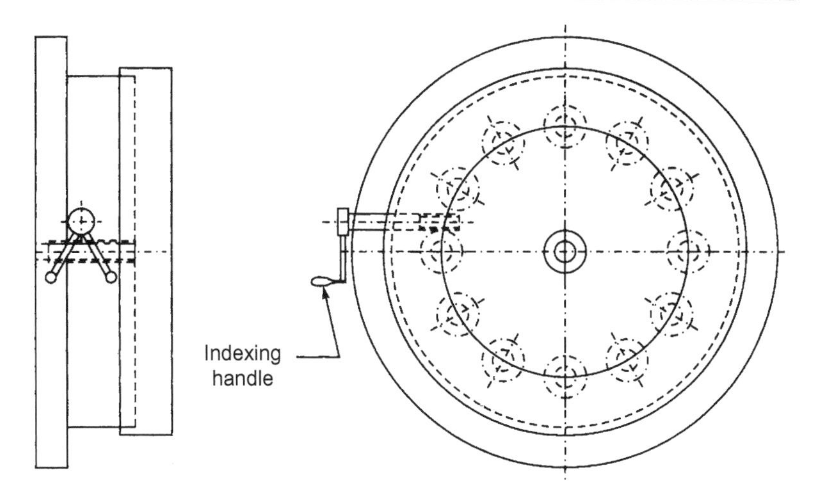

Fig. 4.9 *Standard indexing table*

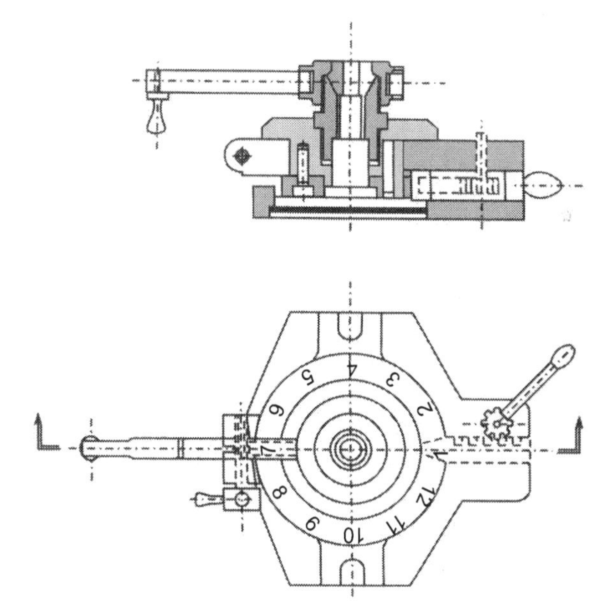

Fig. 4.10 *Standard dividing fixture*

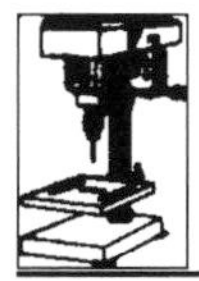

CHAPTER 5

Drill Jigs

Locating and clamping elements in drill jigs are subjected to high torque in the direction perpendicular to the axis of the cutting tool. The jig and the workpiece are also subjected to thrust in the direction of the feed of the tool.

The following are the requirements of a good drill jig:

1. Quick and accurate location of the workpiece.
2. Easy loading and unloading of the workpiece and prevention of wrong loading.
3. Prevention of bending or movement of the workpiece during drilling.
4. Ample chip clearance with facilities for swarf removal and cleaning.
5. Light weight to minimise operator fatigue due to repeated handling.
6. Prevention of loss of loose parts by chaining them to the jig body.
7. Clearance for overshoot of the drill.

Drill Bushes

Drill jigs use bushes to guide drills, reamers and other cutting tools to the workpiece. Bushes are made of water hardening carbon steel with 0.85–1% carbon and 0.5–0.9% manganese and are hardened to R_C 60–64 to minimise wear due to contact with hard, rotating tools. Bushes are generally finished by grinding the inside and outside diameters within 0.001 mm concentricity. The inside diameter is ground precision running fit (*F*7) with the drill/reamer which needs to be guided whereas the outside diameter is made press fit (*p*6), precision location fit (*h*6) or precision running fit (*f*6), depending upon the function and application of the bush.

Press Fit Bushes

Press fit bushes are the most common type of bushes and are pressed interference fit in the bush plates also referred to as jig plates. These bushes are used in batch production where the bushes often outlast the life of the jig.

Headed bushes (Fig. 5.1) are preferable to headless bushes because the collar provides positive stop against the jig plate. Moreover, it is found that the chances of the bush getting loose in the jig plate and sliding axially with the drill are lesser in the collared bushes. However, when the spacing of the bushes is close or the top surface of the jig plate is required to be free from the projecting collars, headless bushes are used (Fig. 5.2).

Press fit bushes are also used as liners for renewable and slip bushes.

Bushes fitted in soft materials are sometimes knurled instead of machining to p6/s6 tolerance to provide more interference with the softer housing.

Knurling is also used to salvage interference fit parts whose external diameter is machined underrsize inadvertently, due to error or lack of skill. Although far from good the remedy helps salvage, otherwise unusable, costly parts with many dear operations.

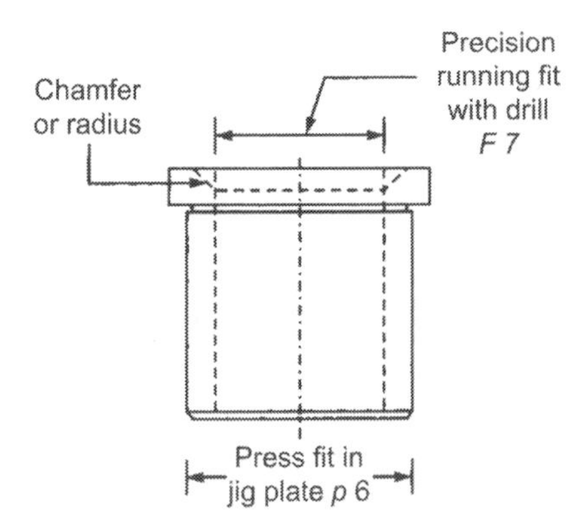

Fig. 5.1 *Headed collared press fit bush*

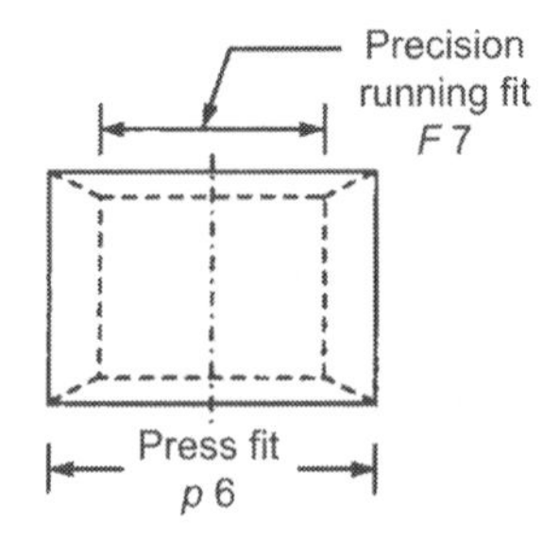

Fig. 5.2 *Headless press fit bush*

Renewable Bushes

For continuous or large batch production, the inside diameter of the bush is subjected to severe wear due to continuous contact with hard cutting tool. The guide bushes require periodic replacement. The replacement is simplified by making the outside diameter precision location fit (*h*6). The bushes can then be assembled manually without any press. The use of liner in the jig plate provides hardened wear resistant mating surface to the renewable bush (Fig. 5.3). The renewable bush must be prevented from rotating and moving axially with the cutting tool. This is accomplished by provision of a flat on the collar. The flat arrests with the collar of the retainer shoulder screw to prevent rotation. The bush flange below the collar of the shoulder screw prevents the bush from getting lifted with the cutting tool.

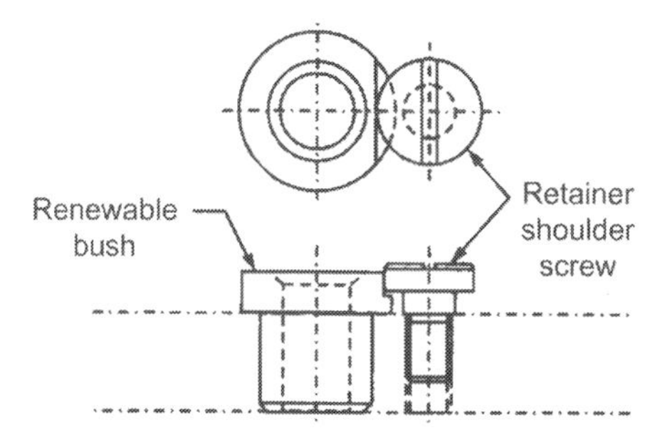

Fig. 5.3 *Renewable bush*

Slip Bushes

When a hole in the workpiece requires two operations such as drilling and reaming, it is necessary to use two different guide bushes for the different tools. The hole is first drilled using a bush having a bore suitable for the drill. After drilling, the drill bush is removed and a reaming bush is used to guide the reamer. In mass production the changeover of these bushes should be effected quickly. This is accomplished by provision of slip bushes. There are a number of different types of slip bushes in use. In the most common type, the bush is provided with a flat on the head similar to the renewable bush and a circular cutout in the flange to facilitate quick assembly and removal (Fig. 5.4).

For loading or unloading of the slip bush, the cutout in the flange is aligned with the collar of the retainer shoulder screw. The bush can be moved freely axially in this position. For assembly, the slip bush is aligned with the shoulder screw and inserted into a liner. When the bush collar touches the jig plate, the slip bush is rotated clockwise to arrest the flat on the bush flange against the collar of the retainer shoulder screw. This

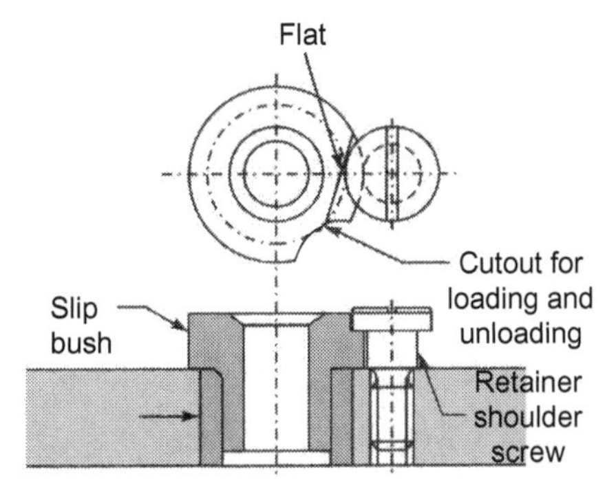

Fig. 5.4 *Slip bush*

prevents rotation of the bush during drilling. The bush flange below the collar of the shoulder screw prevents the slip bush from rising up with the cutting tool. For removal, the slip bush is rotated anti-clockwise to align the bush cutout with the shoulder screw collar. Then the bush can be lifted axially out of the liner. In a variation of the slip bush, the straight flat is replaced by a circular step (Fig. 5.5b).

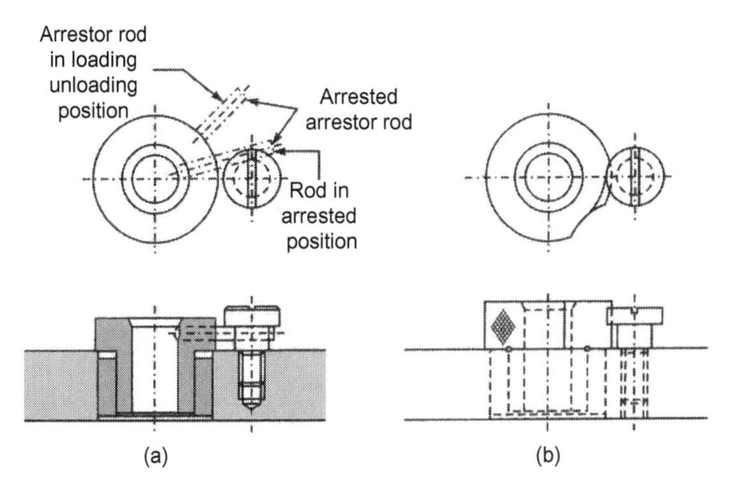

Fig. 5.5 *Other types of slip bushes*

In another design, the head of the slip bush is fitted with a rod as shown in Fig. 5.5a. For assembly, the rod is turned to arrest it against the shoulder of the retaining screw to prevent rotation. In this position, the collar of the shoulder screw prevents the rod and the bush from being lifted with the cutting tool. For removal, the bush is rotated anti-clockwise to turn the rod clear of the collar of the shoulder screw. Then, it can be removed axially from the liner.

Threaded Bushes

The bushes used for clamping the workpiece are threaded on the outside. There should be another plain guiding diameter for accurate location of the bush (Fig. 5.6). The collar of the liner bush is usually placed on the opposite side to take the axial thrust of the screw. The liner bush should be prevented from rotation by a grub screw or a flat on the collar (Fig. 5.6). The flat mates with a machined step on the jig plate.

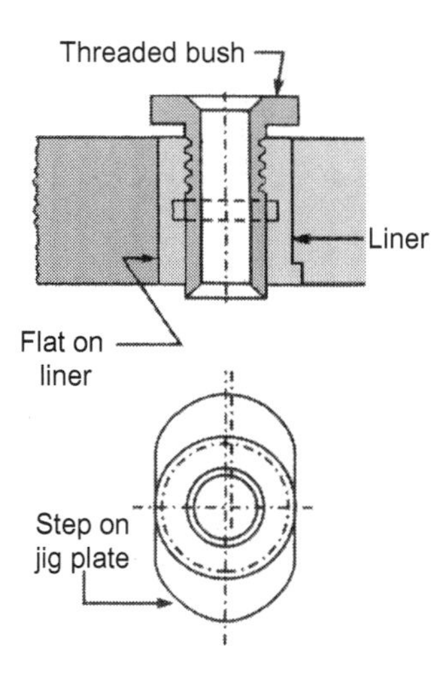

Fig. 5.6 *Threaded bush*

Alternatively, an unthreaded bush can be clamped with a spring-loaded lever (Fig. 5.7). The pressure of the spring holds the bush pressed against the workpiece boss. For unclamping, the lever is pressed down to compress the spring. This raises the pivoted bush up, thus, releasing the hold on the workpiece.

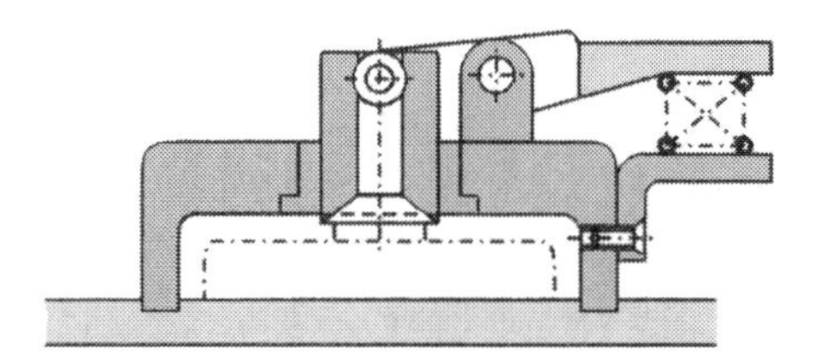

Fig. 5.7 *Spring-loaded clamping of threaded bush*

Special Bushes

Some workpieces or operations require unusual types of bushes. In many instances, these involve simple modifications in the standard bushes.

A twist drill tends to slide down inclines and curves (Fig. 5.8). This causes bending and breakage of the drill. The problem can be countered by altering the shape of the drill bush to provide better support and resistance against bending. This generally involves matching the end of the bush with the profile of the workpiece (Fig. 5.9).

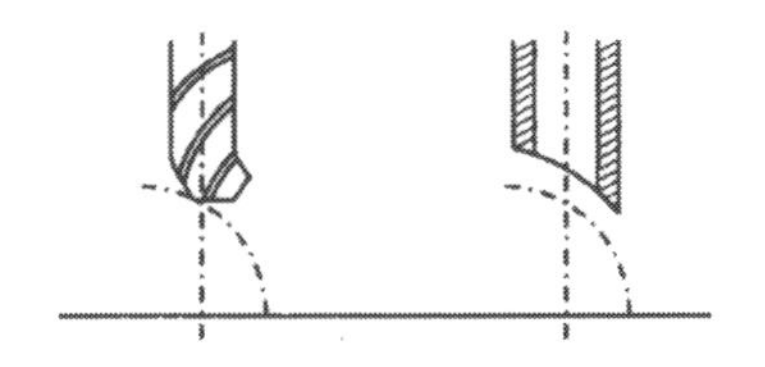

Fig. 5.8 *Drill bush for curved surface*

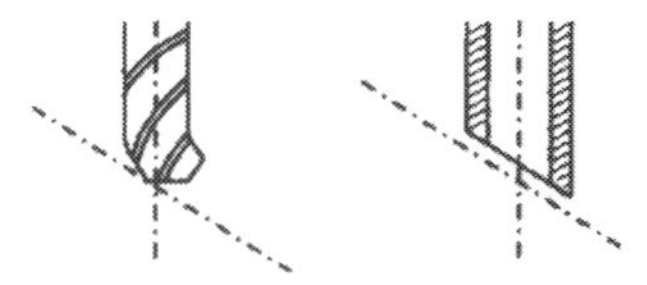

Fig. 5.9 *Drill bush for inclined surface*

Sometimes, the centre of the drilled holes are placed so close that it is just impossible to provide any drill bushes in the jig plate (Fig. 5.10). The bushes shown by the chaindotted lines in Fig. 5.10 obstruct each other. Consequently, there would be little wall material between the two holes for the bushes. Under such circumstances, a combined plate-type of bush is used (Fig. 5.11).

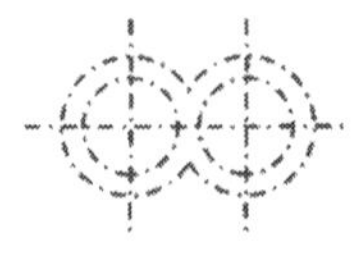

Fig. 5.10 *Problems due to close centre distance in drilling holes*

The plate bush is made of tool steel. A number of bushes can be combined into a single plate bush. The plate bush is screwed and dowelled to the jig plate.

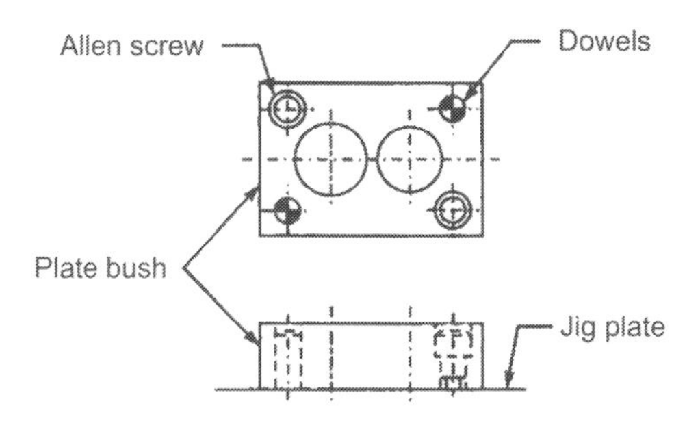

Fig. 5.11 *Plate bush*

Various Types of Jigs

Depending upon their construction and method of operation, drill jigs can be broadly classified as follows:

1. Plate jigs and channel jigs with workpiece pots
2. Angle plate jigs
3. Turn-over jigs
4. Leaf or latch jigs
5. Box jigs
6. Trunnion-type indexing jigs
7. Sandwich and pump jigs
8. Jigs for multi-spindle machines

Plate-type Jigs

Plate-type jigs mainly consist of a single bush plate with a provision for location and the clamping of workpiece. Figure 5.12 shows a plate-type of jig for the shown workpiece. The workpiece profile is located by six location pins and clamped by two knurled screws against the location pins. Sometimes, it is economical to make the jigs channel shaped in order to simplify location and clamping (Fig. 5.13). It can then be called a channel jig. In any drill jig, the workpiece should be supported adequately against bending due to the downward thrust of the drill. Furthermore, there should be enough clearance below the workpiece for overshoot of the drill after passing through the workpiece. This can be achieved by providing a resting pot for the workpiece (Fig. 5.14). The pot is machined with bigger slots or holes for passage of the drill and disposal of chips. These slots must be aligned with the drill bushes in the jig (bush) plate. This is accomplished by providing a location pin in the pot and a corresponding slot in the jig plate. As shown in the figure, the pot is also used for anchoring the clamping stud.

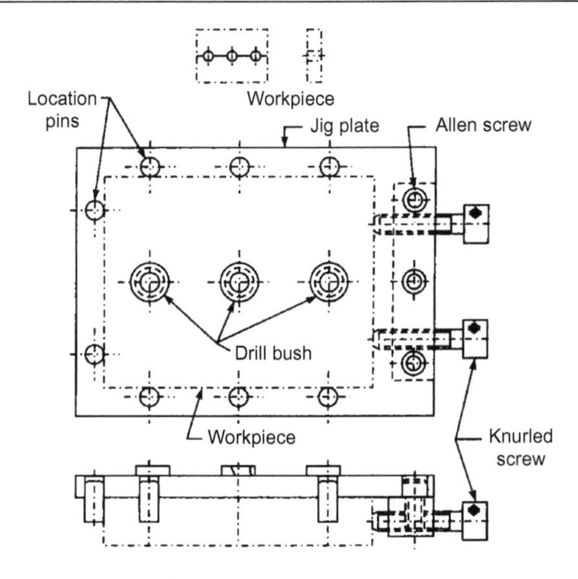

Fig. 5.12 *Plate drill jig*

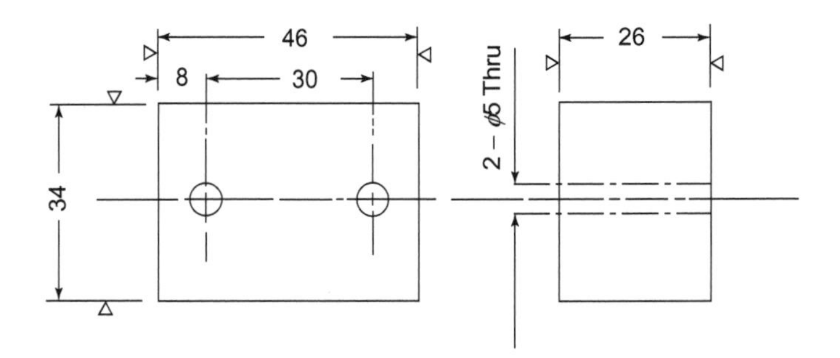

Fig. 5.13a *Workpiece for channel jig in Fig. 5.13b*

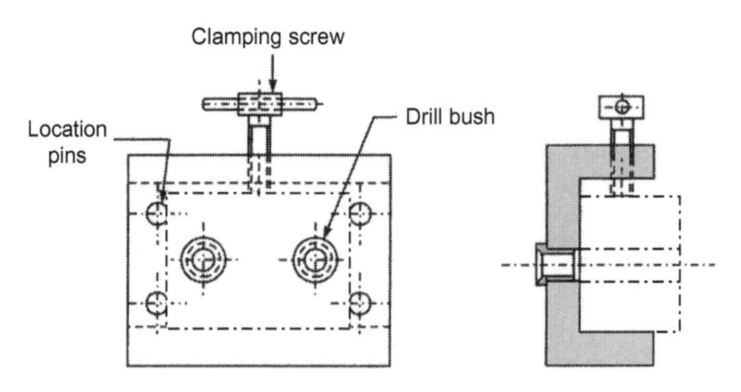

Fig. 5.13b *Channel drill jig*

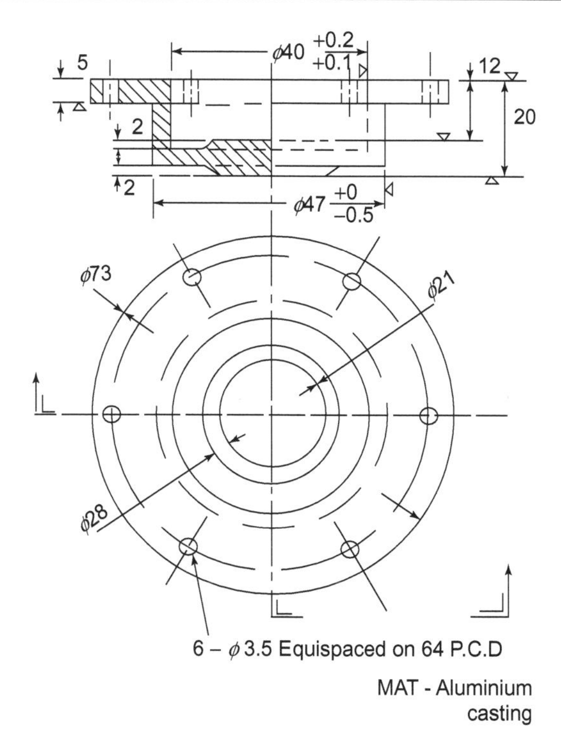

Fig. 5.14a *Workpiece for pot drill jig in Fig. 5.14b*

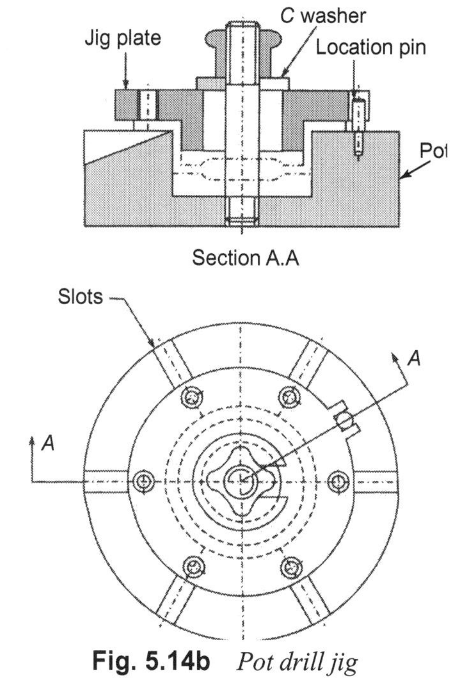

Fig. 5.14b *Pot drill jig*

Moreover, the base of the pot also provides a square resting surface for drilling. The jig plate locates the workpiece with a spigot which engages into the machined bore of the workpiece. The C washer facilitates quick sandwich clamping of the workpiece between the pot and the plate jig.

Angle Plate Jigs

In angle plate jigs, locators are generally fixed to the vertical wall of the angular body (Fig. 5.15). The workpiece is located by a central locator and a diamond pin for angular position. A 'C' washer is used for quick clamping of the workpiece. The central locator must have a groove for passage of the drill after breaking through the workpiece.

Turn-over or Table-type Jigs

Workpieces having no suitable resting surface for drilling can be drilled conveniently with turn-over jigs. Turn-over jigs are plate jigs with jig feet. The feet provide square resting surface to the jig during drilling. The resting diameter of the jig feet should be bigger than the slots of machine table to prevent the feet from falling into the slots.

Figure 5.16 depicts a turn-over jig for drilling 13 mm holes in the depicted workpiece. It is located on a 100 ϕ machined bore for concentricity and three location pins for angular position. A 'C' washer and a handknob provide quick clamping. The height of the feet must be longer than the clamping stud to provide proper resting face during drilling.

All turn-over jigs must be turned over for the loading and unloading the workpiece. After loading the workpiece, the jig must be turned over again to rest on the jig feet for drilling as shown in the figure. Turn-over jigs are very convenient for drilling flanged workpieces which must be drilled from the flange end.

Leaf of Latch Jigs

These generally have a hinged jig (bush) plate (Fig. 5.17). The jig plate can be swung aside as shown by the chaindotted lines to provide clear path for loading and unloading the workpiece from the top. The jig plate must have positive resting face to ensure that the axes of bushes are vertical during drilling. The jig plate must be clamped against the resting face by an eyebolt. The open slot in the jig plate and swinging eyebolt facilitate quick clamping and unclamping of the jig plate. The hand knob needs to be loosened by only half-a-turn and the eyebolt swung to the position as shown by the chaindotted line, in order to permit swinging of the jig plate aside for loading and unloading of the workpiece from top.

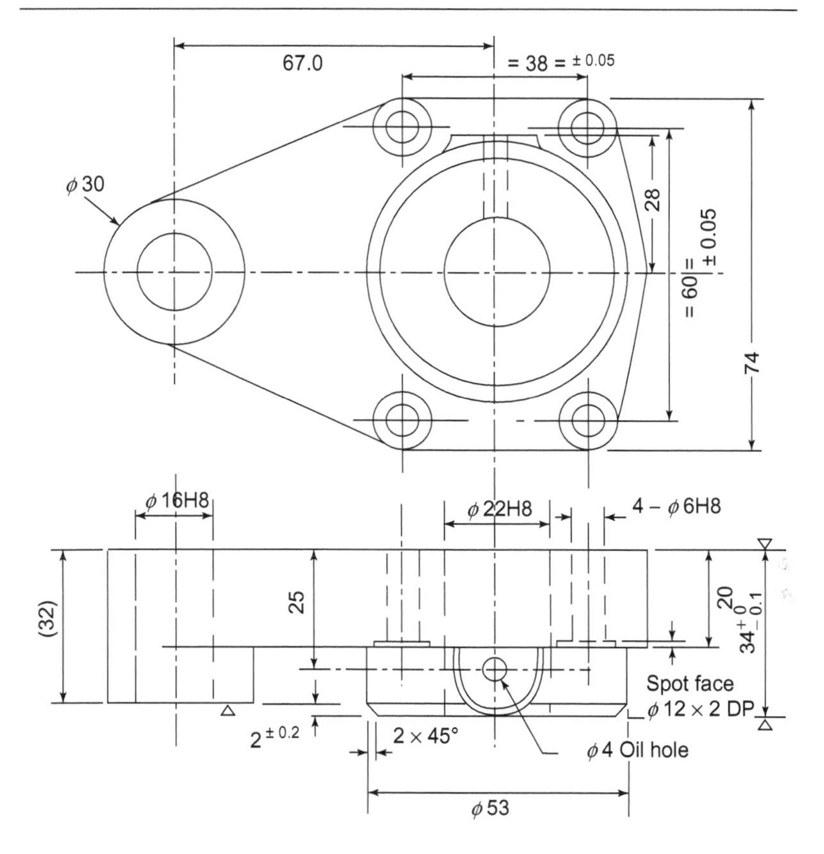

Fig. 5.15a *Workpiece for angle plate jig in Fig 5.15b*

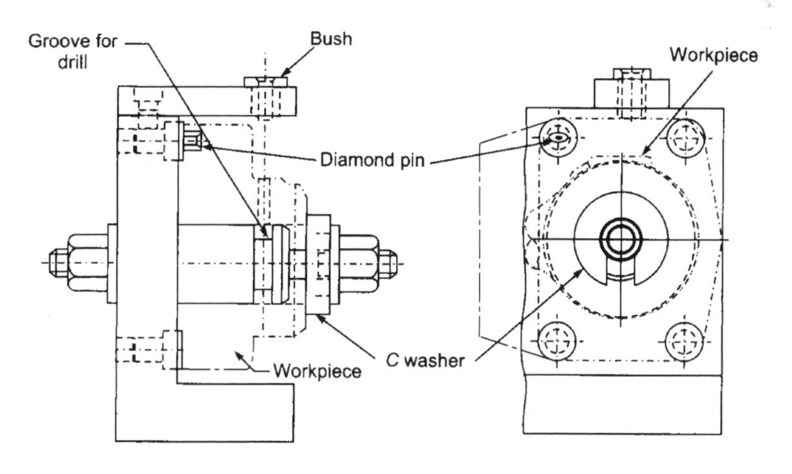

Fig. 5.15b *Angle plate jig*

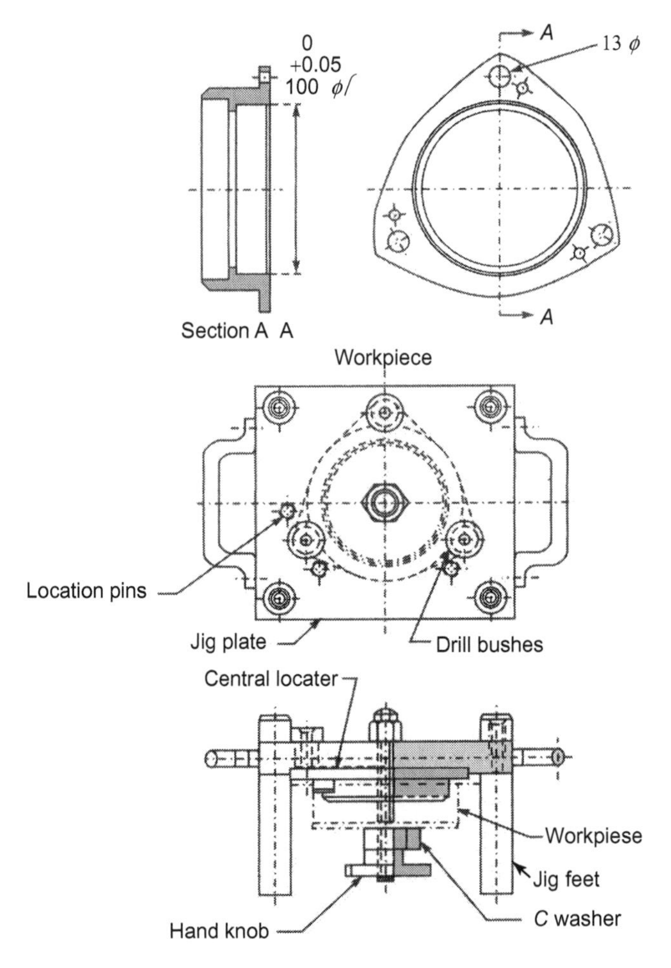

Fig. 5.16 *Turn-over or table jig*

Leaf-type jigs are particularly suitable for workpieces having location surfaces and holes to be drilled on opposite sides. As shown in the figure, the jig plate is often used to house the clamping screw.

Box Jigs

Workpieces having holes on a number of sides can be drilled economically with box jigs. The jig body is generally shaped like a box with one side open for loading and unloading the workpiece. The open side is provided with a hinged latch which often houses bushes and clamping screws. The jig is fitted with bushes on various sides and suitable jig feet on the opposite sides.

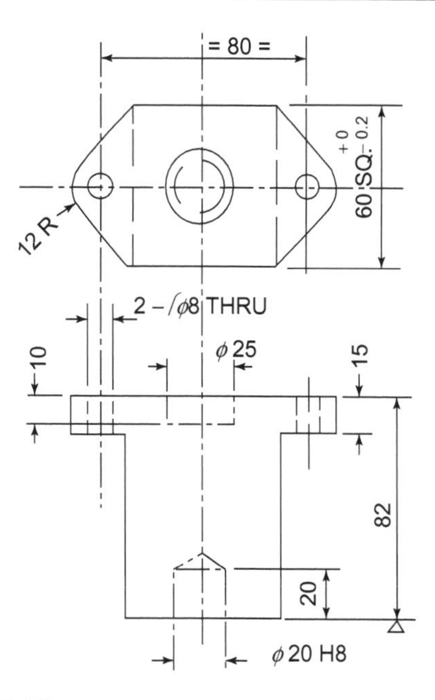

Fig. 5.17a *Workpiece for leaf jig in Fig. 5.17b*

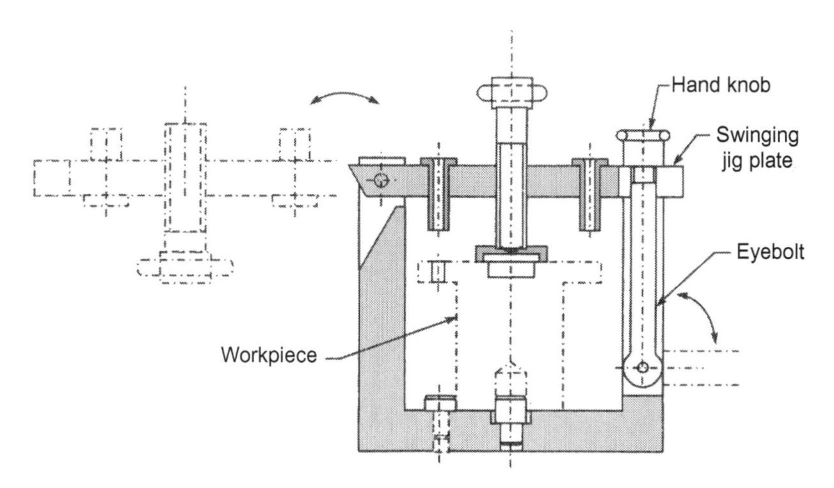

Fig. 5.17b *Leaf or latch jig*

Figure 5.18 shows a box jig for the workpiece shown in the diagram. The workpiece rests on the machined base of the jig plate. It is located by four profile location pins and an adjustable *V* block which centralises the boss and pushes the workpiece against the location pins. The workpiece is clamped by a detachable latch clamp with open slots for two shoulder screws which provide anchorage to the latch during clamping. Jig plate for 12 diameter side holes are fixed to the main jig plate with Allen screw and dowels.

Jig feet are made rectangular to facilitate resting of the jig on (Fig. 5.18) two square faces. The feet are provided with location slots to accommodate thickness of the main jig plate. The location slot along with the feet clamping screw hold the feet parallel and square to the main jig plate. One side of the rectangular feet provides a square resting surface during drilling of 12 diameter side holes. The ends of the jig feet provide resting surface for drilling a 16 diameter hole in the flange of the workpiece.

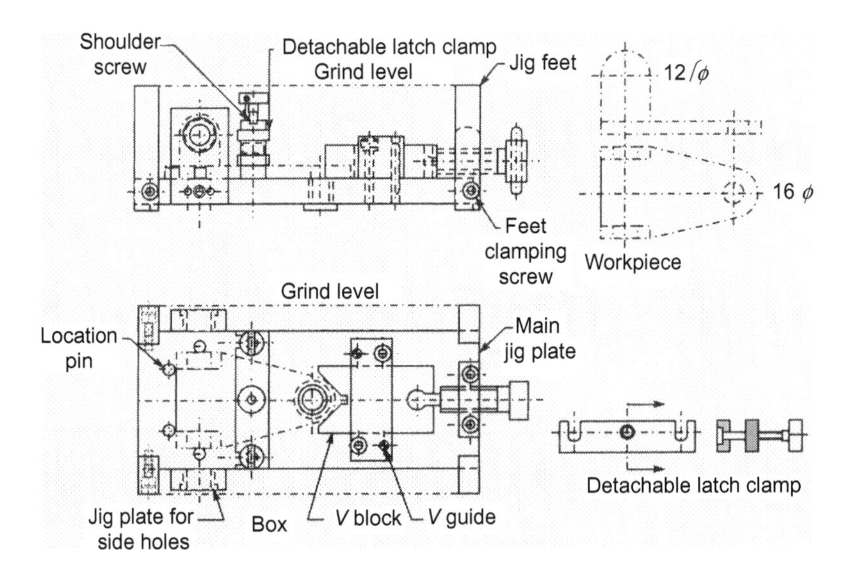

Fig. 5.18 *Box jig*

Thus, the box jig permits drilling of holes in three sides of the workpiece with a single location and clamping operation. This saves time and increases production. Moreover, box jigs have built-in accuracy. The precision positional relationships between jig bushes in the different planes are passed on to the workpiece. For example, the box jig illustrated in Fig. 5.18 provides positive relationship between the 16 diameter flange hole and 12 diameter side holes. This would be rather difficult to achieve if the 16 diameter flange hole and the 12ϕ side holes are drilled separately instead of with a single box jig.

Trunnion Jigs

When large, heavy workpieces are to be drilled from a number of sides, the jig is constructed like a box with jig bushes on various sides. Due to the large size and weight of the workpiece and the jig, it is impossible to tumble the jig manually for drilling the holes on the various sides.

To ease this operation, the jig body is provided with pivots at both ends. The pivots are supported with ball bearings in the supporting brackets at both ends (Fig. 5.19). This reduces friction and consequently, the force required to turn the jig around the pivots. On one side of the jig is attached an indexing plate with location bushes for indexing. When the indexing plunger is engaged with one of the indexing bushes, the workpiece and jig is held in position for drilling holes on one side. For drilling holes on the other side, the indexing plunger is withdrawn from the bush and the jig is rotated to drill holes on the other side. When the indexing plunger enters the indexing bush in the indexing plate, we can be sure that the drill jig is held accurately for drilling holes on one side.

Thus, trunnion facilitates moving and positioning of heavy workpieces and jigs for drilling holes on various sides. The heavy jig and trunnion remain stationary during drilling. The drill machine spindle must be moved to align with the drill bushes in the jig. Consequently, trunnion-type jigs can be used only on moveable spindle machines such as a radial drilling machine.

Sandwich and Pump Jigs

These are plate jigs with guide pillars for alignment of jig plate with the base plate (Fig. 5.20). The workpiece is located on the base plate by pins. The base is aligned with the jig plate by guide pillars which locate by engagement with guide bushes in the jig plate. Thus, guide pillars position the drill bushes correctly with respect to the workpiece located on the base plate.

Sandwich Jig In sandwich jig, the workpiece is clamped like a sandwich between the base plate and the jig plate. The clamping can be accomplished by two swinging eyebolts and corresponding open clamping slots in the jig plate. The tightening of the hexagonal nuts in the position shown clamps the jig plate against the workpiece and the base plate.

For unclamping, the hexagonal nuts need to be loosened by only half-a-turn to permit eyebolts swung aside through the open slots in the jig plate (Fig. 5.20).

The jig plate can now be removed from the pillars and kept aside while the drilled workpiece is removed and a new one is loaded and located on the base plate. After that, the pillar guide bushes in jig plate are aligned with

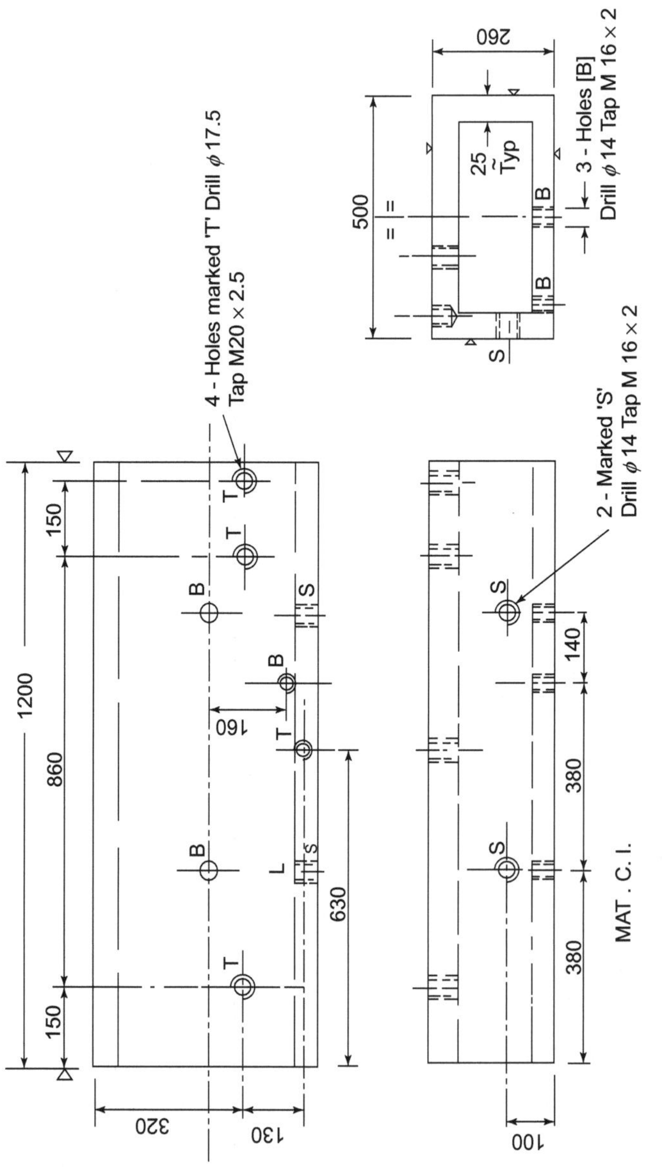

Fig. 5.19a *Workpiece for trunnion jig in Fig. 5.19b*

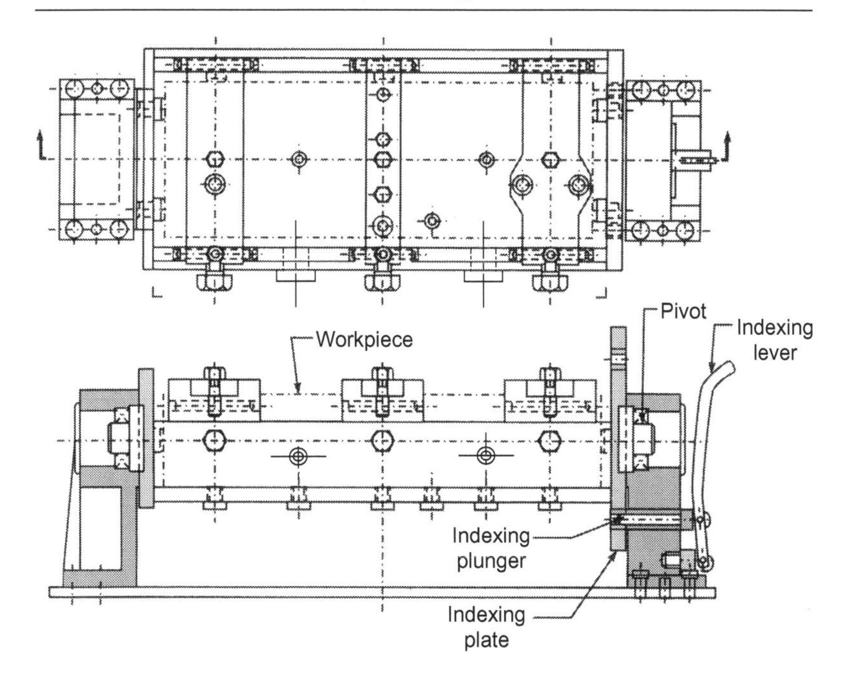

Fig. 5.19b *Trunnion jig*

the pillars on the base and the jig plate is slid down on guide pillars to touch the workpiece. The swinging eyebolts are swung vertical through the slots in the jig plate to the position shown. The operator has only to tighten the hexagonal nuts by half-a-turn to sandwich clamp the workpiece between the jig plate and the base plate. Sandwich type of jigs are particularly suitable for workpieces which have parallel machined surface square to the axis of drilling. If the workpiece has got only one machined surface, it should be rested on the base plate. The jig plate should be fitted with a spherical-ended pad or an equaliser clamp to facilitate clamping on the unmachined top surface of the workpiece.

Pump Jigs These are smaller versions of sandwich jigs. Instead of removing the jig plate completely from guide pillars, it is merely raised above to provide passage for loading and unloading of the workpiece (Fig. 5.21). The guide pillars attached to the jig plate have rack gear teeth on one side. The pinion gear meshing with the rack can be rotated by a handle to raise or lower the rack pillars and the jig plate attached to them. The jig plate is lowered to touch and clamp the workpiece. After drilling, the jig plate is raised to permit replacement of the drilled workpiece with a new one. Pump jigs are very convenient for drilling workpieces having parallel surfaces such as rolled plates and flats.

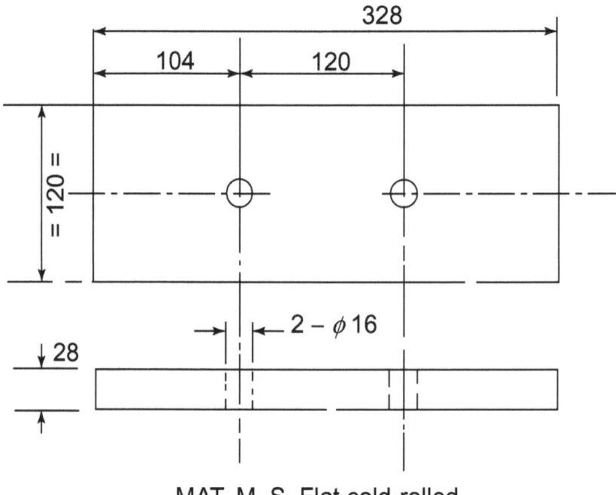

Fig. 5.20a *Workpiece for sandwich jig in Fig. 5.20b*

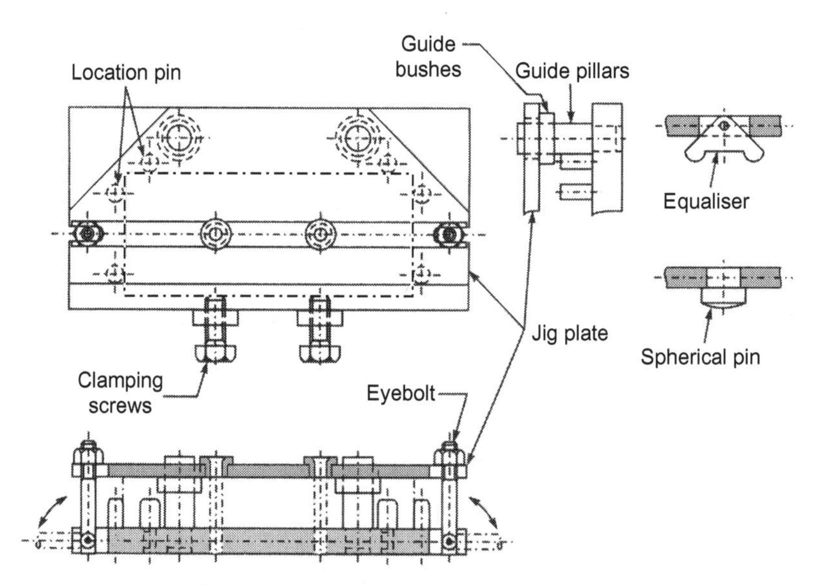

Fig. 5.20b *Sandwich jig*

Workpieces having only one machined surface can be clamped by fixing a spherical pin in the jig plate (Fig. 5.20). As they are rather heavy, pump jigs cannot be slid easily on the machine table. Consequently, pump jigs are suitable for drilling only a single hole on a fixed spindle drilling machine. The jig is generally clamped on the machine table. If a radial drilling ma-

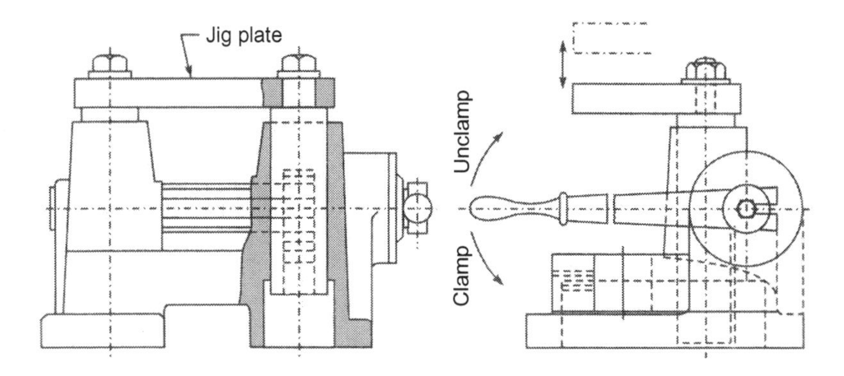

Fig. 5.21a *Pump jig*

chine is available, pump jigs can be used for drilling more than one hole as the moving spindle can be brought to each drill bush. Standardised pump jigs are readily available in the market. These reduce the manufacturing time for a jig substantially. Moreover, one pump jig can be used for a number of workpieces by providing detachable jig plates and base plates for different workpieces.

Figure 5.21b and the accompanying table gives the dimensions of some models of pump jigs along with the details of the holes for locating the replaceable locators for different workpieces.

Jigs for Multi-spindle Machines

Figure 5.22 shows a drill jig for a multi-spindle drill head. The design is similar to the sandwich jig in some respects. The base plate is clamped firmly on the machine table. The base is provided with location and clamping arrangement for the workpiece. The jig plate is suspended on the drill head with four columns having resting nuts. The jig plate is held against the nuts by springs which also provide force for sandwich clamping of the workpiece (Fig. 5.22). For loading and unloading the workpiece, the multi-spindle drill head and the suspended jig plate are raised to provide clear passage for the workpiece. For drilling, the drill head is brought down. The suspended jig plate touches and clamps the workpiece before drilling commences.Thus, in addition to guiding the drills through bushes, the jig plate also automatically clamps and unclamps the workpiece. It functions somewhat like a spring-loaded top stripper plate in a press tool.

The jig plate also carries two location pillars which engage in the guide bushes in the base plate to align both the plates precisely with each other and the workpiece.

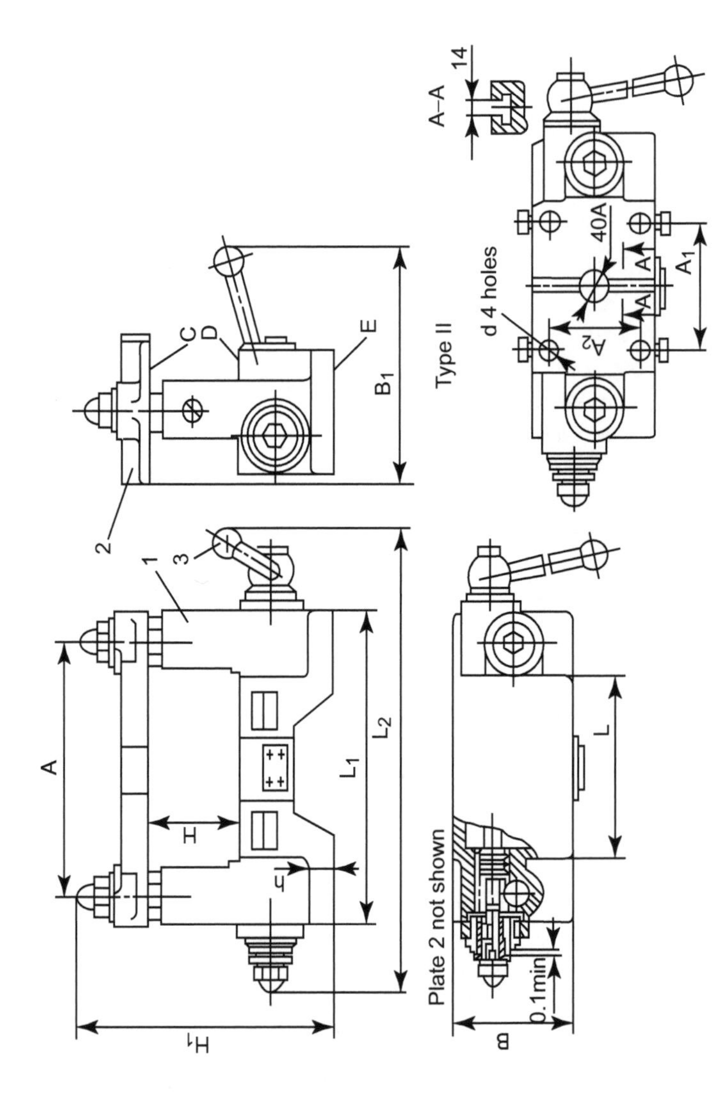

Fig. 5.21b *Overall locating dimensions of standard pump jigs (Cont.)*

Dimensions (mm)

	A (±0.01)	A_1	A_2	B	L	H		d(H7)	B_1	L_1	L_2	H_1	h	Clamping force, (kgf)	Mass (kg)
		±0.02				min	max								
1	250	125	110	140	180	80	120	—	305	310	520	265	20	45.0	32
2								10							
1	320	160	125	160	240	120	180	—	315	390	575	340	30		40
2								12							
1	400	210	180	220	320		200	—	470	470	680	360		68.5	65
2								16							

Fig. 5.21b *Overall locating dimensions of standard pump jigs*

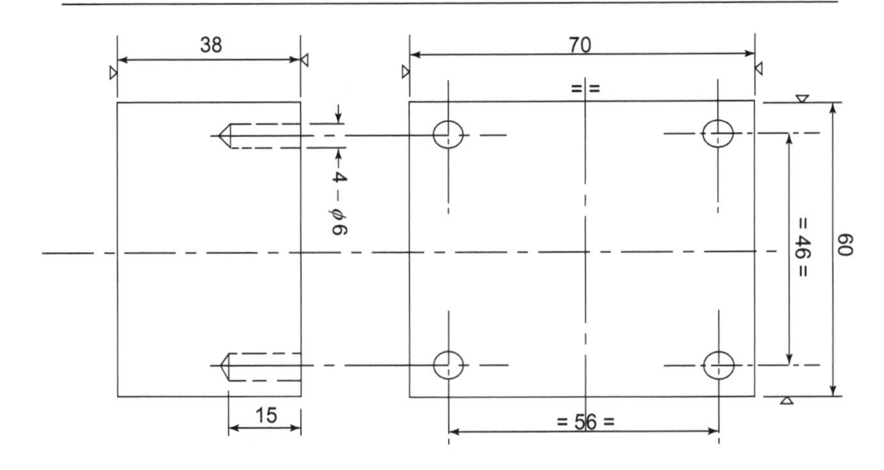

Fig. 5.22a *Workpiece for a jig for multi-spindle drilling m/c or head in Fig. 5.22b*

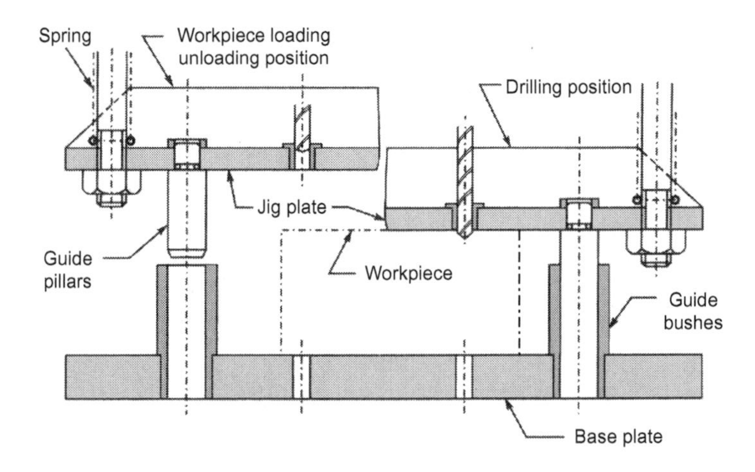

Fig. 5.22b *Jig for multispindle drilling machine*

Adjustable Jigs

Workpieces made from the same size of rolled steel angles, channels, squares, flats and round bars can often be drilled in a single adjustable jig. The differences in positions and or sizes of the holes can be taken care of by making the locators and jig plates adjustable. The variation in sizes of holes can be accommodated by using renewable bushes of required size.

Figure 5.23 shows three workpieces which can be drilled in the common adjustable jig shown in Fig. 5.24.

All the workpieces are made from 30 Sq. (outside) tube with a wall of 1.6 mm thickness. The section is located by pins for centrality of the holes along width 30. Another pin locates the workpieces for longitudinal position of the holes from the left hand end. Section P–P shows the clamping arrangement while section Q–Q shows the adjustable jig plate. It has got a key-way location fit with the key fitted on the jig base. The jig plate is clamped to the base by two Allen screws. Note the stepped flat welded below the channel. It provides seating surface for the nuts mating with the Allen screws. The step engages with one of the flats of the nuts and prevents their rotation when the Allen screws are tightened. It is convenient to provide a removable location pin for quick, precise setting of the jig plate in the required position.

Removable renewable bushes take care of the variation in the sizes of the holes. A slot in the base provides drill overshoot clearance while drilling through holes.

Figure 5.25b shows an adjustable jig for central holes in round bars. The *V* block can accommodate a range of round bars. The adjustable screw location enables changing of the position of the hole from the end face of the workpiece bar. Such jigs are used widely for drilling split-pin holes in shafts.

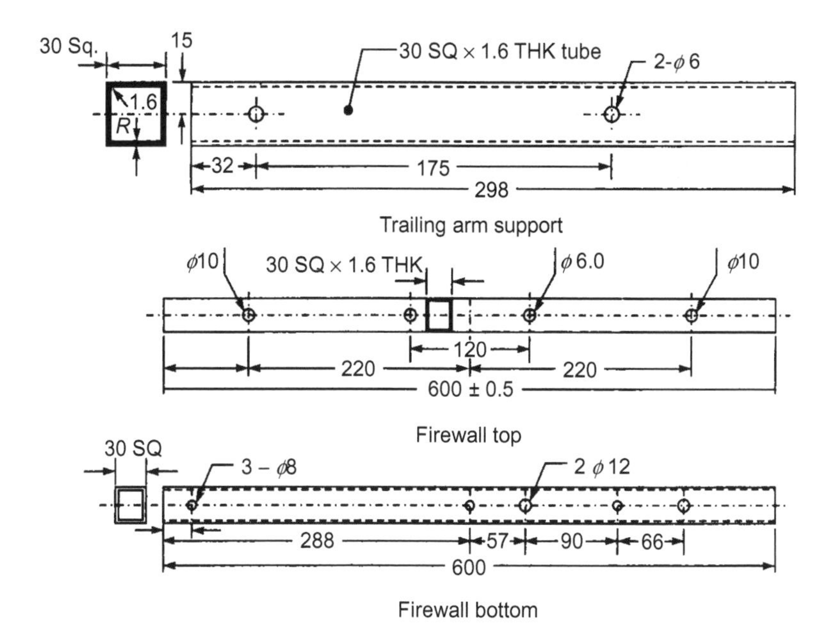

Fig. 5.23 *Workpieces for adjustable jig*

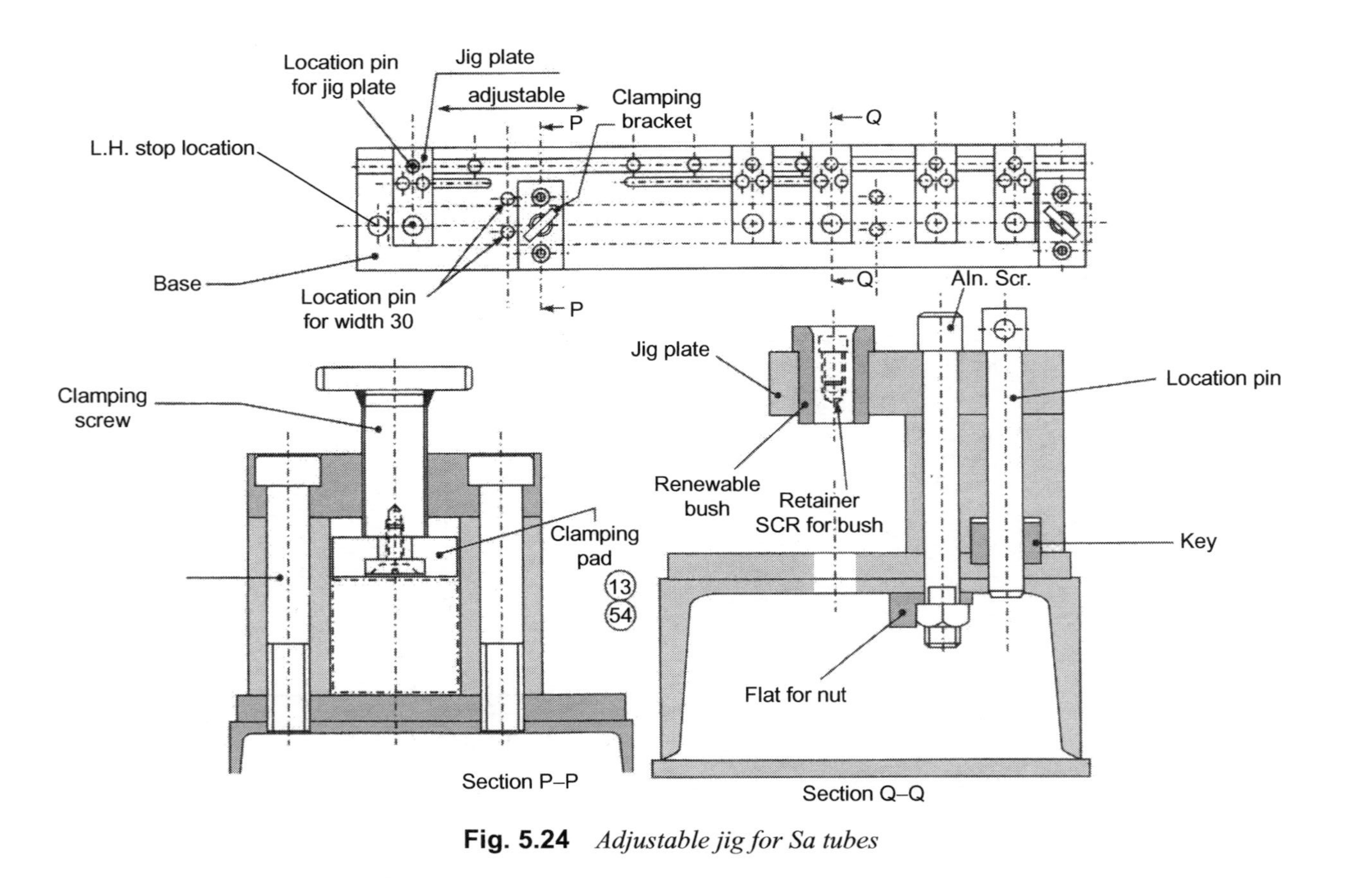

Fig. 5.24 *Adjustable jig for Sa tubes*

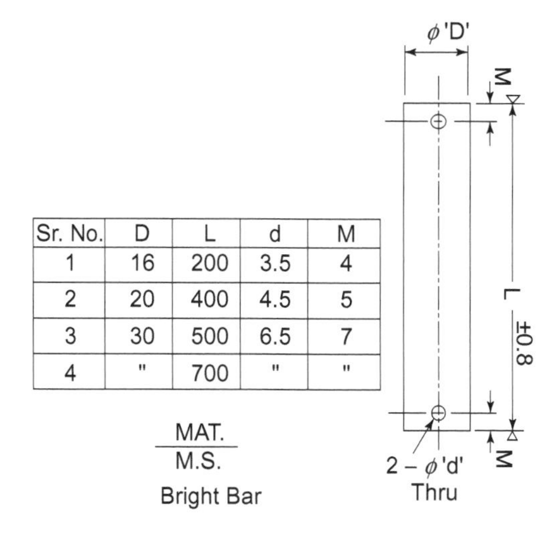

Sr. No.	D	L	d	M
1	16	200	3.5	4
2	20	400	4.5	5
3	30	500	6.5	7
4	"	700	"	"

Fig. 5.25a *Workpiece for drill jib in Fig. 5.25b*

Drilling Very Deep Small Diameter Holes

A drilled hole is considered deep when its depth exceeds 11 times its diameter. Drilling deeper holes poses the following problems.

1. Drill tends to run out, which increases as the hole depth increases.
2. Chip disposal becomes difficult, particularly in materials which give discontinuous chips (e.g. C. I.). It is common practice to withdraw drill after drilling to depth of 3 times the drill diameter, to remove the chips. For the chips can choke up the twist drill flutes and jam the drill in workpiece.
3. Delivering the coolant to farther cutting point becomes a bit difficult.

Transmission elements like crank-shaft call for very deep oil holes. What is more these holes are often angular at the point of the drill entry. The angle acts like a children's play slide and pushes the drill away from the entry face. Deflection of a hardened drill beyond certain limit causes its breakage.

Removal of a broken drill from workpiece is a tough task. Sometimes slow, costly spark erosion is the only option available. Also scrapping the crankshaft is generally costly.

The problem can be alleviated to some extent by providing a square surface at the drill entry point (Fig. 5.26b). The surface can be milled by a slot drill; a sturdy milling cutter which can be fed axially like a drill.

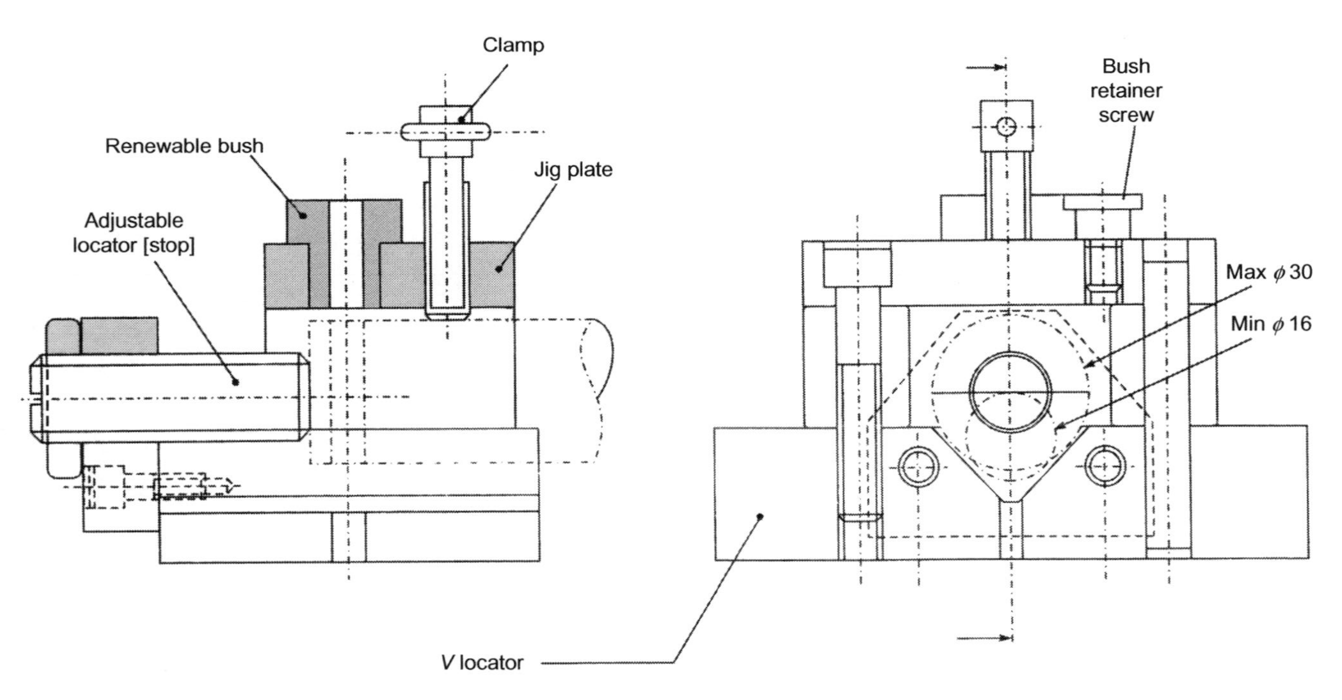

Fig. 5.25b *Adjustable jig for holes up to 8.5ϕ in 16–30ϕ bars*

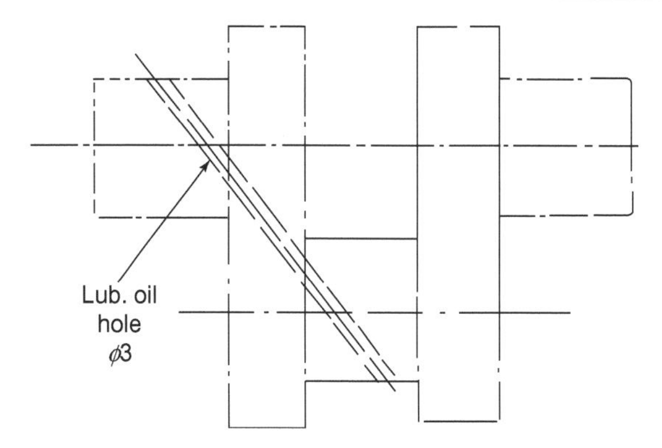

Fig. 5.26a *Crank-shaft with deep angular oil hole*

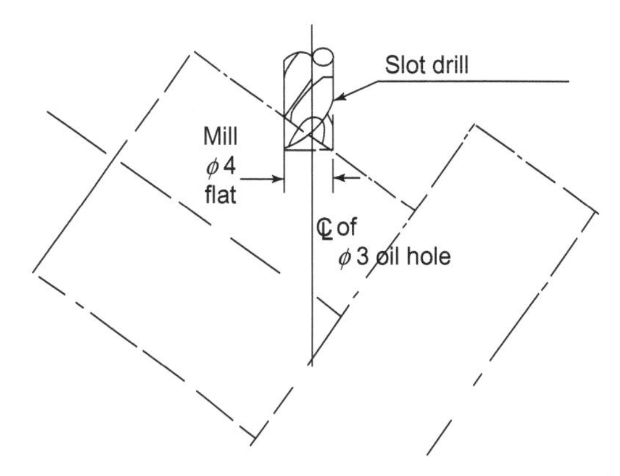

Fig. 5.26b *Milling a flat at entry point of angular holes*

Other solution is to use a centre drill for starting the hole (Fig. 5.27). Centre drill is much more sturdy than a twist drill and hence much lesser vulnerable to deflection . In fact many experienced tool-makers commence drilling important holes by drilling a centre hole first to guide the following twist drill. *The centre drill small (entry side) diameter should be bigger than the web thickness of the following twist drill. The bigger diameter of the centre drill too must be slightly bigger than the twist drill outside diameter.*

Special single flute drills are also available. These are particularly convenient for drilling materials with non-continuous chips like cast iron. The drill has got a tip with a single flute having a coolant hole. The tip is brazed with a tube, which floods the coolant into the tip. As supplying coolant to a rotating drill is tricky, it is better to rotate the workpiece and hold the special drill steady. This may not be possible for some workpieces like a crankshaft.

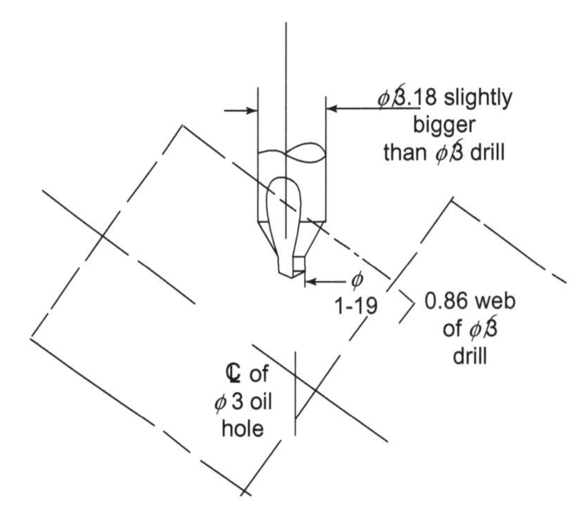

Fig. 5.27 *Using centre drill for starting angular holes*

Large Drill Jigs

For bigger workpieces like end-frames of textile spinners or a railway engine, it is impossible to load the heavy workpiece onto a drilling machine table; forget moving the workpiece to align with the machine spindle.

Work pieces measuring a few meters can be loaded within the reach of an appropriate radial drilling machine. The workpiece can be loaded on floor and the face to be drilled made horizontal by a spirit level,and wedges between the floor and the workpiece resting face. The drill jig is loaded and clamped onto the workpiece. The spindle of the radial drilling m/c is moved to align it with each drill bush in the drill jig.

Some workpieces are so heavy that they can be handled only by crane. Even large jigs for such workpieces may call for crane.

Jig weight can be reduced by using a lighter material for the jig body. Aluminium weighs only one third of steel, while fibre only one sixth. Some large jigs are made of a fabrication of a thin steel sheet reinforced by strengthening ribs and a peripheral angle iron frame. I have seen a German drill jig made of fibre body strengthened by an angle iron frame. Instead of machining to p6/s6 tolearance, the press fit diameters of the drill bushes were knurled to enhance the interference with the softer housing material.

Medium size (50–150 kg) workpieces can be moved to align m/c spindle with the various drill bushes by providing some handling arrangement with wheels/roller conveyors to change face friction to rolling friction. This reduces the operator fatigue to facilitate manoeuvring the heavy workpiece and

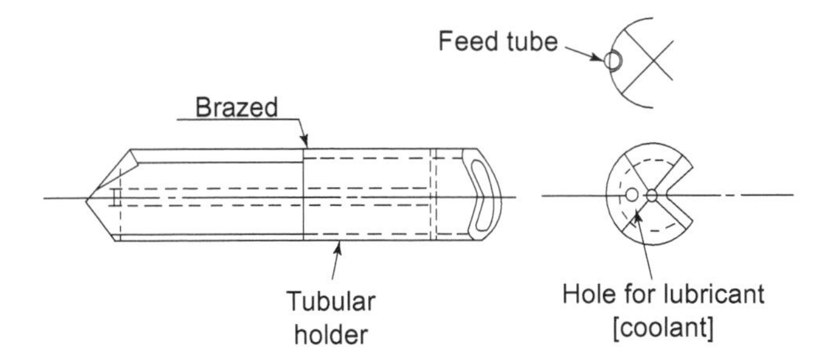

Fig. 5.28 *Single flute holed deep hole drill*

the jig. The handling arrangement should be such that the surface to be drilled remains square with the m/c spindle for all the drilling positions. A long workpiece should not tilt due gravity while drilling the holes near the ends.

Very large workpieces like a railway engine are almost impossible to move or level. In such cases the jig is clamped onto the workpiece and drilled with a hand-held drilling m/c which can be moved to any angular position. Also some drilling machines are provided with a magnetic base which can be clamped magnetically to any flat surface, like the magnetic table of a surface grinder. The magnetic base enables clamping the m/c onto the workpiece for drilling a hole square with the face.

Summary

1. A good jig facilitates precise location and easy foolproof loading/unloading of the workpiece. It also prevents bending of the workpiece. It has ample chip space and is light in weight.
2. Drill bushes have *G7/F7* hole to guide the drill. They are made of steel hardened to RC 62/65.

Types of Bushes

1. Press fit bushes for short runs.
2. Renewable bushes for high wear applications.
3. Slip bushes for multiple operations: drilling, reaming, counter-boring.
4. Threaded or spring-loaded bushes to combine clamping with guiding.
5. Special bushes with end shaped suitably to prevent drill deflection.
6. Plate bushes combining two or more bushes for very closely spaced holes.

Types of Jigs

1. Plate jigs for workpieces having parallel machined faces on sides to be drilled and used for resting.
2. Angle plate jigs for holes square to the machined bores.
3. Turn-over or table jigs for workpieces having the machined surface on the same side as the holes (and also square to the holes).
4. Leaf or latch jigs for workpieces having the machined surface on the side opposite to the holes (and square to the holes).
5. Box jigs for drilling holes from a number of sides in light workpieces.
6. Trunnion jigs for drilling holes from a number of sides in heavy workpieces.
7. Sandwich and pump jigs for workpieces having parallel machined surfaces on the side to be drilled and the side to be rested.
8. Jigs for multi-spindle machines with jig plate fixed to the machine spindle and aligned by guide pillars with the workpiece holding the fixture clamped on the machine table.
9. Adjustable jigs with adjustable locators and jig plates for workpieces having similar shape but different hole positions. Renewable bushes to vary hole size.

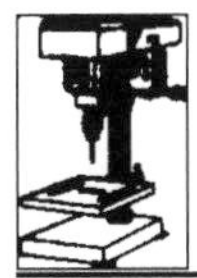

CHAPTER 6

Milling Fixtures

The direction and intensity of forces in milling depend considerably upon the type of milling machine, cutter and direction of feed.

Types of Milling Machines

Vertical Milling Machine

In this, the axis of the rotating cutter is vertical. This causes inevitable milling torque in the horizontal plane. Milling fixture elements should be able to withstand this torque and thrust of the milling cutter.

Horizontal Milling Machine

These drive cutters around a horizontal axis. Depending upon the direction of feed, the workpiece is lifted up or pressed down against the table. Horizontal machines often use a gang of many cutters. This increases the total cut and the resultant cutter thrust. Consequently, milling fixtures for horizontal machines should be able to bear torque in the vertical plane and thrust in the horizontal direction.

Types of Cutter

Bigger cutters such as face milling cutters develop higher cutting torque and thrust than smaller cutters like end mills and slitting saws. The helix angle of the cutting teeth develops axial thrust, which is passed onto the drawbolt and arbour nut. If two similar cutters are used simultaneously, they should be mounted in such a way that the helix angles of the two cutters are in opposite directions. Their axial thrusts should oppose and neutralise each other.

Direction of Feed

Up Milling (Conventional) The directions of feed and cutting oppose each other (Fig. 6.6b). The cutter tends to lift the workpiece and fixture from the table. This calls for heavy downward clamping. The thrust resulting from the cutting force should be directed to a solid, fixed part of the fixture instead of the clamp or other movable parts.

Down Milling (Fig. 6.5b) The feed direction is the same as the direction of cutting force. The cutter tends to press the fixture and workpiece down on the table. This subjects the machine to vibrations and so old, worn-out machines with excessive clearance between slides and lead screws are unsuitable for down milling.

Essentials of Milling Fixtures

1. ***Strength*** Milling fixtures should be heavy and robust to withstand heavy forces and severe vibrations developed in milling. Cast iron is a suitable material for milling fixtures. It can withstand vibrations well.
2. ***Thrust*** Heavy thrust caused in milling should be transmitted to strong solid structures. The thrust should not be directed towards a clamp or a movable part. If a vice is used, it is better to direct the thrust towards the fixed jaw instead of the movable jaw.
3. ***Cutter Setting*** Suitable cutter setting pieces should be provided for easy and accurate tool setting. It is customary to keep 0.40–0.5 mm gap between the cutter and setting piece. This gap facilitates cutter setting with the help of a feeler gauge (Fig. 6.1).
4. ***Machine Location Tennons*** Milling fixtures are generally fixed with locating tennons (tongues). These are fixed in slots machined on the resting face of the base (Fig. 6.2). Tennons are made close sliding fit in machine T slots. Tennons align the milling fixture with the longitudinal stroke of the machine.
5. ***Rigid Clamping*** The fixtures must be clamped firmly to the machine table in order to prevent sliding due to cutter thrust and vibrations. This is accomplished by a provision for *U* slots in the fixtures (Fig. 6.2). These facilitate direct clamping with *T* bolts, instead of external clamps. A minimum of two clamping slots are provided. In case of heavy cut and thrust, the number of clamping slots are increased to four or six.

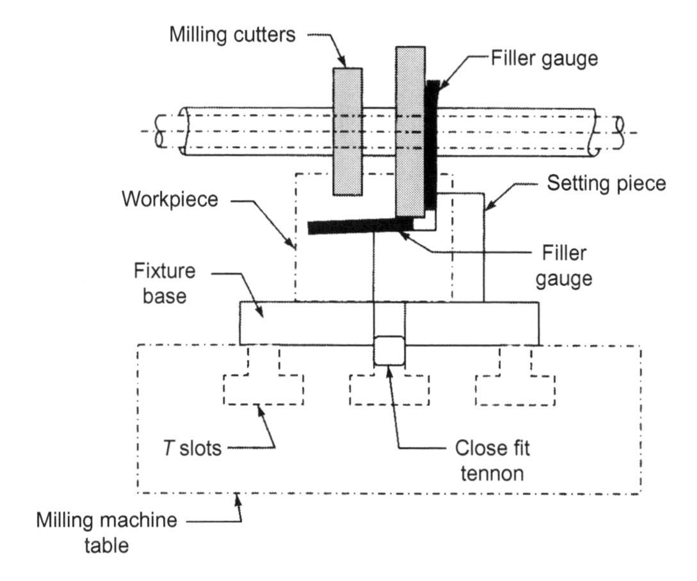

Fig. 6.1 *Cutter setting piece*

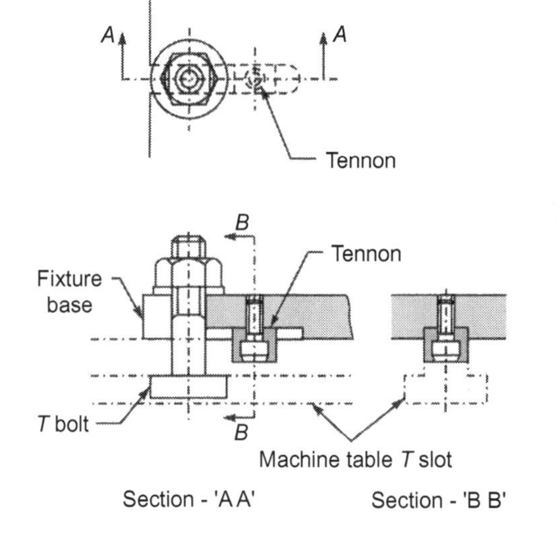

Fig. 6.2 *Machine location and clamping arrangement for milling fixtures*

6. ***Motion Economy*** Clamping time can be reduced by securing more than one workpiece with a single clamp (Figs 6.11b and 6.12b). In large scale continuous production, pneumatic or hydraulic power clamping should be considered. Generally, clamping time can be overlapped with machining time by using more than one fixture (Figs 6.7, 6.8–6.9).

7. ***Swarf Disposal*** Unlike drilling, milling chips are discontinuous. In case, swarf gets accumulated in closed pockets, big chip removal gates should be provided for cleaning the fixture.

Special Vice Jaws

For simple workpieces in small batches, a machine vice can be used conveniently. Many machine vice jaws have vertical and horizontal *V* grooves which facilitate holding of round workpieces in vertical or horizontal position. Many odd-shaped workpieces can be held in a vice by using suitable special jaws. The capacity of a vice can be increased by using extension jaws (Fig. 6.3a). Vice jaws can also be affixed with locators. Figure 6.3b shows a fixed jaw with an angular slot and rest pin to provide nesting location and vertical stop to the workpiece. The other movable jaw is plain surfaced as it is used only for clamping. Some workpieces require locators on both the jaws as shown in Fig. 6.3c. In such cases both the jaws should be positively aligned with each other. This can be accomplished by providing guide pins and bushes. Some machine vices have location slots for precision positioning of jaws. The jaws are provided with close-fitting location tongues (tennons) as shown in Fig. 6.3d.

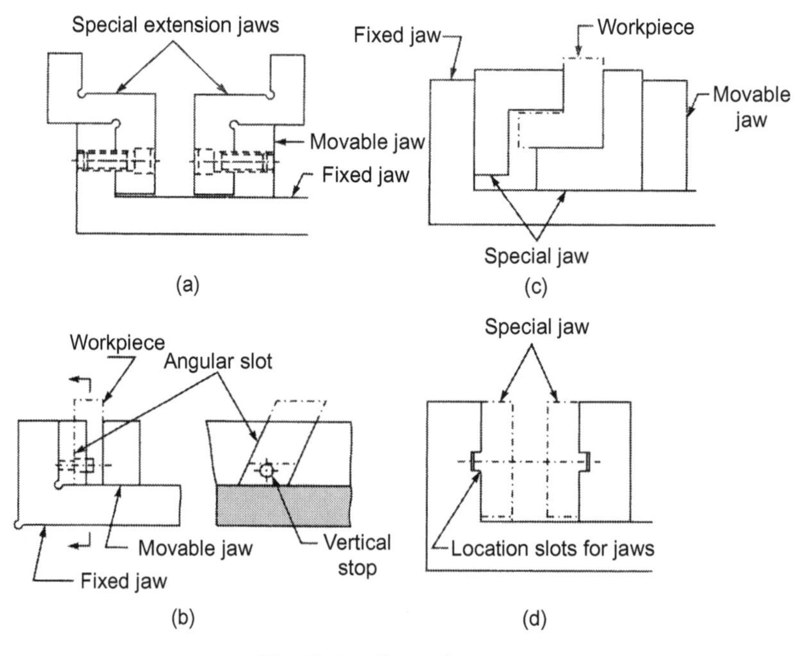

Fig. 6.3 *Special vice jaws*

Milling operations can be broadly classified as:

1. Facing
2. Slotting

Facing Fixtures

Milling machines are used extensively for facing seating and mating flat surfaces. Milling is often the first operation performed on the workpiece. Figure 6.4b shows a simple face-milling fixture.

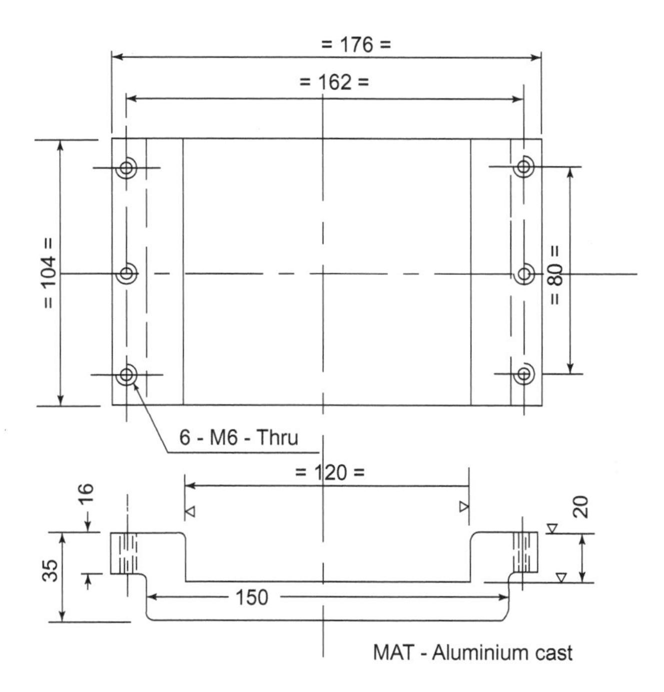

Fig. 6.4a *Workpiece for face milling fixture in Fig. 6.4b*

The workpiece is supported by three adjustable spherical-ended pads *A* which are adjusted to suit the variation in casting and locked in position by check nuts. Two-self adjusting supports are pushed upwards by light springs which ensure that supports are positively in contact with the workpiece. Supports can be locked in this position by clamping screws *D*. The tightening of edge clamp pushes the casting against fixed jaw *F* which is keyed in the fixture body to provide solid support to the workpiece against the heavy thrust developed during operation. The cutter should be fed to the

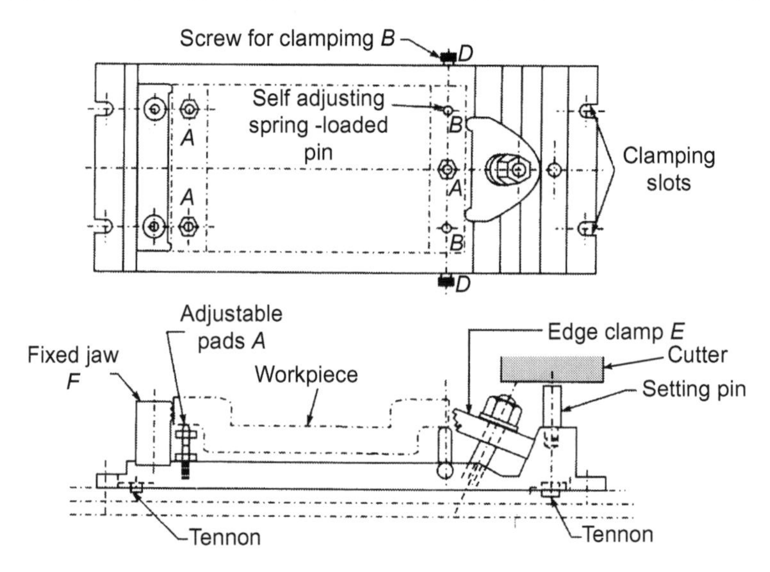

Fig. 6.4b *Face milling fixture*

workpiece in such a way that the milling thrust is directed towards the solid support of the fixed jaw. Setting piece S is placed in the path of the cutter so that it can be set before it commences facing operation. Generally, locating tennons are not necessary in plain face milling operations. An approximate location effected through clamping slots is adequate enough. The position and size of the clamping slots should match with the spacing of T slot on the

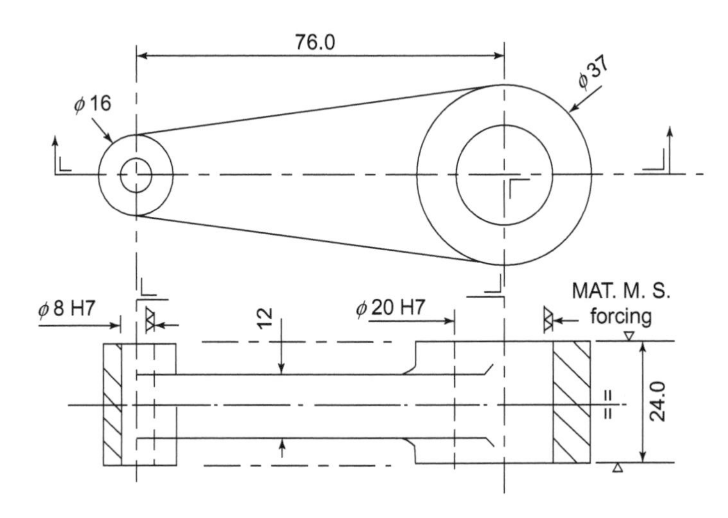

Fig. 6.5a *Workpiece for straddle milling fixture in Fig. 6.5b*

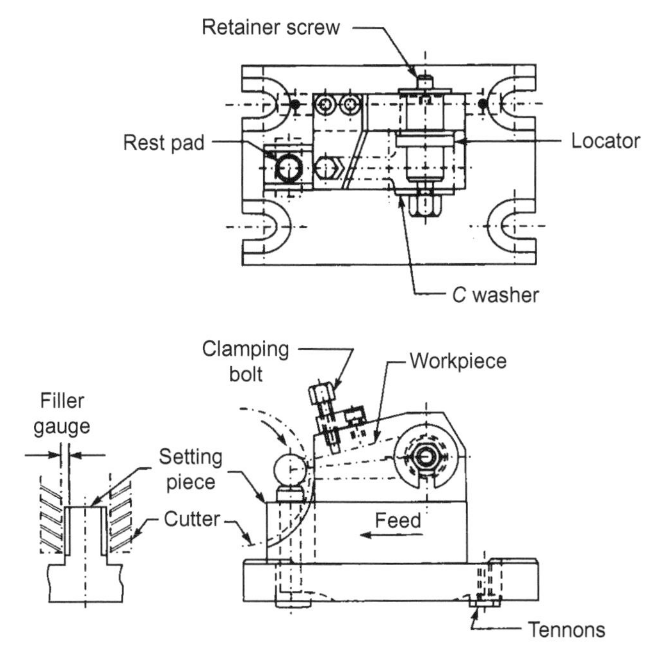

Fig. 6.5b *Straddle milling fixture*

machine table. Four clamping slots are provided to counter the heavy forces developed during operation. Generally, two clamping slots are sufficient for lesser cutting load.

Figure 6.5b illustrates a fixture for simultaneous facing of two sides of a boss. This method of milling is called straddle milling. The workpiece is located on the machined bore and face of the bigger boss of the workpiece. It is clamped against the face of the resting pad by a bolt. The hexagonal nut and *C* washer hold the workpiece against the collar of the locator.

The two milling cutters face both sides of the boss simultaneously. The milling thrust is directed toward the rest pad which passes it on to the solid fixture body. The fixture is located in machine table T slots by two tennons. Four U shaped slots in the fixture base simplify clamping on the machine table. The machined side faces of the casting below the rest pad are used for cutter setting. The cutters are positioned at 0.5 mm from the faces of the casting with a feeler gauge.

Straddle milling is widely used for milling precisely the parallel opposite faces of a workpiece.

Figure 6.6 depicts a gang milling fixture for milling one slot and a number faces in the workpiece shown. A gang of three side and face cutters is used to mill seven faces on the workpiece.

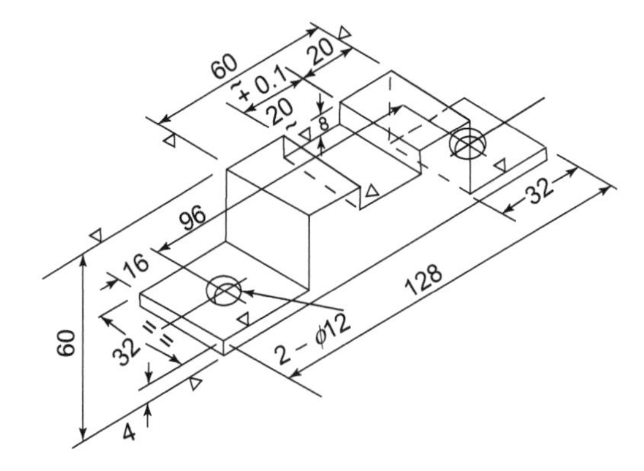

Fig. 6.6a *Workpiece for gang milling fixture in Fig. 6.6b*

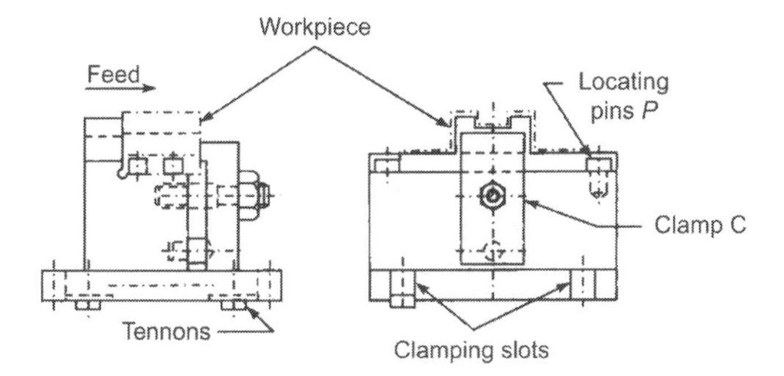

Fig. 6.6b *Gang milling fixture*

The workpiece is located by four pins *P* and it is clamped against a solid section of the body against which the milling thrust is directed. Clamp *C* has got a downward angle at the clamping point. In addition to holding the workpiece against the vertical face, the angular clamping face also exerts downward pressure on the workpiece, pressing it against the horizontal face.

Most of the clamps used in horizontal milling exert some downward force on the workpiece to prevent it from getting lifted during conventional upmilling feed (Fig. 6.4).

The profiled portion of the body also serves as a cutter setting piece. It is made 0.5 mm underrsize to facilitate use of feeler gauge for cutter setting.

The fixture is provided with two locating tennons at the base to align it with table T slots. Four *U* shaped clamping slots facilitate strong clamping to withstand the heavy thrust due to the three cutters.

A large part of industrial milling consists of milling a single mounting and reference face of the workpiece. Such plain facing work can be speeded up by overlapping the workpiece loading and clamping time over the machining time. While one workpiece is being machined, the previously machined piece is unclamped and unloaded; and the next piece to be machined is loaded and clamped. The new piece is ready for machining before the preceding piece is machined completely. This can be accomplished by the following methods:

1. Index milling
2. Rotary milling
3. Reciprocal milling

1. *Index Milling* It uses a multi-station indexing table on which a number of fixtures are mounted. In a two-station fixture shown in Fig. 6.7, while workpiece *A* is milled at the machining station, the previously machined workpiece is removed and replaced by a fresh piece at the loading and unloading station. When machining of *A* is over, the indexing device is rotated and indexed to bring the new workpiece *B* to the machining station. The machined workpiece *A* can be replaced by a fresh workpiece while piece *B* is being machined.

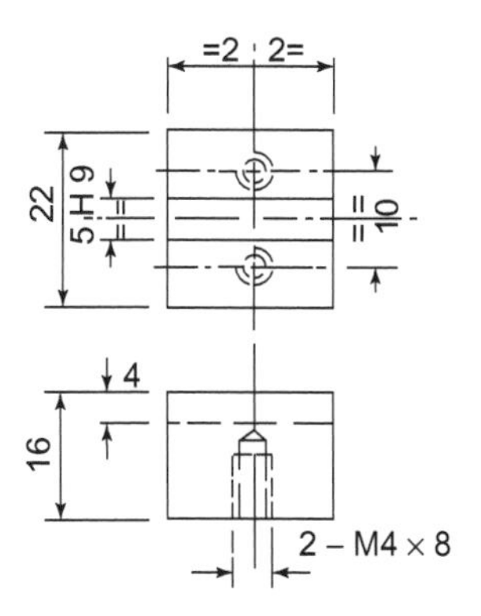

Fig. 6.7a *Workpiece for index milling (Fig. 6.7b) on fixture (Fig. 6.7c)*

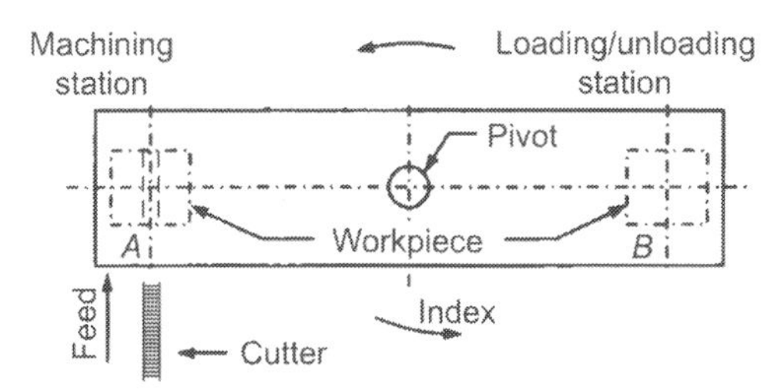

Fig. 6.7b *Index milling*

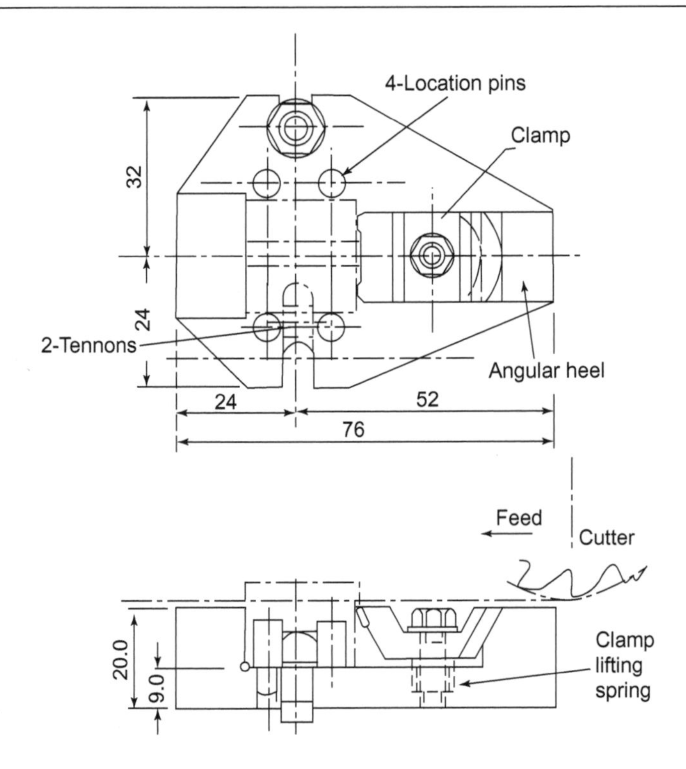

Fig. 6.7c *Fixture for milling workpiece in Fig. 6.7a by index milling (Fig. 6.7b)*

2. ***Rotary Milling*** In this, a number of workpieces are mounted on a rotary fixture which is rotated to feed the workpiece stream to the milling cutter. At the opposite end of the rotary table the machined workpieces are replaced by fresh ones even while the rotary fixture is moving (Fig. 6.8). Figure 6.8a shows workpiece for rotary in milling. Figure 6.8c shows the milling fixture.

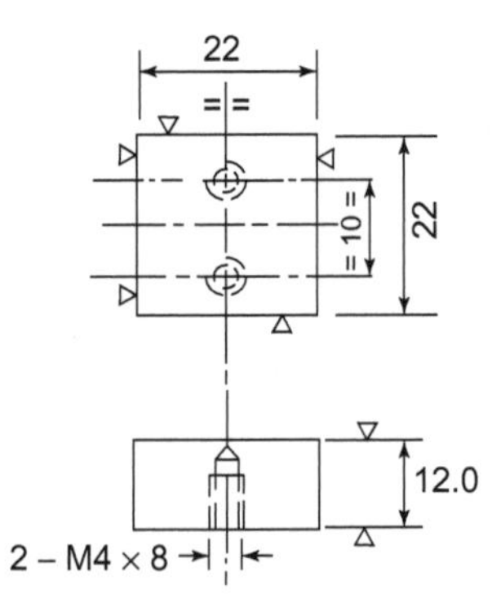

Fig. 6.8a *Workpiece for rotary milling in Fig. 6.8b*

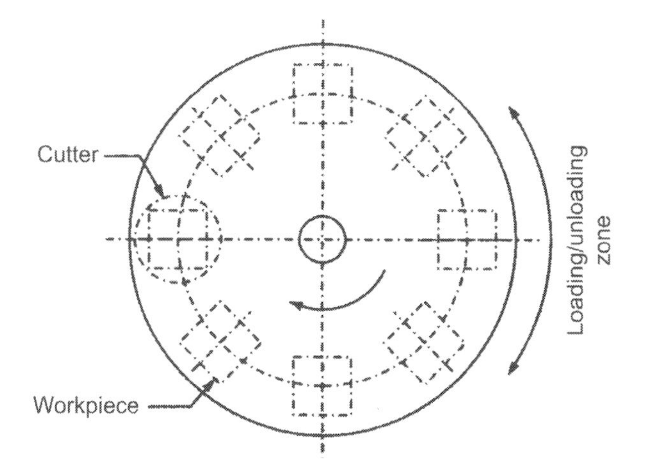

Fig. 6.8b *Rotary milling*

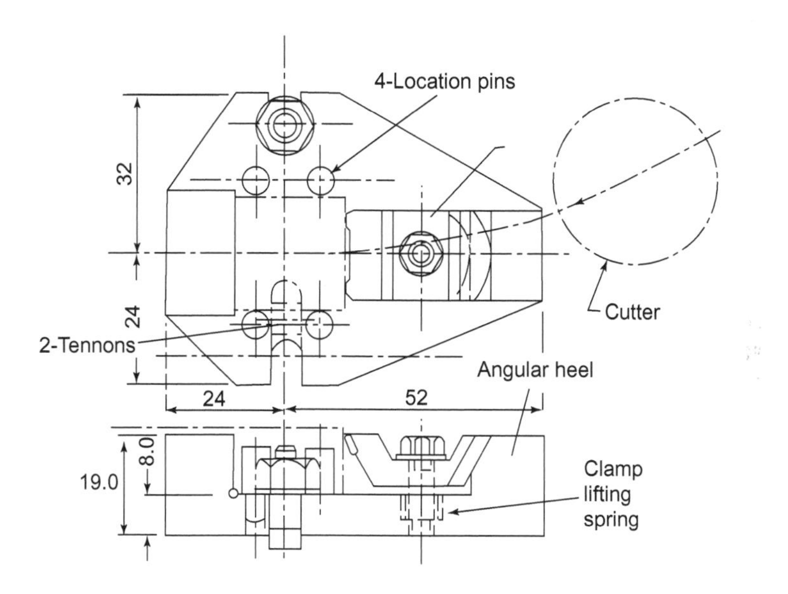

Fig. 6.8c *Fixture for milling workpiece in Fig. 6.8a on rotary milling m/c with radial 'T' slots*

3. ***Reciprocal or Pendulum Milling (Fig. 6.9)*** In this, two fixtures are mounted at the two ends of the machine table. The machined workpiece at one end is replaced by a fresh one while the workpiece at the other end is being machined. After completion of machining, the machine table is traversed to feed the workpiece at the other end of the table. While this is being

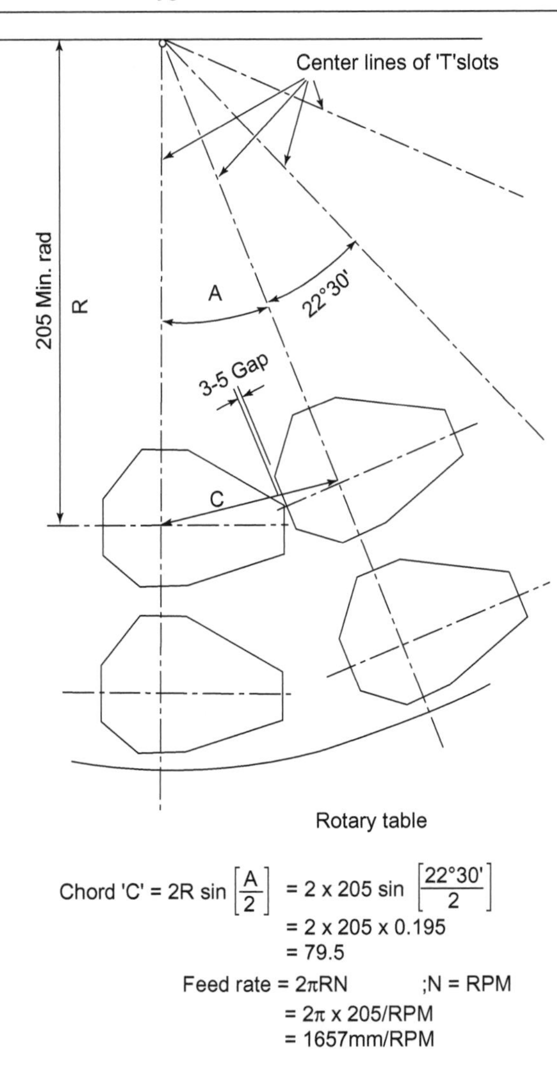

Fig. 6.8d *Layout of fixtures in Fig. 6.8c on rotary table*

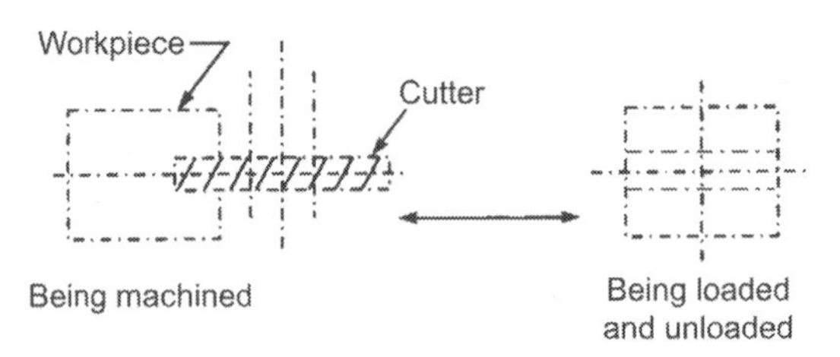

Fig. 6.9a *Pendulum or reciprocal milling*

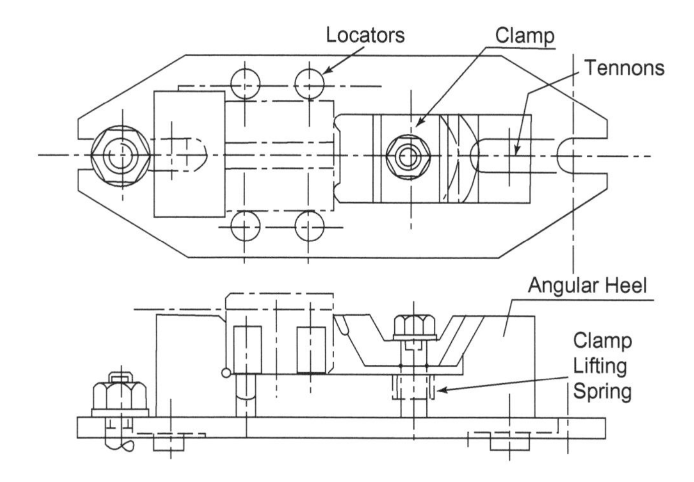

Fig. 6.9b *Fixture for milling workpiece in Fig. 6.7a by pendulum milling on hor. milling m/c*

machined, the preceding machined workpiece at the idle end is replaced by a fresh one. Thus, the table is reciprocated like a pendulum to machine alternately the workpieces at both the ends of the table.

Slotting Fixtures

In slotting fixtures, the workpiece should be clamped as close to the portion being machined as possible. Figure 6.10 shows a slot milling fixture for a lever. The lever is located on two previously machined holes. The bigger locator as well as the angle plate are slotted to permit passage of the slotting cutter. The slot can be used for setting the cutter. The workpiece is clamped against the angle plate by a swinging strap clamp. The clamp is loosened and turned anti-clockwise to the chaindotted position to clear the path of loading and unloading the workpiece. The base is slotted for locating tennons which align the fixture with the machine traverse.

Figure 6.11b depcits a key-way milling fixture for shafts. The shafts are located and supported by *V* blocks. A single clamp secures two shafts simultaneously. Both the shafts are milled simultaneously for key-ways by a gang of two cutters, which can be set with the help of the setting piece. A stopper locates shaft axially and takes the milling thrust. The fixture is aligned with the machine table by two tennons and clamped through *U* slots.

Round parts can be slotted economically on a standard string milling fixture as shown in Fig. 6.12. The workpieces are held between *V* blocks which slide freely in a guide slot in the body.

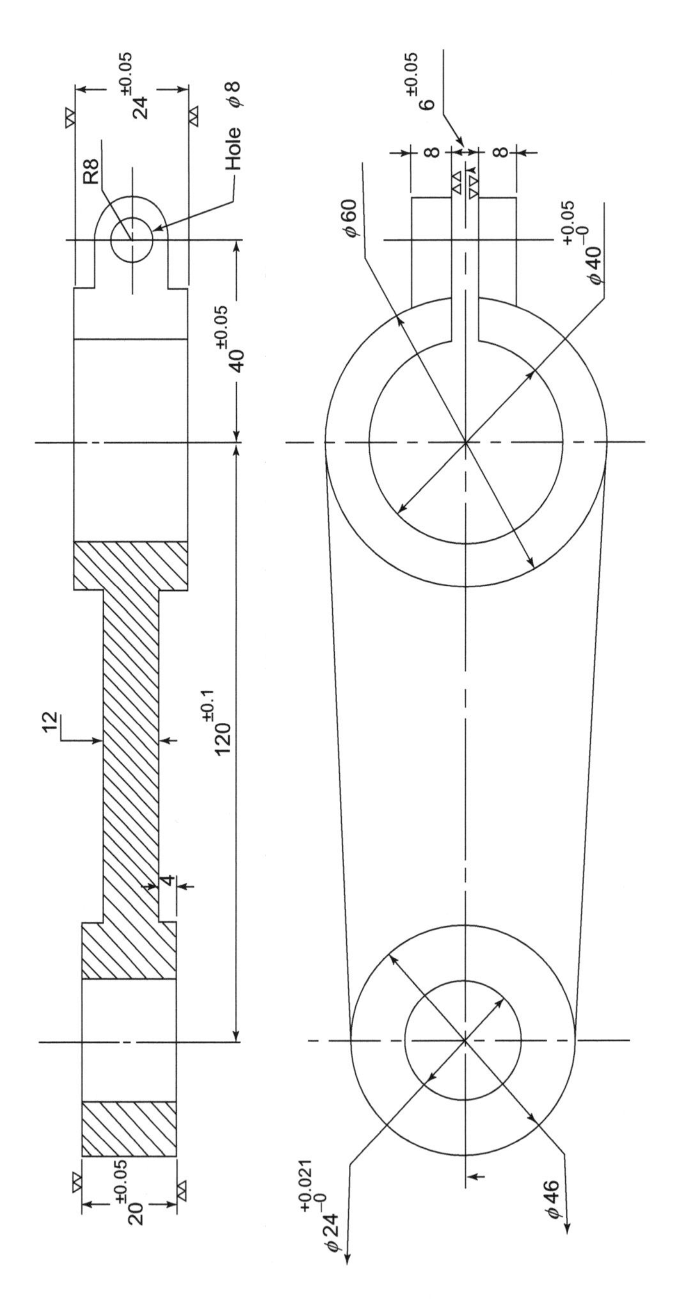

Fig. 6.10a *Workpiece for slotting fixture in Fig. 6.10b*

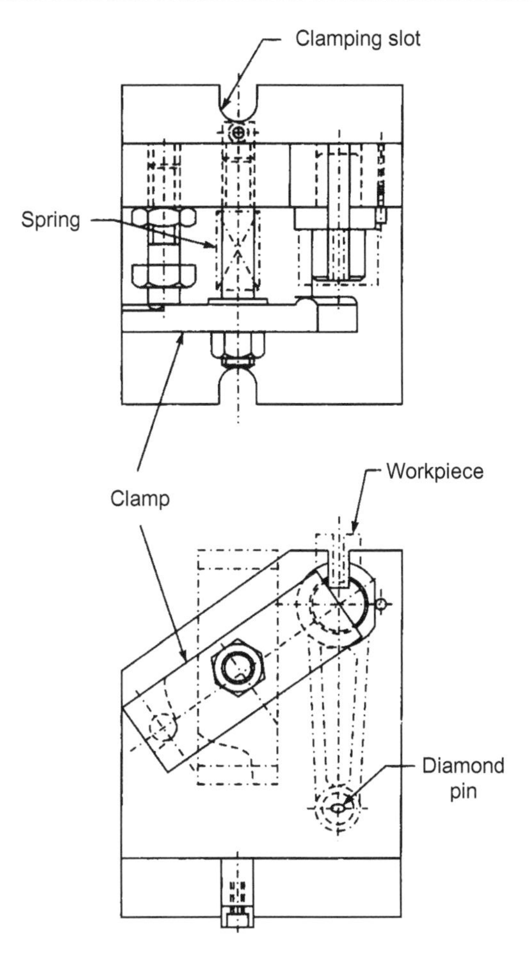

Fig. 6.10b *Slotting fixture*

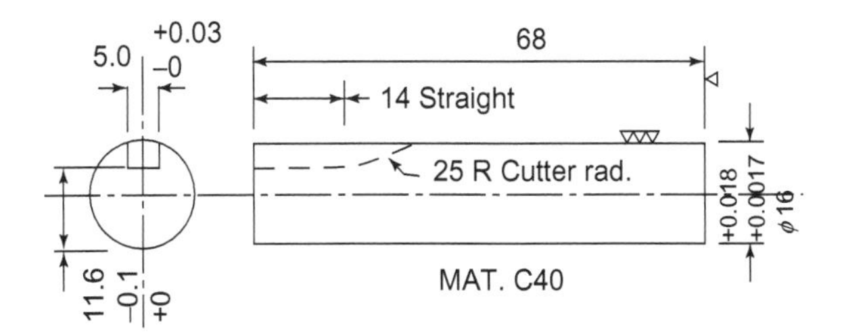

Fig. 6.11a *Workpiece for key-way milling fixture in Fig. 6.11b*

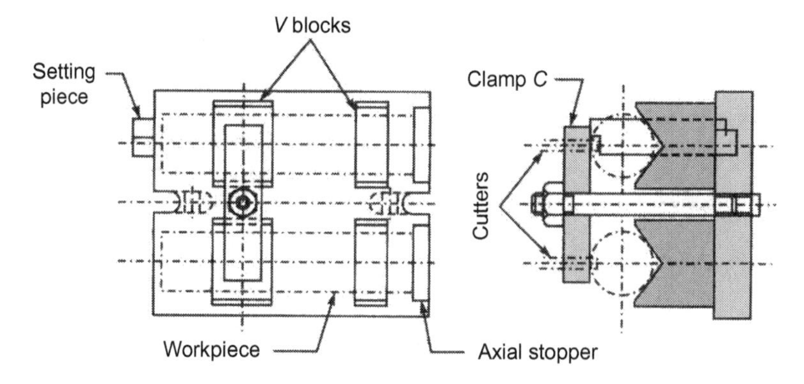

Fig. 6.11b *Key-way milling fixture*

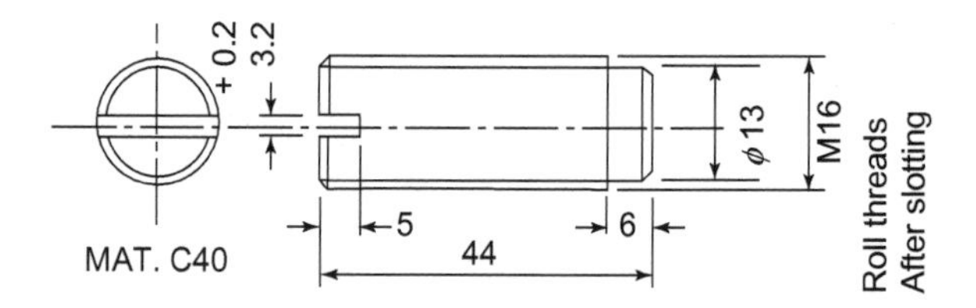

Fig. 6.12a *Workpiece for standard string milling fixture in Fig. 6.12b*

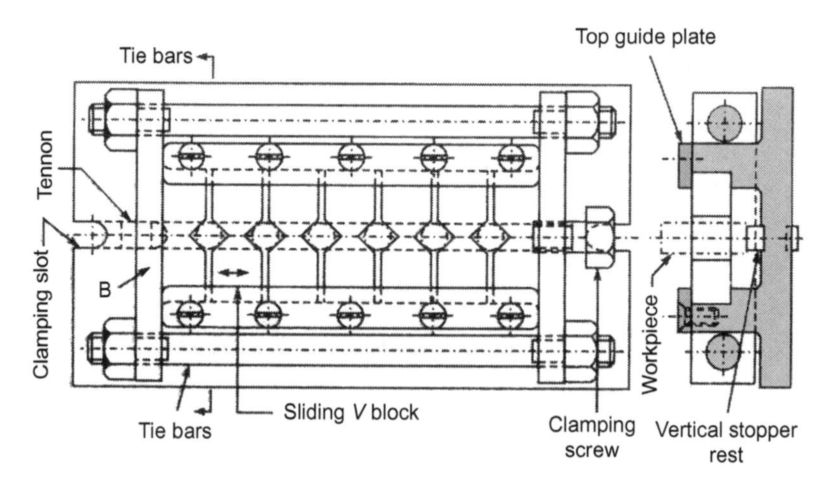

Fig. 6.12b *Standard string milling fixture for round parts*

The top guide plate prevents *V* blocks from getting lifted up during milling. The *V* blocks can grip a wide range of round diameters. Axial location can be provided by a rest plate which acts as a vertical stopper for the workpieces. This plate can be changed for different workpieces.

Large chip removal gates must be provided for removal of the chips falling into the box-like structure of the fixture body. The cutter thrust should be directed towards fixed plate B. A number of workpieces are clamped simultaneously by a single hexagonal-headed bolt which holds the workpieces like a multi-layered sandwich of alternate *V* blocks and workpieces. Two tennons at the bottom align the fixture with the machine travel and the *U* slots serve as integral clamps.

String milling can be used conveniently for many workpieces requiring only a short machine stroke for operation. It utilises a large part of the machine stroke. Numerous workpieces are machined in a single traverse. The number of workpieces which can be milled in a single stroke depends upon the accuracy of the machine slide movement along the traverse and permissible centrality tolerances on the workpiece slot.

Milling Half Cylindrical Surfaces

Although milling cutters are much more sturdy than twist drills they, too deflect (lesser than a twist drill) under load. Furthermore milling cutters have very wide (j 16) manufacturing tolerance on diameter. Even on a 16 diameter cutter, the tolerance is 1.1 mm. And the tolerance is bilateral (+ or –). So the cutter supporting arrangement must have adjustment to take care of the diameter variation as well as the reduction due to re-sharpening cut on the diameter. Fig. 6.13a shows a workpiece with a half cylindrical 11R surface to be machined. Fig. 6.13b shows the special half cylindrical bush for preventing deflection of a slot drill while milling the half-cylindrical seat. Note that the diameter (radius) of the cutter guiding portion of the bush should be suitable for the maximum diameter (16 + 1.1) of the slot drill. The bush is provided with two screws for adjusting its position to suit the cutter diameter. Two studs along with four hexagonal check nuts secure the bush in the set position. The adjustment facilitates re-setting the bush after the cutter wear , thus prolonging its life.

The semi-cylindrical bush facilitates machining the semi-cylindrical seat on a drilling machine. Of course we can machine the half cylinder on a turning machine. However the fixture cost as well as the machining cost will be higher.

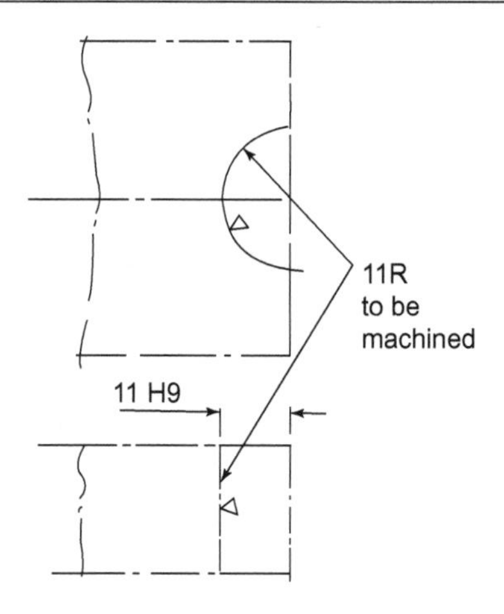

Fig. 6.13a

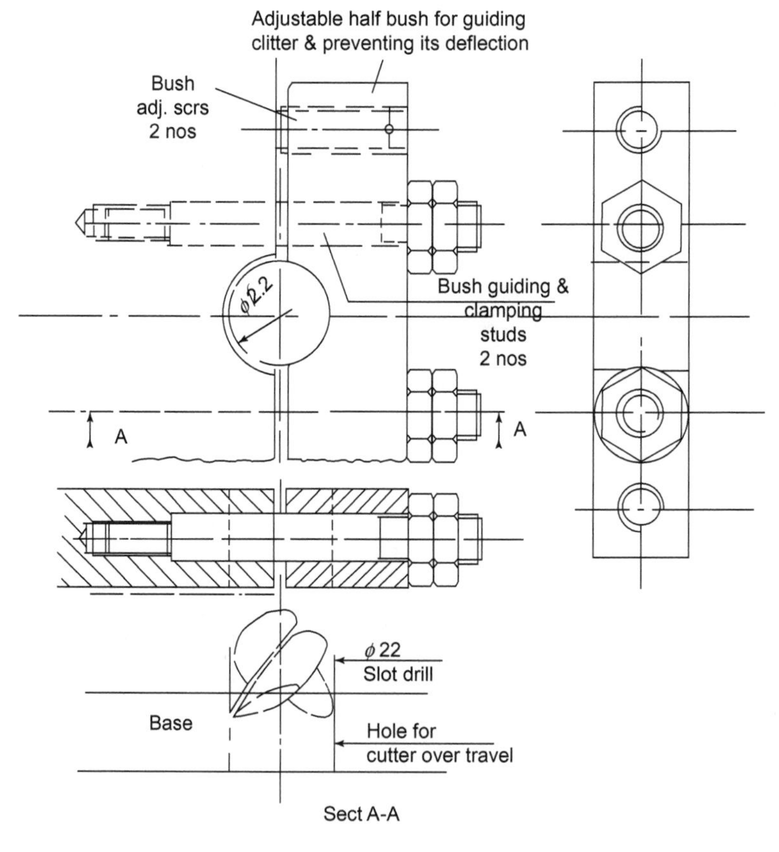

Fig. 6.13b

Summary

Milling Machines

1. Vertical (spindle) milling machines generate torque in the horizontal plane and thrust in the feed direction.
2. Horizontal (spindle) milling machines tend to lift or press the downwards workpiece and generate thrust in the direction of the feed.

Cutter Types

1. Bigger the cutter, more the torque and thrust. Helix angle of the cutting teeth leads to axial thrust.

Feed Direction

1. Up milling feed in direction opposite to the cutting force. Tends to lift the workpiece and fixture.
2. Down milling feed in direction of the cutting force. Tends to press the workpiece and fixture downwards. Severe vibrations.

Essentials of Milling Fixture

1. Strength to withstand heavy forces.
2. Thrust should be directed towards a strong, solid structure.
3. Cutter setting piece should be provided.
4. Milling fixtures should be aligned with locating tennons.
5. Rigid clamping.
6. Motion economy through multiple/power clamping.
7. Gates for chip removal.

Special Vice Jaws

They enable usage of a standard vice with replacable jaws for milling.

Facing Fixtures

No part of the fixture should be in the path of the cutter.

1. Straddle milling uses two cutters for milling two parallel faces of a workpiece simultaneously.
2. Gang milling uses a number of cutters to mill many faces of a workpiece simultaneously.
3. In index milling, a machined workpiece is unloaded and a fresh one is loaded on the idle station of the indexing table while another workpiece is being milled at the other station.
4. In rotary milling, a table mounted with a number of workpieces rotates continuously. The milled workpieces are unloaded and fresh ones are loaded on the table in the part away from the cutter.
5. Pendulum or reciprocal milling uses two fixtures at opposite ends of the machine. The loading and unloading of the workpiece at one end of table is done while the workpiece at the other end is being milled.

Slotting Fixtures

They often use clamps with a slot for the cutter to accomplish clamping of the workpiece as close as possible to the part being milled.

1. Key-way milling fixtures for horizontal machines often use double clamping and a gang of two cutters to mill two shafts simultaneously.
2. String milling fixtures place a number of similar round workpieces in one line for milling them in a single traverse of the cutter.

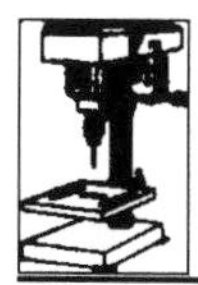

CHAPTER 7

Turning Fixtures

Turning fixture mainly consists of workpiece locating and clamping elements. These fixtures are used for facing, boring and turning operations. For all these operations, the workpiece must be positioned correctly with respect to the rotating machine spindle. For boring and turning, the axis of the bore or the outside diameter to be machined must be aligned with the machine spindle axis.

Generally, turning machine spindles have accurately machined spigots for location and threads for clamping of locators and work holders (Fig. 7.1).

Most of the machines are provided with a back plate, which is permanently mounted on to the machine spindle. The back plate, is used to locate and clamp turning fixtures, chucks and other workholders on the machine. The outside diameter of the back plate is generally machined precisely to

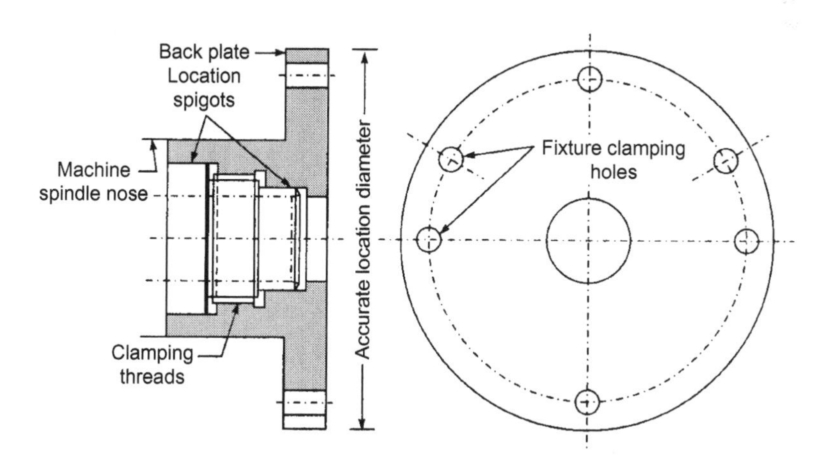

Fig. 7.1 *Back plate for turning fixtures*

the sixth grade of tolerance. It is used as a locating spigot for aligning axis of rotation of the fixtures with the machine spindle. The back plate is provided with three or more equi-spaced holes for clamping turning fixtures. Generally, the fixtures are provided with clamping studs which are inserted in the clamping holes in the back plate and secured by hexagonal nuts (Fig. 7.2). Even the standard chucks and commercial workholders are fixed to the back plate in a similar manner.

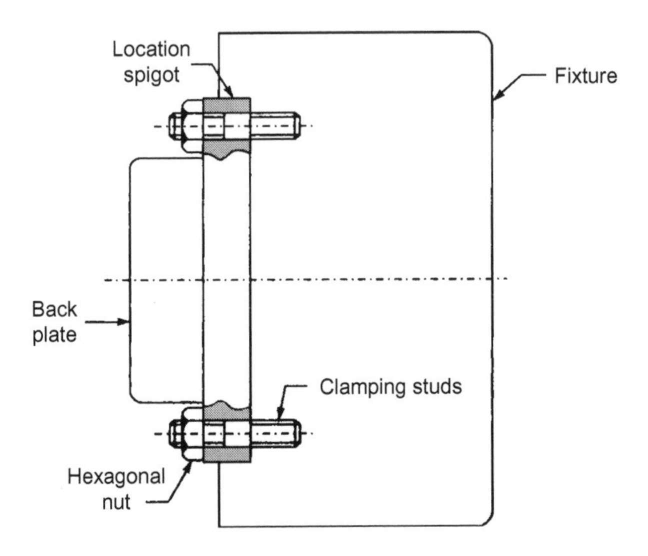

Fig. 7.2 *Location and clamping of turning fixtures*

The majority of workpieces processed on turning machines (lathe, capstans, turrets and autos) are circular in shape. Most of these can be held and located (centralised) satisfactorily in the standard commercial, chucks and collets. Many rectangular and other odd shapes can be clamped satisfactorily on the standard face plates. As a matter of fact, most of the turning fixtures are special face plates designed to facilitate quick loading, locating and clamping of workpieces in mass production.

Standard Chucks

Self-centreing Three-jaw Chucks

In this, all the jaws move simultaneously and are operated by rotating a screw with a chuck key. The standard jaws always remain concentric with the axis of the chuck during movement. This centralises the workpiece.

Figure 7.3 illustrates a typical three jaw-scroll chuck. Self-centreing chucks are also available in two or four jaw varieties.

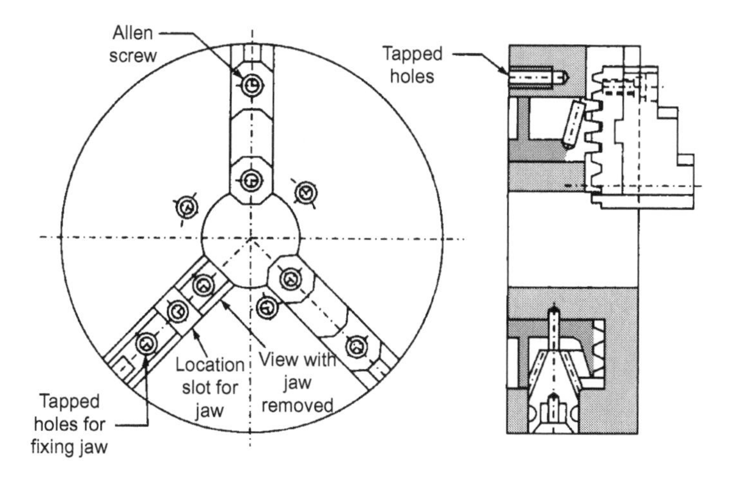

Fig. 7.3 *Three-jaw self centreing scroll chuck*

Independent Four-jaw Chucks

In this type, each one of the four chuck jaws can be moved independent of the other jaws. This helps in making the jaws deliberately non-concentric to centralise an offset bore in a rectangular workpiece (Fig. 7.4). Independent jaw chucks are also used for most accurate centralising of round workpieces. They are also available in two-jaws variety.

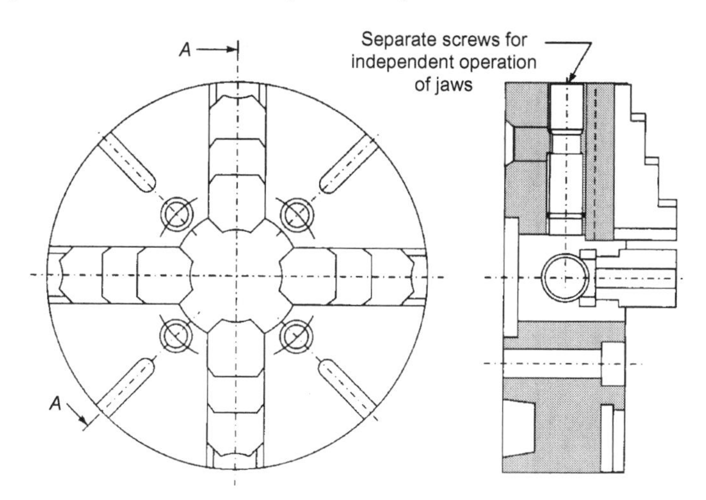

Fig. 7.4 *Independent four-jaw chuck*

Combination Chucks

These combine the advantages of the independent jaw and self-centreing chucks.

Each jaw can be moved towards or away from the centre of the chuck by a separate adjusting screw. This facilitates location of odd shaped workpiece (Fig. 7.5). After adjustment, all the jaws can be moved simultaneously by the master socket for quick clamping and unclamping of the workpiece.

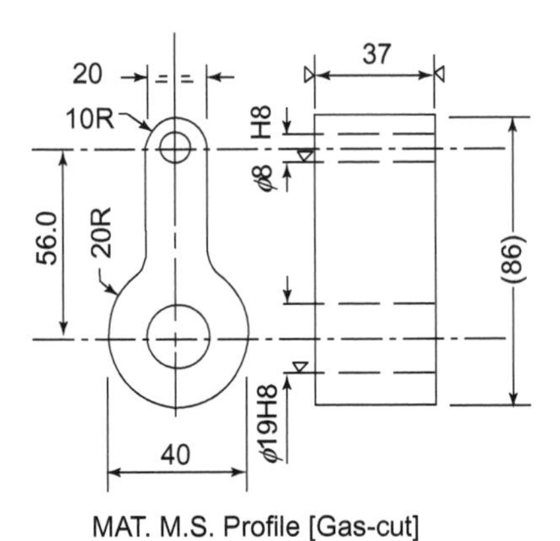

Fig. 7.5a *Workpiece for using radial adjustment of combination chuck jaw to centralise ϕ 19 offset bore (see Fig. 7.5b)*

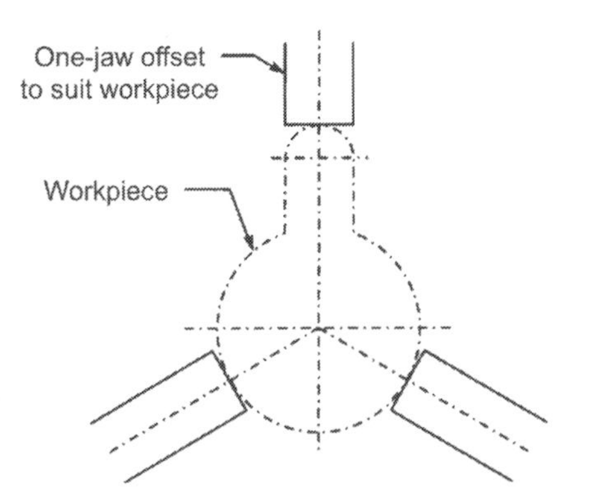

Fig. 7.5b *Combination chuck*

Power-operated Chucks

In this, the use of compressed air or pressurised hydraulic oil for moving the jaws reduces operator fatigue and facilitates fine control of clamping pressure. Moreover, the clamping force can be varied during rough and finish machining. For example, a workpiece is clamped with 4 kg/cm^2 air pressure during roughing heavy cut. During light cut finishing, the air pressure is reduced to 1 kg/cm^2. This releases the workpiece from the temporary distortion caused by high clamping force used in roughing. Finishing under low force clamping prevents inaccuracies due to distortion of the workpiece.

Special Jaws

A wide variety of odd-shaped workpieces can be located and clamped satisfactorily by modifying the shape of the standard jaws. Figure 7.6 depicts typical standard jaws.

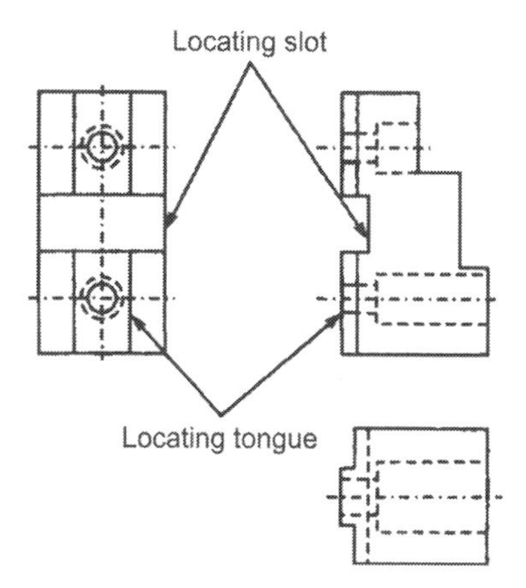

Fig. 7.6 *Standard jaws*

For frail and thin-walled parts the length and area of the clamping face of the jaw is increased considerably to distribute clamping pressure over a wider area. This reduces distortion and damage of the workpiece (Fig. 7.7).

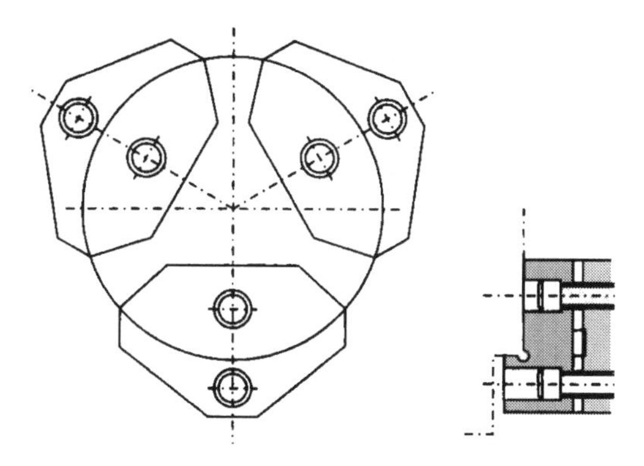

Fig. 7.7 *Special jaws to increase clamping area*

Soft Jaws

They are used for highly concentric second operation machining. These jaws are not hardened. They are machined to size after assembly on the chuck just before commencing manufacture.

Before starting production of every batch, a light cut is taken on the soft jaws to ensure high degree of concentricity during second operation machining of the workpiece. A clamping ring is necessary to hold the jaws in tight position during the cut.

The shape of the jaw clamping face can be modified to suit the workpiece profile (Fig. 7.8). This helps in quick location and clamping of odd-shaped workpiece on the standard chuck. A combination chuck is more convenient for use of such jaws. For, the different jaws can be positioned independently by individual adjusting screws. After setting the jaws to suit the workpiece,

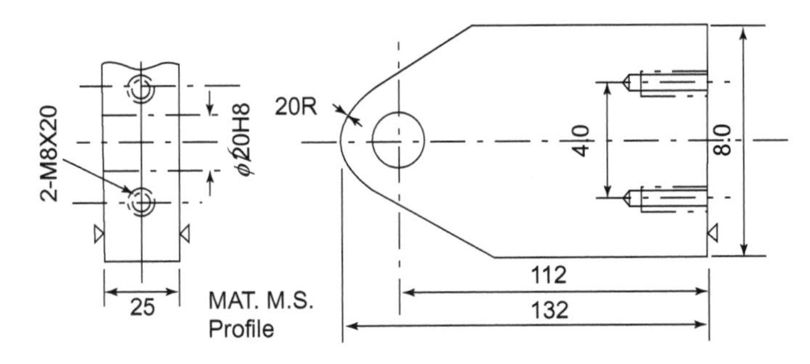

Fig. 7.8a *Workpiece calling for special Jaw (Fig. 7.8b)*

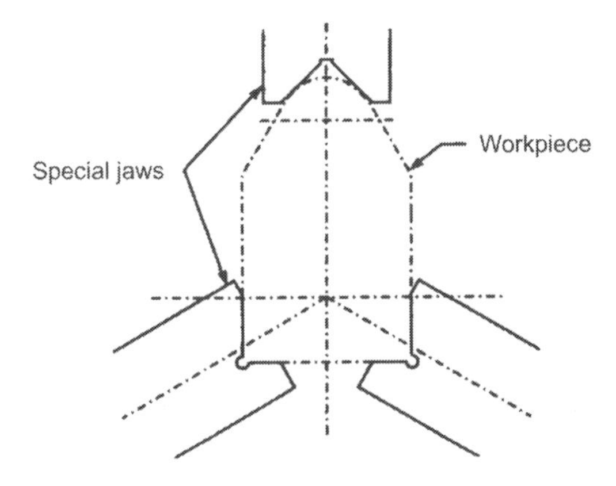

Fig. 7.8b *Special jaws for odd-shaped workpiece*

all the jaws can be operated simultaneously by the master socket for quick clamping and unclamping.

Face Plate

The standard face plate can be used conveniently for machining simple, short height components. The addition of locators and clamps on the face plate facilitates quick location and clamping of the workpiece (Fig. 7.9). Face plate fixtures are particularly suitable for facing a number of workpieces simultaneously on the lathe (Fig. 7.10).

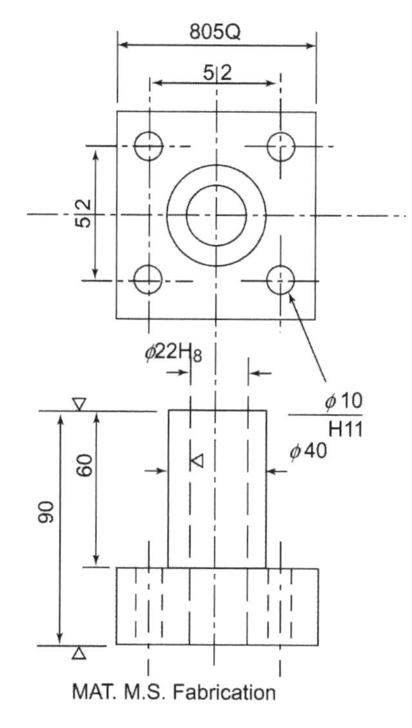

Fig. 7.9a *Workpiece for face plate fixture in Fig. 7.9b*

Spring Collets

Cold rolled round bars can be centralised accurately and clamped/unclamped quickly by using hardened collets. However, these can be operated only within a limited range of about 0.15 mm. Consequently, different

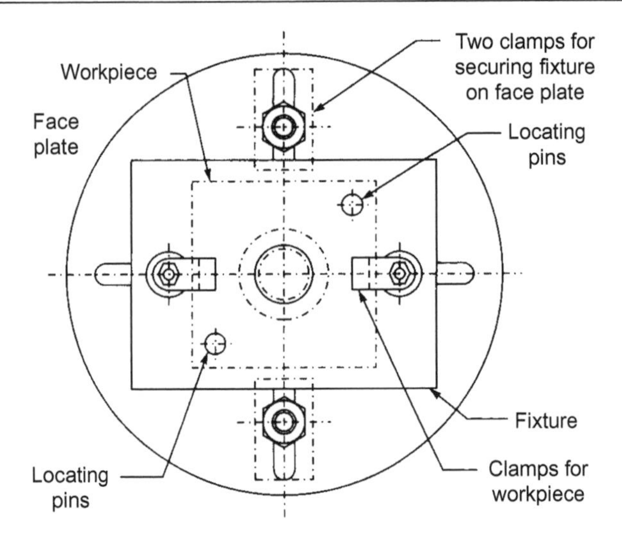

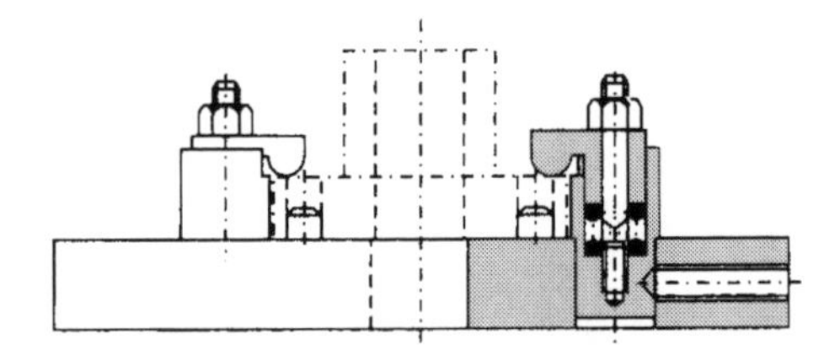

Fig. 7.9b *Face plate fixture*

collets must be used for different sizes of bars, and the variation in the bar size should be less than 0.15 mm.

The compactness of collets permits the cutting tool to be taken very close to the griping point. The stock is held almost all around the periphery. This distributes the clamping pressure over a wide surface of the bar and prevents distortion and clamping dents.

Most of the collets have got a clamping cone, which bears against the conical bore on the spindle nut. For gripping the bar, the collet is pressed against the conical surface in the nut. This is mostly done manually by a handle which moves a draw tube in the machine spindle. In some machines, the tube is moved by a pneumatic cylinder.

Collets can be broadly classified into three types:

1. Push-out collets
2. Pull-in collets
3. Dead length collets

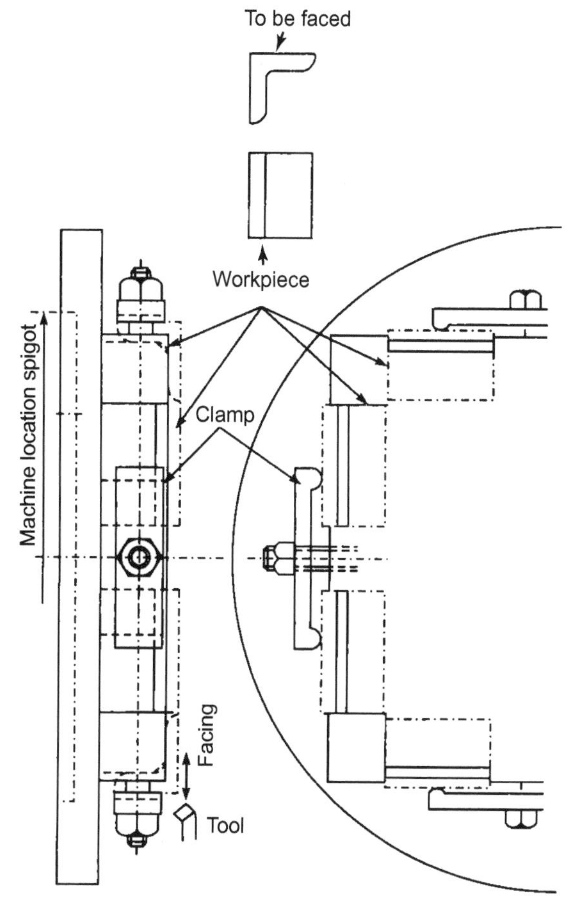

Fig. 7.10 *Angles facing fixtures*

Push-out Collets

For clamping the bar, the push tube pushes the collect against the conical seat of the spindle nut as shown in Fig. 7.11b. This bends the gripping portion of the collet inwards to clamp the bar. Push-out type collets tend to push the stock outwards. This is good for the first operation in which the bar is pushed against the stopper. For changing the collet, it is necessary to remove the nut from the spindle. Collets are made of spring steel and are hardened and tempered. The gripping portion is slotted to permit bending to facilitate clamping. The wall at the bending point is thinned to reduce the force required for bending during gripping.

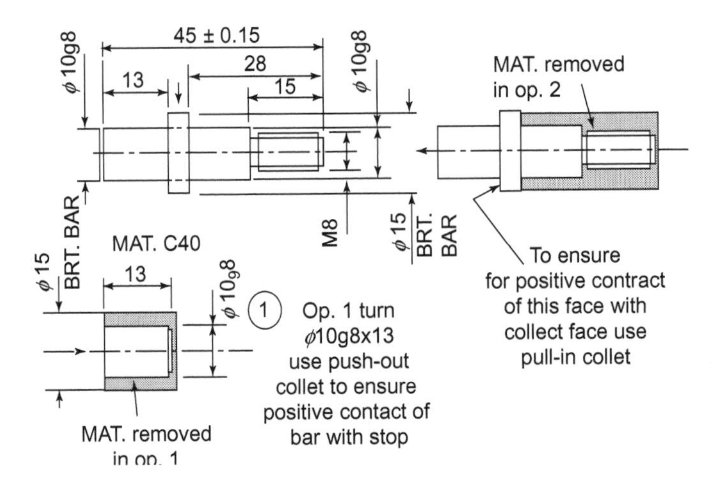

Fig. 7.11a *Workpiece for push-out and pull-in collets in Figs 7.11b and 7.12*

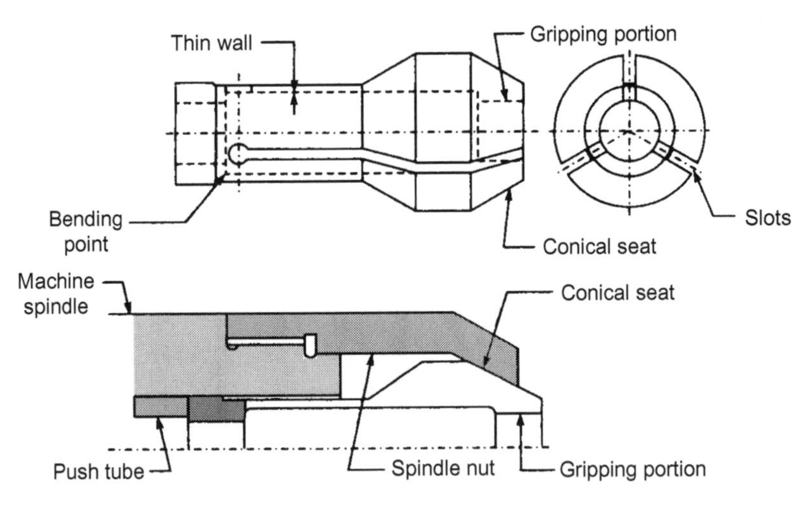

Fig. 7.11b *Push-out collet*

Pull-in Collets

Pull-in collets (Fig. 7.12) are threaded at the rear end. A draw tube is screwed into the collet. For gripping the bar, the draw tube pulls the collet against the conical seat of the nut. This bends the gripping portion of the collet inwards to clamp the bar.

Pull-in collet tends to move the stock towards the machine spindle during gripping. This type of collet can be changed over without removing the spindle nut.

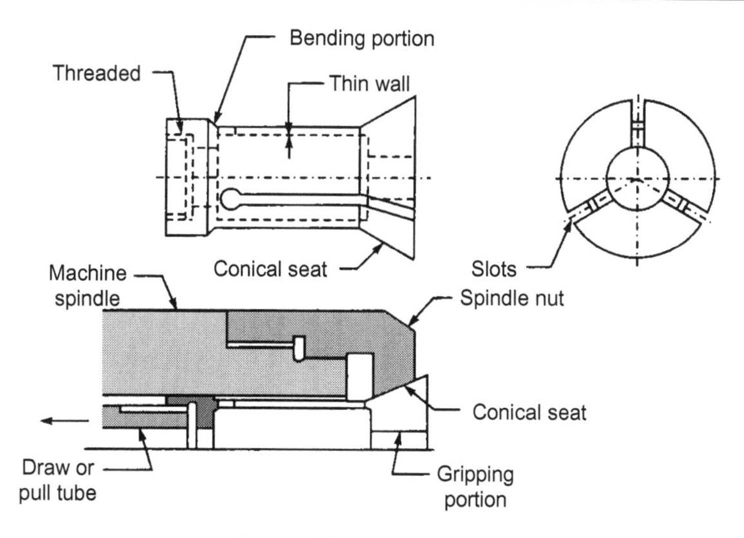

Fig. 7.12 *Pull-in collet*

Dead Length Collets

Dead length collet (Fig. 7.13) has two conical seats. The tapered portion on the machine spindle side bears with the cone on the pressure sleeve whereas the angular seat on the opposite side matches with the angle on the nut. The tightening of nut squeezes the collet between the two conical seats to clamp the stock. Consequently, dead length collets do not move the stock inwards or outwards like pull-in or push-out collets.

This type of collet is also less economical as the manufacture of the two conical mating surfaces increases machining cost. Moreover, the collet

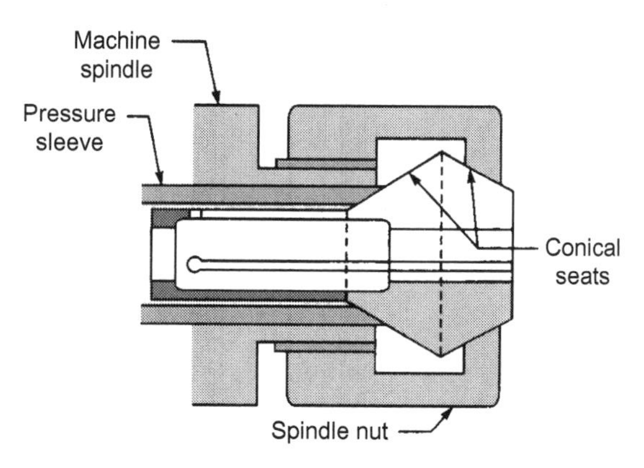

Fig. 7.13 *Dead length collet*

must be tightened or loosened manually by rotating the nut. This takes a little more time than handle or air operated push-out and pull-in collets.

Cylindrical Liners

Collets of bigger size can be used for gripping smaller stock by using cylindrical split-bush type liners (See Fig. 7.14a). As the liners do not have any conical seats, they cost less than conical collets. Liners serve mainly as packing between the collet and the stock. The wall of the liner must be thinned at the bending point.

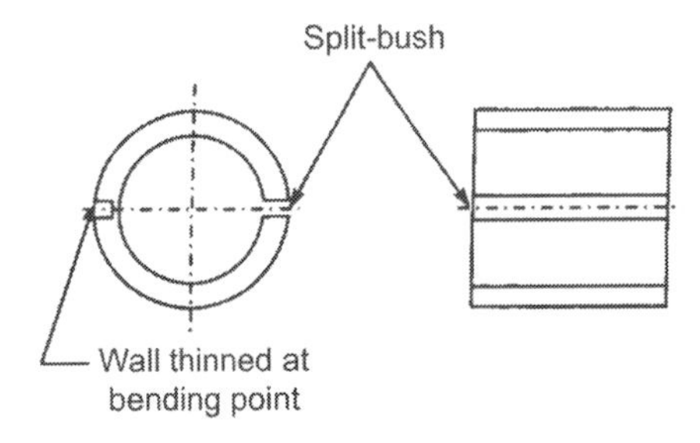

Fig. 7.14a *Split-bush liner*

Hydraulic Collets

These compress a thin-walled cylinder from outside to decrease its bore to grip the workpiece all around the circumference.

The collet has no slits. The collet-holder is mounted on the machine spindle nose thru a back plate (Fig.7.14b). The housing contains hydraulic oil/petroleum jelly/PVC paste. The fluid is pressurised by tightening the clamping screw. It pushes a small ram against the fluid to develop 150–450 bar (kg/sq. cm) hydraulic pressure. This compresses the thin wall of the collet from outside to reduce its bore by 0.01–0.15 mm to grip the cylindrical workpiece from outside on the entire periphery.

While filling the hydraulic fluid, the pressurising (clamping) screw should be in a vertical plane. Furthermore, there should be a provision for escape of the air displaced by the fluid: a bleeding port and the port closing screw. Furthermore the inter-faces accessible to the fluid should be sealed to prevent the leakage.

Figure 7.17d, for a hydraulic expanding, shows the bleeding screw and port and the hydraulic seals necessary. The related text explains the requisites for proper functioning of the system.

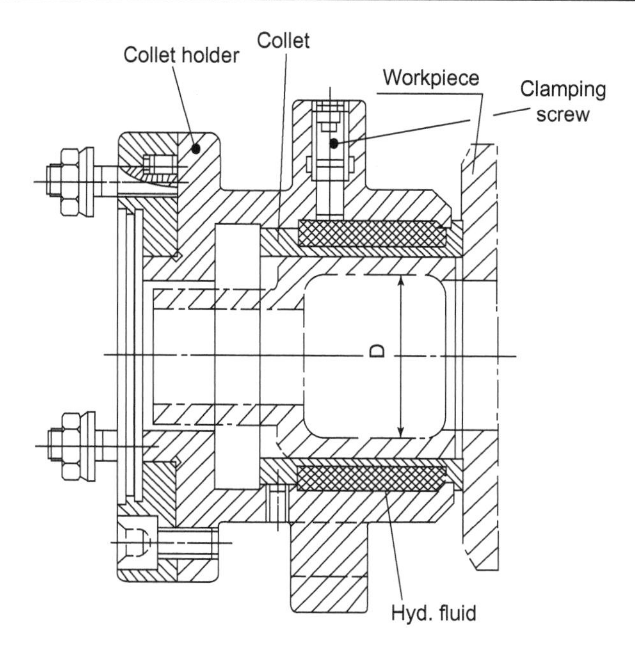

Fig. 7.14b *Hydraulic collet*

Mandrels

Mandrels are internal locators used for machining of the outside diameter of the workpieces concentric with finished bores. Mandrels can be classified as below:

1. Tapered mandrels
2. Axial clamping mandrels
3. Expanding mandrels
4. Threaded mandrels

Tapered Mandrels

These are tapered bars with centre at the ends for aligning with the machine axis and a flat for fixing the drive carrier (Fig. 7.15). Taper generally ranges from 0.4 to 0.5 mm per metre. This limits the variation in the bore of the workpieces and so, for wide difference in the bores, different mandrels must be used. The taper facilitates friction drive for the workpiece, which is generally pressed on the mandrel with an arbor press. For repeated use, the

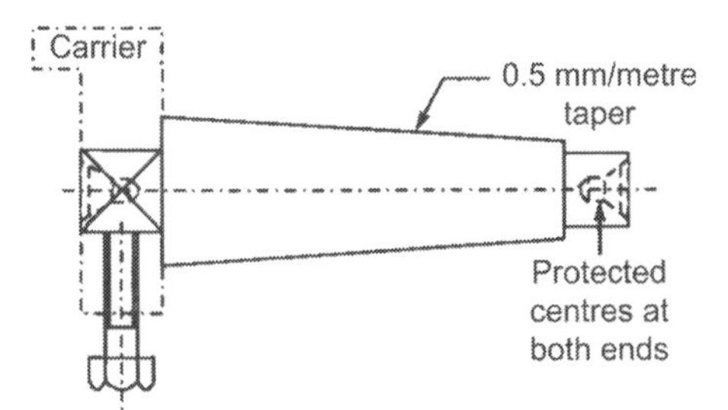

Fig. 7.15 *Tapered mandrel*

mandrels should be hardened and the centres protected by counterbores to prevent damage due to accidental fall. Tapered mandrels are rarely used in mass production as they require longer workpiece loading and unloading time.

Axial Clamping Mandrels

These are used extensively for grinding outside diameter of bushes. The locating diameter must be close push fit with the minimum size of the workpiece bore. Consequently, the maximum bore size workpiece would be loose on the mandrel by the amount equal to the workpiece tolerance. Thus, the possible concentricity between the inside and outside diameter of the workpiece would be equal to the tolerance on the bore of the workpiece. For example, if the bore of a workpiece is between 50.00 and 50.04 mm the diameter of the mandrel should be push fit with 50.00 mm bore to permit usage of the mandrel for all workpieces. A workpiece having 50.04 mm bore would, naturally, be loose by 0.04 m on the mandrel, and its concentricity can vary from 0.00 to 0.04 mm with respect to the bore. The workpiece is clamped axially with a C washer and a hexagonal nut which permit quick loading and unloading (Fig. 7.16). The drive pin serve as an integral drive carrier. The mandrel is provided with protected centres and is hardened to minimise wear on the locating diameter.

Expanding Mandrels

For a high degree of concentricity, expanding mandrels should be used. These permit adjustment of the locating diameter to suit the variation in the bore size of the workpiece. In fact, expanding mandrels clamp the workpiece on the bore as a collet grips the bush on the mandrel's outside diameter. Consequently, there is no clearance between the mandrel outside and the workpiece inside which explains the high degree of concentricity.

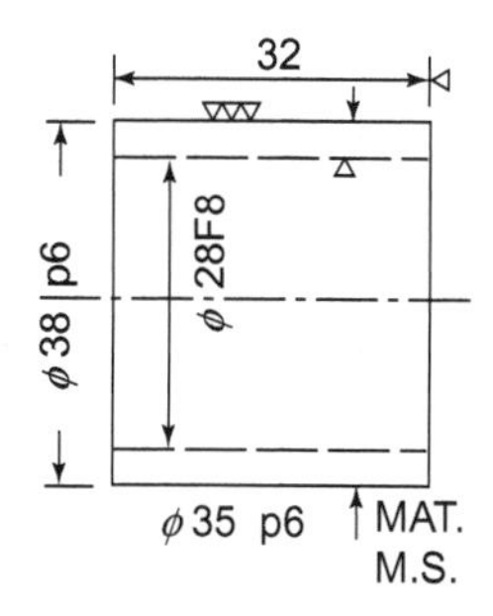

Fig. 7.16a *Workpiece for axial clamping mandrel in Fig. 7.16b*

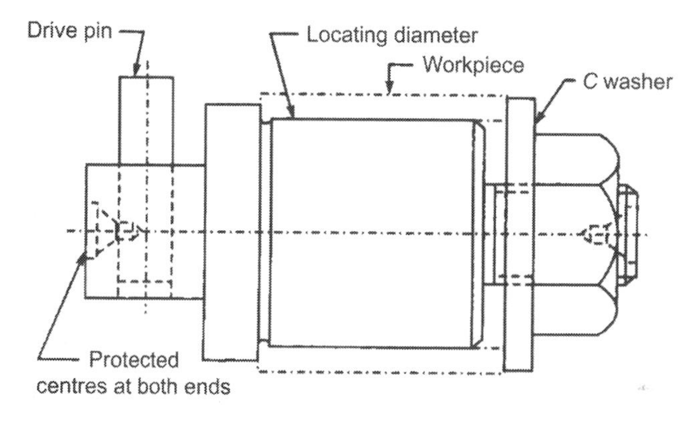

Fig. 7.16b *Axial clamping mandrel*

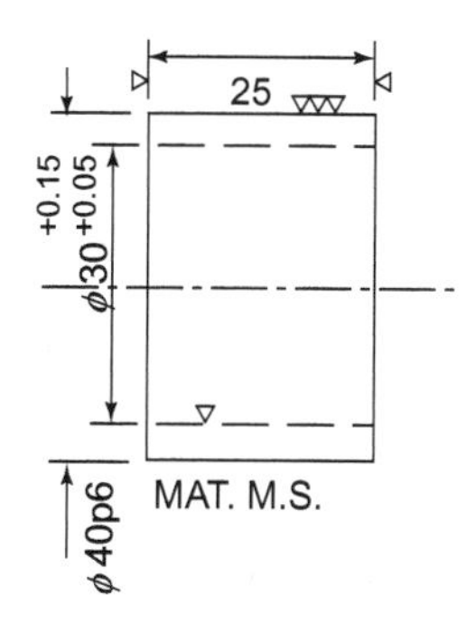

Fig. 7.17a *Workpiece for Fig. 7.17b*

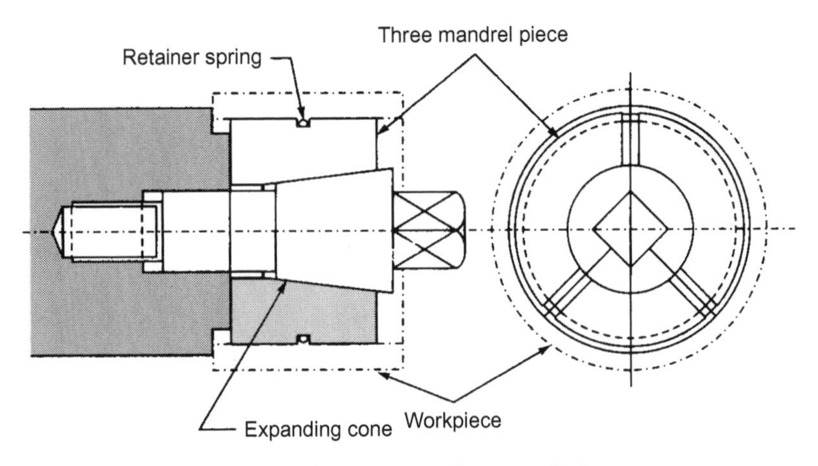

Fig. 7.17a *Expanding mandrel*

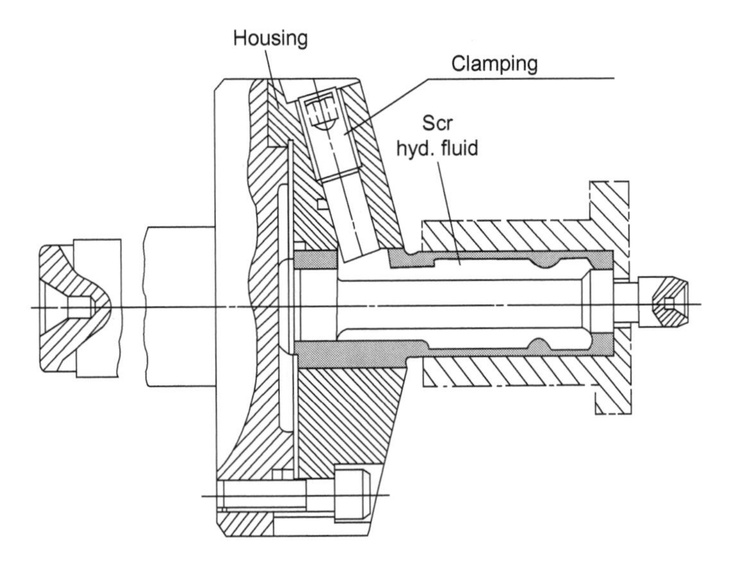

Fig. 7.17b *Hydraulic expanding mandrel*

The mandrel is split into three or four pieces as shown in Fig. 7.17a, and are held against the expanding cone by a retainer spring. The clockwise rotation of the cone pushes the mandrel pieces outwards against the workpiece to locate and clamp it. The rotation of the cone in the opposite direction reduces the distance between the mandrel pieces which are pressed inwards by the retainer spring. This contracts the mandrel to provide clearance between the mandrel and the workpiece for easy loading and unloading.

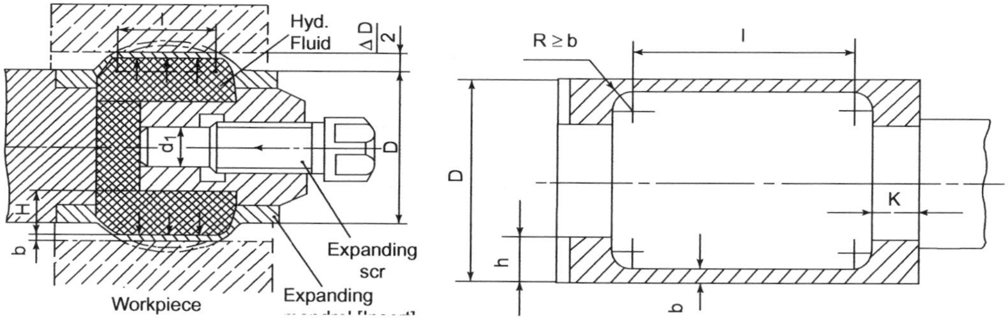

D	l = 0.5 D						l = 0.75 D						l = D						l = 1.5 D					
	M_t	ΔD	p	b	h	k	M_t	ΔD	p	b	h	k	M_t	ΔD	p	b	h	k	M_t	ΔD	p	b	h	k
20	25	0.02	350	0.5	2.5	4	25	0.04	350	0.7	3	3.5	25	0.05	400	1.0	3	5	85	0.03	250	0.5	2.5	2.5
	50	0.01	450	0.8	2.5	5	60	0.03	450	0.9	3	4.5	250	0.01	450	0.6	2	6	270	0.02	450	0.8	2.5	5
30	90	0.03	350	0.8	3.5	5	90	0.06	300	1.0	4	6	85	0.07	450	1.5	4.5	7	250	0.05	250	0.8	4	5
	200	0.02	450	1.3	3.5	7	200	0.05	450	1.4	5	7	800	0.02	450	0.9	3	8	900	0.03	450	1.2	4.5	7
40	200	0.04	250	1.0	5	6	200	0.08	300	1.4	5.5	8	200	0.09	450	2.0	6	9	650	0.07	250	1.0	5	8
	450	0.02	450	1.7	6	8.5	450	0.06	450	1.8	6	10	2000	0.03	450	1.2	4.5	10	2000	0.05	450	1.6	6.5	9
60	700	0.05	250	1.5	7	8	750	0.11	350	2.0	8	10	670	0.13	450	3.0	10	13	2000	0.10	250	1.5	8	10
	1500	0.04	450	2.5	8.5	11	1500	0.09	450	2.7	10	12	7000	0.04	450	1.8	7	13	7000	0.07	450	2.4	10	12
80	300	0.10	150	1.2	6	10	300	0.19	200	2.0	10	13	-	-	-	-	-	-	750	0.10	150	1.3	10	15
	1600	0.07	250	2.0	7	10	1700	0.15	300	2.8	12	15	1600	0.18	450	4.0	12	18	5000	0.13	250	2.0	10	15
100	600	0.15	150	1.5	7.5	14	600	0.23	200	2.5	10	15	3100	0.2	450	5.0	15	22	1500	0.22	150	1.6	8	15
	3000	0.10	250	2.6	10	15	3400	0.18	300	3.5	14	17	-	-	-	-	-	-	9500	0.17	250	2.5	11	13

Designations: M_t = torsional moment created by cutting by force, kgf.cm; p = pressure in PVC- paste required for deformation of locating sleeve, kgf/cm^2;
ΔD = defomation of the sleeve, mm (at pressure p, kgf/cm^2).

Fig. 7.17c *Hydraulic expanding mandrels*

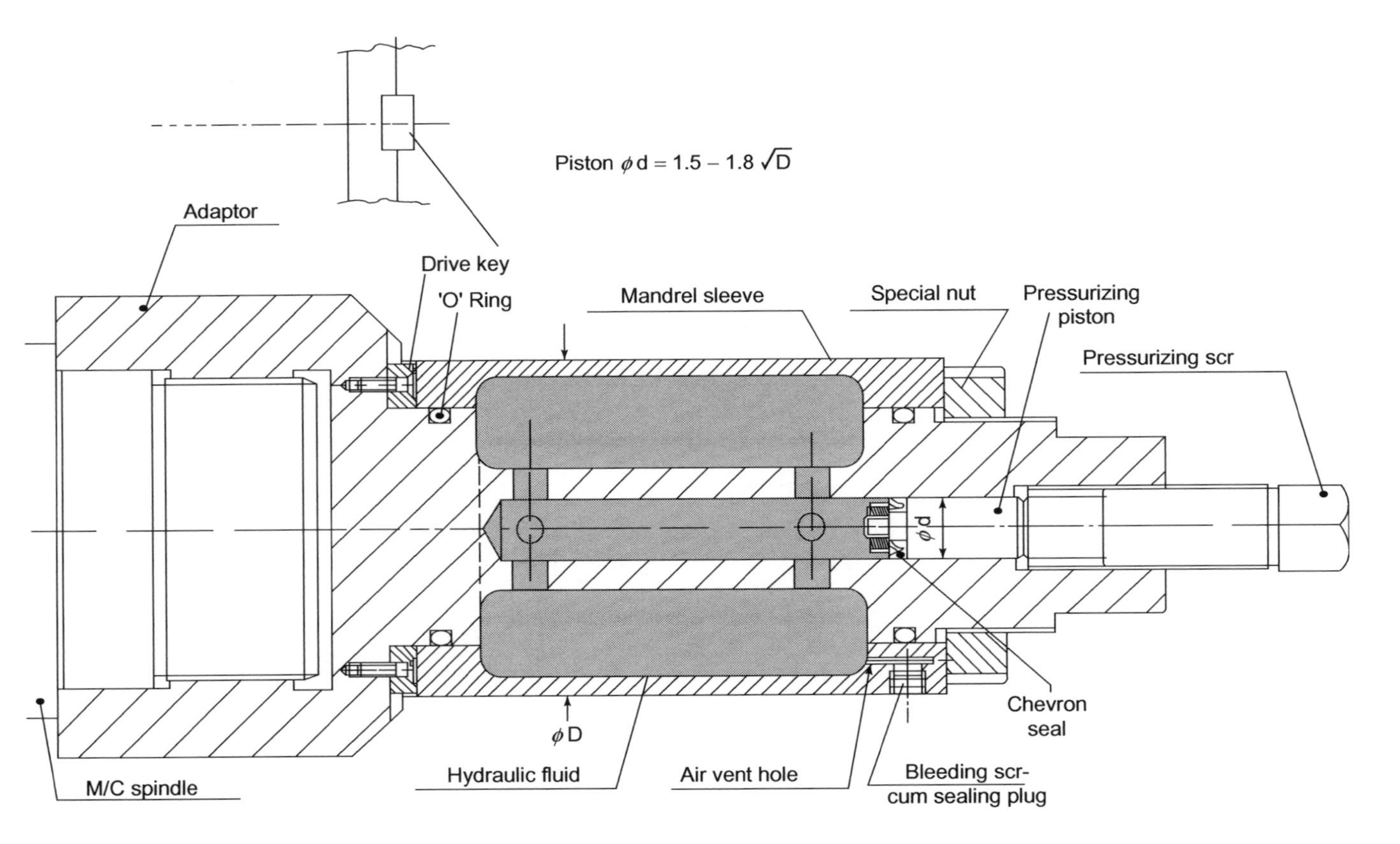

Fig. 7.17d *Hydaulic operation of expanding m anderel*

Hydraulic Expanding Mandrels (Figs 7.17b–d)

The expansion of the mandrel can be effected hydraulically (Fig. 7.17b). Like the collet-holder the housing is fitted to the machine spindle nose by a back plate. It contains hydraulic fluid which is pressurised to 150–450 bar pressure by tightening the clamping screw. Sandwiching the thin-walled mandrel between the pressured oil and the workpiece bore grips it firmly all around its inside periphery. Figure 7.17c gives dimensions of the thin-walled hydraulic mandrels. The table also states the mandrel expansion range and the slip-torque. Figure 7.17d shows assembly of a hydraulic expanding mandrel mounted directly on m/c spindle nose.

The hydraulic fluid should be filled before mounting the mandrel on the m/c spindle. The mandrel should rest on the adaptor face to keep the axis of the mandrel vertical during the filling. The pressurising piston and the screw should be removed to provide access to the fluid. The pressurising end of the mandrel is provided with a small air vent hole and a bleeding screw. It can be loosened or removed during filling. Overflow of the fluid thru the bleeding hole indicates that the hydraulic chamber is full, and the bleeding screw can be tightened to serve as a sealing plug. It should not project outside the mandrel external diameter.

The inter face between the mandrel and the adaptor is sealed with an 'O' ring. The piston is fitted with a Chevron seal. The piston and the pressurising screw are inserted after filling the hydraulic chamber.

The mounting end of the mandrel sleeve has a drive keyways similar to a milling m/c arbor (quick release). The drive keys are mounted in the keyways on the adaptor, using suitable screws. The mandrel sleeve is secured onto the adaptor with a special nut. Tightening the pressurising screw expands the mandrel to grip the workpiece on its bore.

Threaded Mandrels

For workpieces with internal threads, the locating mandrel should have a clamping collar which has internal threads in the direction opposite to the thread in the workpiece (Fig. 7.18). These facilitate tightening of the workpiece and the clamping collar against each other, and prevents the collar from unscrewing during turning operation. For unclamping the workpiece, lug on the clamping collar is knocked in an anti-clockwise direction by a hammer.

Turning Fixtures

Some workpieces require special turning fixtures for quick location and clamping. These are generally special face plates. Their swing should be lesser than that of the machine. The overhang of turning fixtures should be the

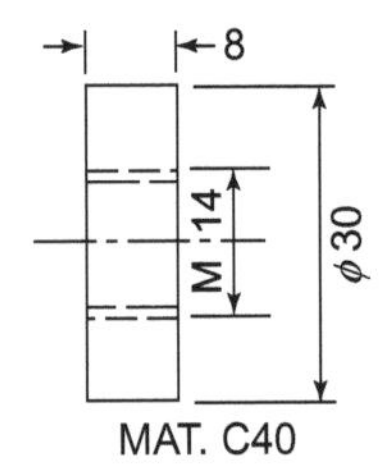

Fig. 7.18a *Workpiece for mandrel in Fig. 7.18b*

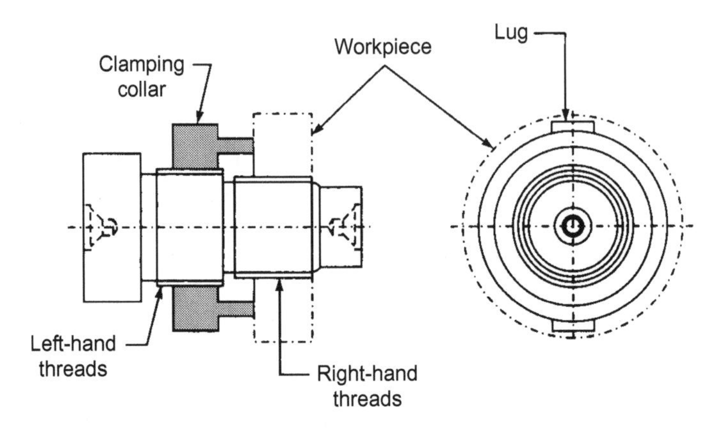

Fig. 7.18b *Mandrel for threaded workpiece*

bare minimum necessary for the operation. The fixtures should be balanced in position with the workpiece. The clamping arrangement should be capable of withstanding the various forces developed during operation—cutting force tangential to the cutting circle, axial and radial forces due to feed of the tool and bending forces due to pressure of tool on the workpiece.

Figure 7.19 shows a typical turning fixture. The workpiece rests on angle plate face *A* and its boss is centralised with the machine axis by a sliding *V* block which can be operated with knurled scores *S*. The workpiece is clamped in this position by two clamps C. The height of the angle plate, sliding *V* and other parts is kept less than workpiece thickness to prevent obstruction to facing tool F. The workpiece is bored through and one side of its boss is faced on this fixture. The eccentric masses due to the workpiece, angle plate and clamps are counterbalanced by balance weight *B*.

Figure 7.20 shows a second operation turning fixture for pump mounting bracket. The workpiece is located on earlier machined spigot *S*, and clamped against the fixture face by two swinging hook bolt clamps H. The clamps are loosened and. swung anticlockwise to the position shown by the chaindotted lines to clear the path of the workpiece during loading and

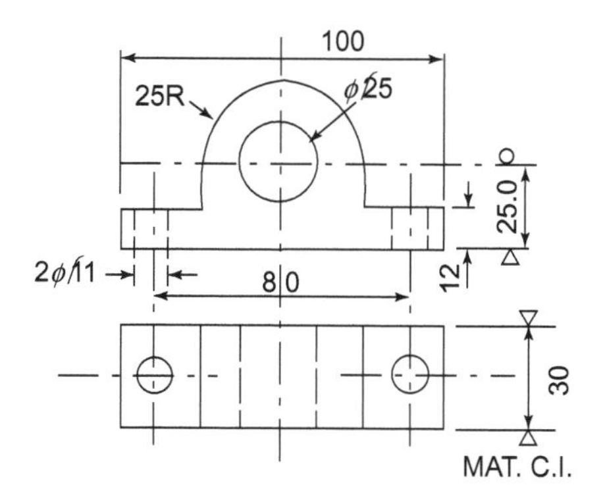

Fig. 7.19a *Workpiece for boring and facing fixture in Fig. 7.19b*

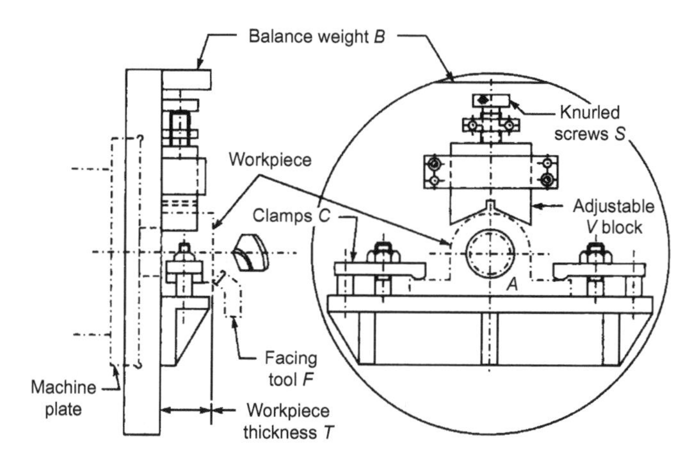

Fig. 7.19b *Boring and facing fixture*

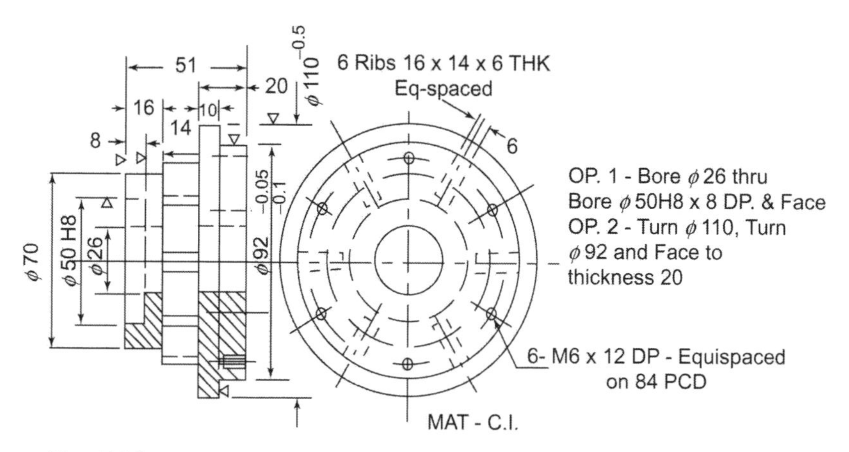

Fig. 7.20a *Workpiece for second operation turning fixture in Fig. 7.20b*

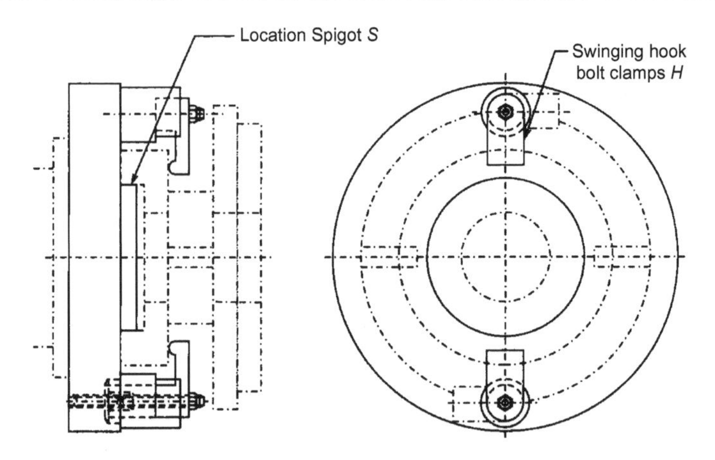

Fig. 7.20b *Second operation turning fixture*

unloading. No balance weights are necessary because of the even and symmetrical distribution of mass around the centre line of the fixture.

Summary

Turning fixtures are mounted precision location fit *(G7/h6)* on the machine spindle. A back plate with internal threads and spigot for the machine spindle, and an external precision *(h6)* spigot (flange) and clamping holes for the fixtures are used as an adaptor.

Standard Chucks

1. Self-centreing three-jaw scroll chucks for cylindrical workpieces.
2. Independent four jaw chucks for odd-shaped jobs.
3. Combination chucks with radially adjustable, changeable, jaws.
4. Special jaws with suitable shapes for odd-shaped or soft/fragile workpieces.
5. Soft jaws with a clamping ring for 2nd operation.

Collets for bars

1. Push-out collets tend to the push the workpiece outwards for the first operation.
2. Pull-in collets tend to pull in the workpiece for the second operation.
3. Dead length collects with double cones are free from pull/push or the bars.

4. Split bush collets for small batch manufacture.
5. Hydraulic collets with no slits.

Mandrels

1. Tapered (0.5/m) mandrel with location centres and flats/square for drive carriers for machining bushes outsides.
2. Axially clamped mandrel with C washer and nut gives lesser concentricity than the tapered mandrel.
3. Expanding mandrel for precise location of the workpiece with the variation in the bore size hydraulic mandrels.
4. Threaded mandrel with opposite hand threads on the clamping collar.

Boring and Facing Fixtures

They should align the bore to be machined with the axis of the machine spindle. Facing fixtures should have the locator and clamps/studs well clear of the tool path, Balance weights for reducing vibrations.

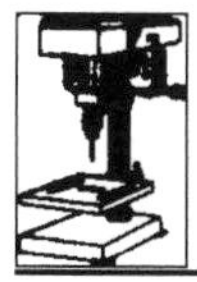

CHAPTER 8

Grinding Fixtures

Surface Grinding

Surface grinding is used widely in industry to finish lengths and thicknesses of the workpieces within precise tolerances. The standard magnetic tables furnished with surface grinding machines can be used satisfactorily for workpieces having resting surface parallel to the surface to be ground. Solid plates can be ground under magnetic clamping alone and no other fixtures are necessary. However, light workpieces having lesser resting area tend to tilt and fly off the magnetic table due to the high speed of the grinding wheel and the high feed used in grinders with reciprocating or rotating tables. As lesser magnetic clamping force is not sufficient to secure the workpiece during the grinding operation, it is necessary to provide additional supports by nesting the workpiece. This can be done by placing solid plates around the workpiece as shown in Fig. 8.1. With more weight and resting area, the nest plates are held firmly by the magnetic force of the table. The nest plates siege the workpiece from outside and arrest its movement in the horizontal plane, thus, preventing it from flying off or tilting due to high speed and feed inherent in the grinding operation.

In mass production, the capacities of the machines should be utilised to the maximum possible extent. Consequently, the maximum possible area of the magnetic table should be utilised to grind as many workpieces as possible in a single batch. To achieve this, the jig and tool design office should furnish a layout of the workpieces on the magnetic table. For round spacers the workpieces are arranged in rows with common supporting nest plates around. The thickness of the nest plates should be lesser than the finish height of the workpiece to prevent obstruction of the grinding wheel (Fig. 8.2).

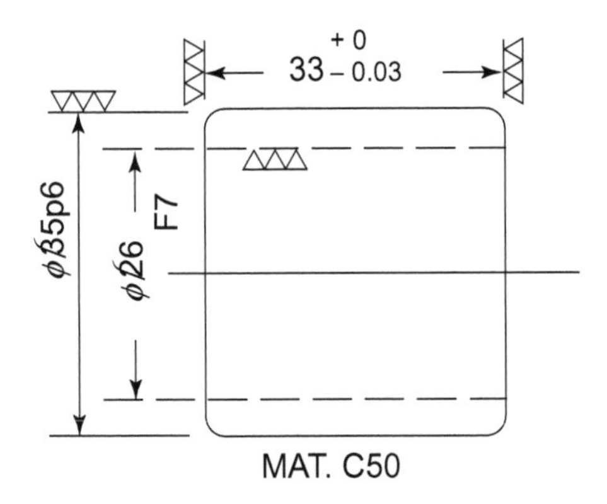

Fig. 8.1a *Workpiece for nesting in Fig. 8.1b*

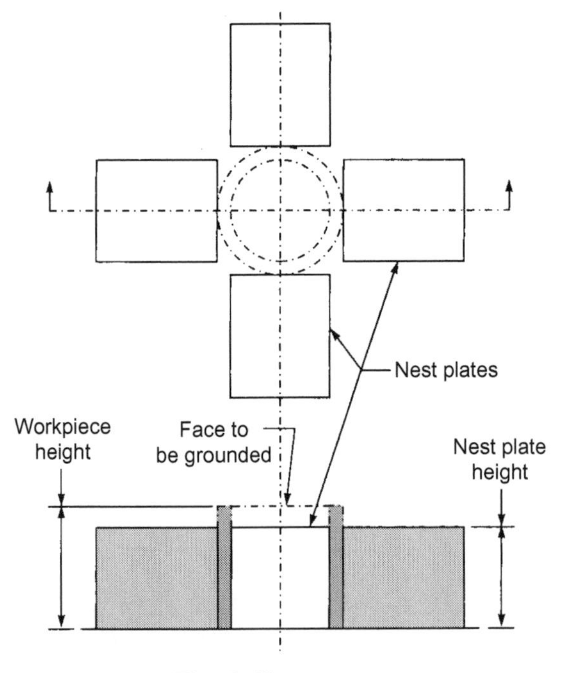

Fig. 8.1b *Nesting*

For odd-shaped workpieces with little variation in size, an epoxy resin nest can be used (Fig. 8.3). The nest prevents the tilting and sliding of the workpieces during grinding operation.

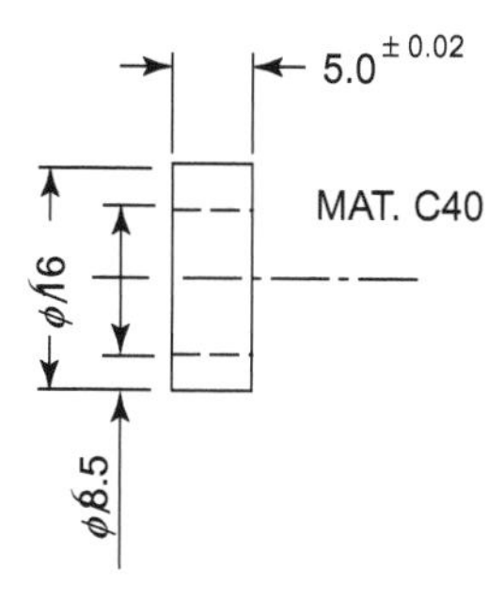

Fig. 8.2a *Workpiece for grinding layout in Fig. 8.2b*

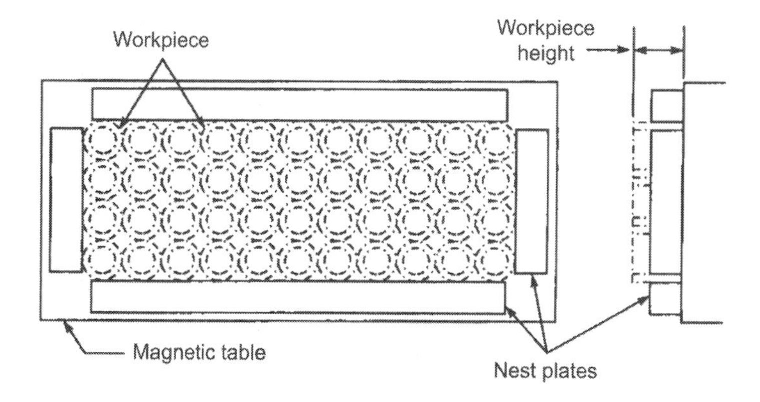

Fig. 8.2b *Surface grinding layout*

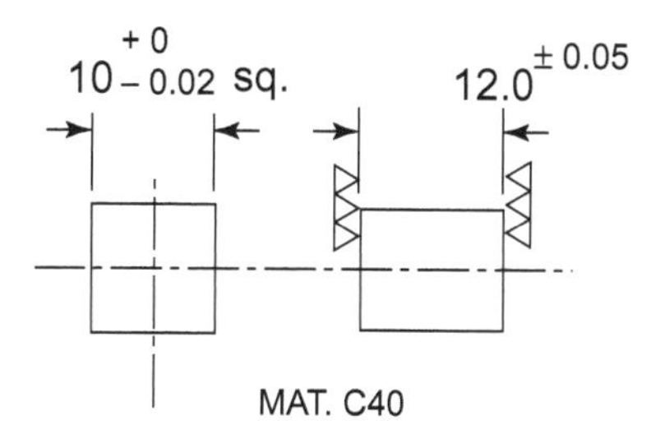

Fig. 8.3a *Workpiece for epoxy resin nest in Fig. 8.3b*

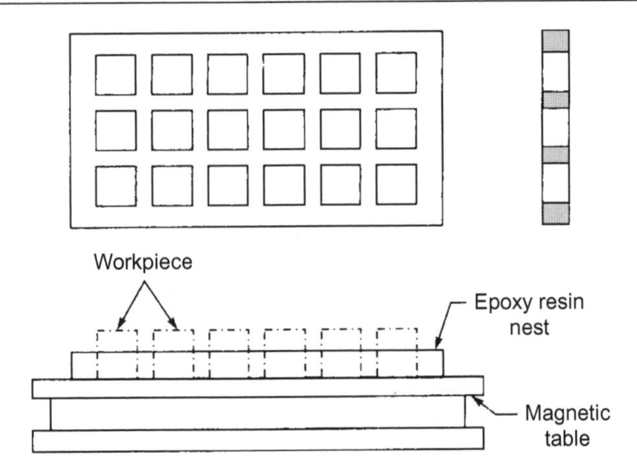

Fig. 8.3b *Epoxy resin nest*

For workpieces unsuitable for magnetic clamping, special fixtures must be designed. Surface grinding fixtures are generally similar to face milling fixtures in design. However, generally face milling is the first operation whereas grinding is done at a much later stage when a number of machined portions of the workpiece are available for location and clamping.

Cylindrical Grinding

Fixtures for cylindrical grinding are similar to fixtures used for turning and boring. A variety of mandrels can be used for grinding the outside diameters of the bushes concentric with the inside diameter. Fixtures used for internal grinding are similar to face plate fixtures used for boring workpieces on turning machines. The design features for location and clamping of the workpiece are similar to those of turning fixtures. Only the arrangement for securing fixtures to the machine spindle should be made suitable for the spindle of the grinding machine.

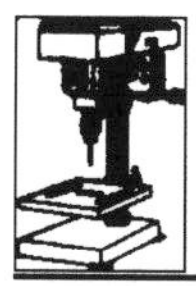

CHAPTER 9

Broaching Fixtures

Broaching is a fast and accurate method of metal cutting. The built-in precision of the broach is reproduced in the workpieces by broaching fixtures which position the workpiece and guide the broach accurately. Consequently, most of the broaching fixtures serve the following functions:

1. Location of the workpiece in the correct position with respect to the machine.
2. Guiding of the broach to suit the dimensional requisites of the workpiece.

Both vertical as well as horizontal broaching machine tables have a round location hole in the table for locating broaching fixtures. The fixtures are provided with a close fitting male spigot which mates with the hole in the table to position the fixture correctly with respect to the machine.

The fixture also positions the workpiece and the broach precisely with respect to each other.

Broaching processes can be broadly classified into the following categories:

1. Internal broaching is used mainly for key-ways, splines, square and hexagonal holes and slots.
2. External broaching is used for outside profiles of connecting rod mating faces, etc.

Key-way Broaching

It is used extensively for cutting internal key-ways in pulleys, gears, sprockets, etc. The broaching process is much faster than other methods such as machining on the slotting machine.

Figure 9.1b depicts a simple broaching fixture for cutting key-way in the workpiece shown in Fig. 9.1a.

The fixture in Fig. 9.1b locates the workpiece on its bore for concentricity. A diamond pin in the hole in the flange positions the workpiece correctly to ensure the required angular relationship between 11ϕ holes and the key-way to be broached.

The broach is guided in the slot provided in the fixture. The depth of the slot depends upon the maximum height of the broach and the key-way depth in the workpiece. For example, if the maximum height of 8 mm key-way broach is 14 mm, the depth of the guide slot for the broach in the fixture in Fig. 9.1b should be 9 mm: BroachHt[14]-Keyway Depth [27–22].

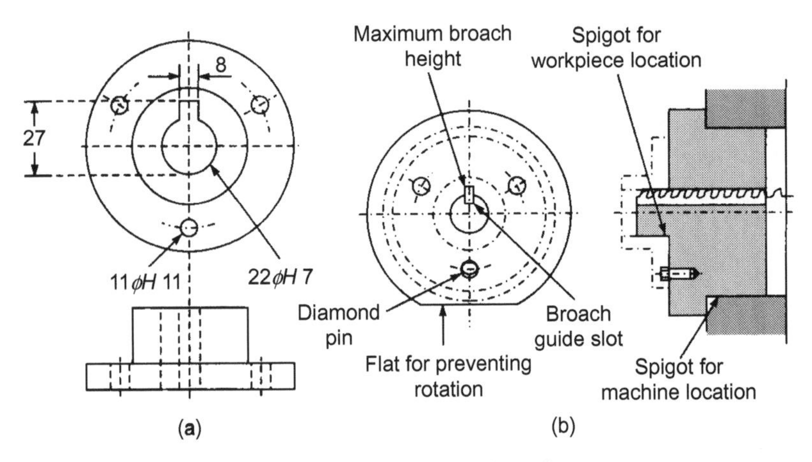

Fig. 9.1 *Key-way broaching fixture*

The fixture is provided with a 110 diameter close-fitting spigot which engages with the machine location bore to position the fixture correctly on the machine table.

For tapered key-ways the workpiece should be held in the tilted position with respect to the machine axis (Fig. 9.2). The tilt facilitates cutting of tapered key-way with a straight broach.

External Surface Broaching

External broaching is used for producing external surfaces and profiles. The workpiece and broaches must be located properly with respect to each other and a supporting guide-way must be provided for the broaches. Often

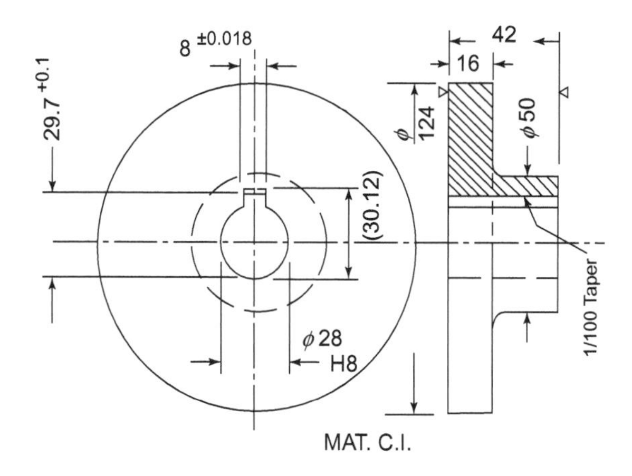

Fig. 9.2a *Workpiece for fixture for tapered key-way in Fig. 9.2b*

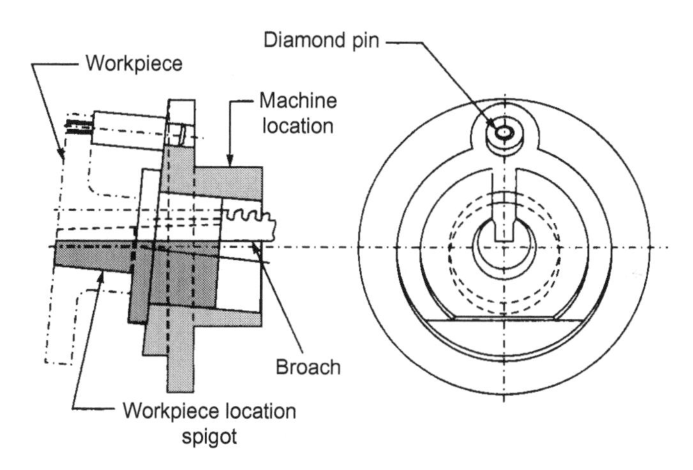

Fig. 9.2b *Fixture for tapered key-way*

packing strips (also called shims or wedges) are used to control the depth of the profile and take care of the wear of the broaches.

Figure 9.3a depicts an arrangement for a broaching bore and mating faces of a connecting rod cap. Figure 9.3b shows the method of broaching the sides and the nut resting faces of the connecting rod.

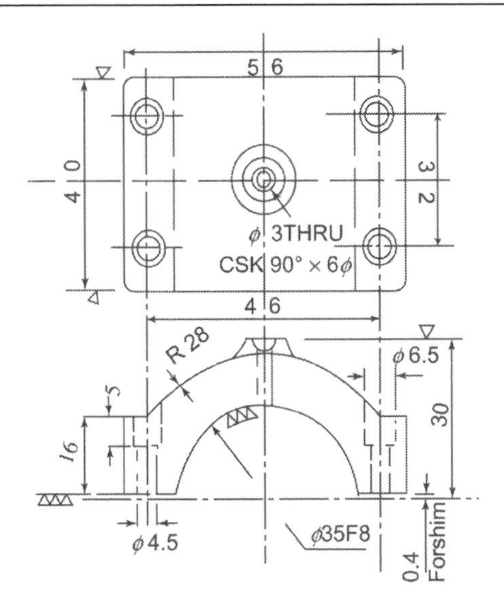

Fig. 9.3a *Workpiece for external broaching arrget in Fig. 9.3c*

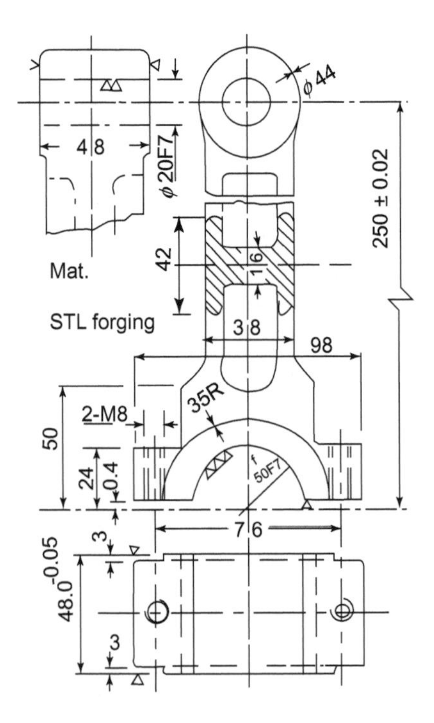

Fig. 9.3b *Workpiece for Fig. 9.3d*

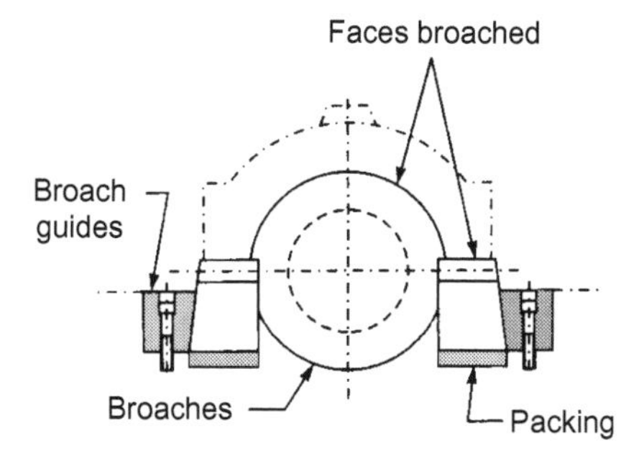

Fig. 9.3c

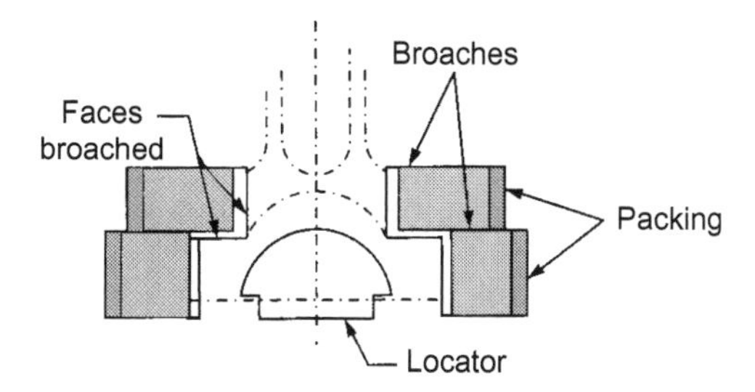

Fig. 9.3d *External broaching*

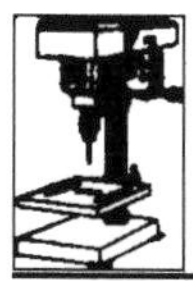

CHAPTER 10

Welding and Assembly Fixtures

Fixtures for joining workpieces by welding comprise the usual locating and clamping elements used in other fixtures. However, effect of heat and prevalence of welding spatter must be taken into account while designing hot joining fixtures. The considerations for welding, brazing and soldering fixtures are given below:

1. Expansion of the heated workpiece and resulting distortion should not affect proper location, clamping, loading and unloading. There should be adequate clearance between the workpiece and locators to permit expansion, contraction and distortion of the workpiece without jamming the fixture. Handles subjected to heating should be made of insulating materials such as wood.
2. Welding spatter should not be allowed to fall on the threaded parts of the clamping elements. The parts near the welding area should not be threaded. Consequently, toggle clamps without the threaded elements are used widely in welding fixtures. These can be operated quickly and provide ample clearance in the unclamped position. Figure 10.1 shows various types of clamps used in welding fixtures.

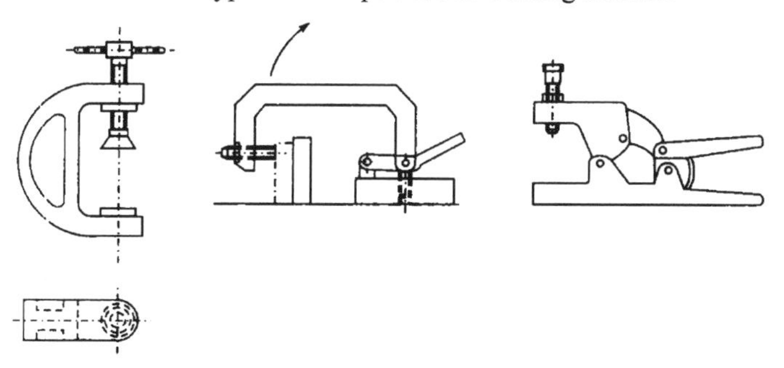

Fig. 10.1 *Welding clamps*

3. Spatter grooves must be provided below the line of welding to prevent the workpiece from getting welded to the base plate by the welding spatter.
4. Care should be taken to check that the joined workpiece does not get locked in the welding fixture after welding. It should be possible to remove the welded workpiece from the fixture after welding.
5. For workpieces requiring welding from a number of sides, a provision for easy tilting or rotating the fixture should be made to ease welding from the various sides.

Figure 10.2 shows a welding fixture for a winged nut. The central boss is located by a loose female spigot to permit expansion due to heat during

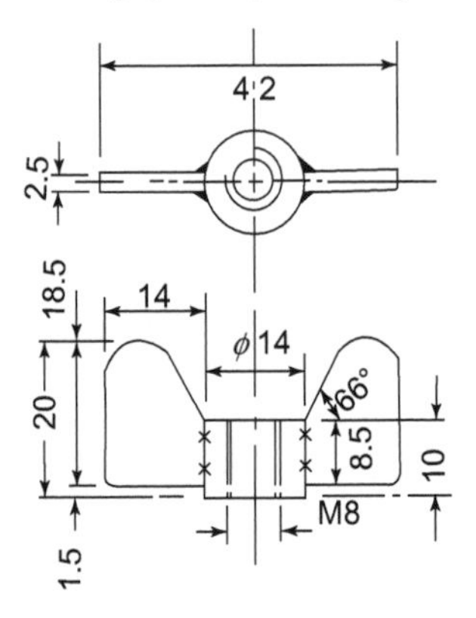

Fig. 10.2a *Workpiece for wing nut welding fixture in Fig. 10.2b*

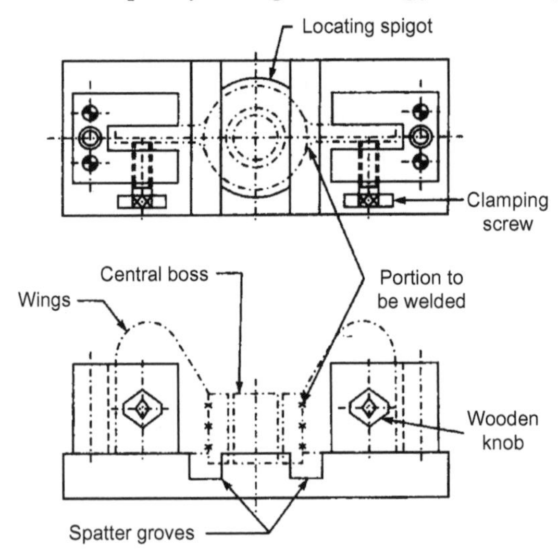

Fig. 10.2b *Wing nut welding fixture*

welding. The wings are located in loose slots which can permit expansion as well as distortion (bending) during welding. The wings are pushed towards the boss to touch it and are clamped in position by the clamping screws with wooden handles.

A spatter groove below the line of welding ensures that the spatter would not weld the boss or the wings to the base plate.

Figure 10.3 shows a fixture for welding four angles to a rectangular frame. Two longer angles are located lengthwise by four plates *A*. The cross-location is obtained by pushing the angles against four channels *B*. One face of each channel is also used to position the shorter cross angles. The other location in the cross direction is provided by the vertical faces of the longer angles.

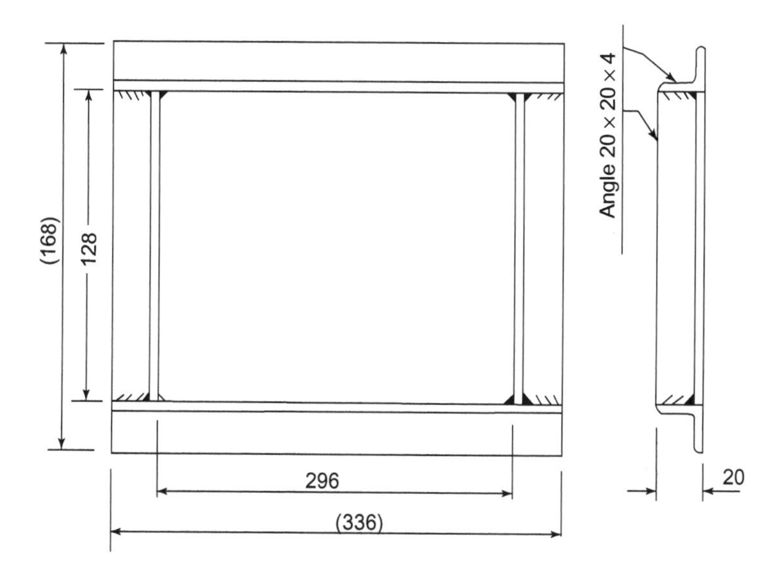

Fig. 10.3a *Workpiece for angle frame welding fixture in Fig. 10.3b*

The angles are clamped against the locators by eight cams which are hammered to the clamping position. For unclamping, the cams are hammered in the opposite direction. The cams are pivoted on shoulder screws and are swung aside after unclamping to clear the path of loading and unloading of the workpiece.

The base plate is milled with pockets below the welding area to provide positive clearance between the workpiece and the base. This prevents the falling welding spatter from welding the workpiece to the fixture base.

Figure 10.4a shows another welding fixture for a pipe fabrication (depicted below the fixture). The pipes are located and supported by

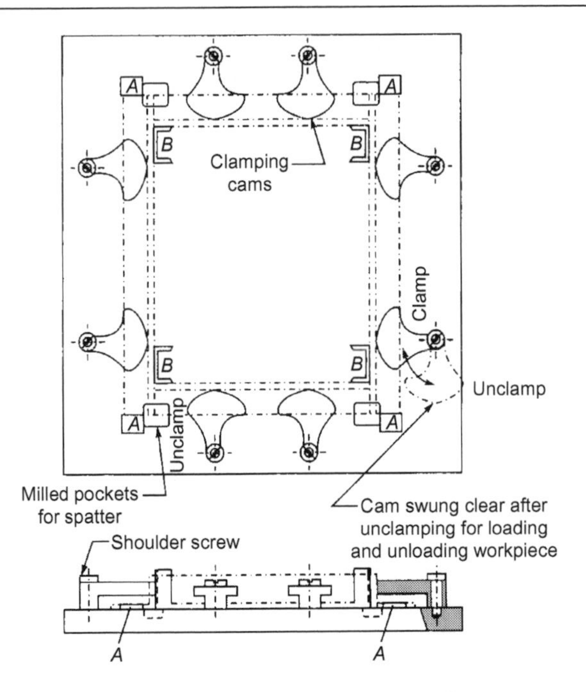

Fig. 10.3b *Angle frame welding fixture*

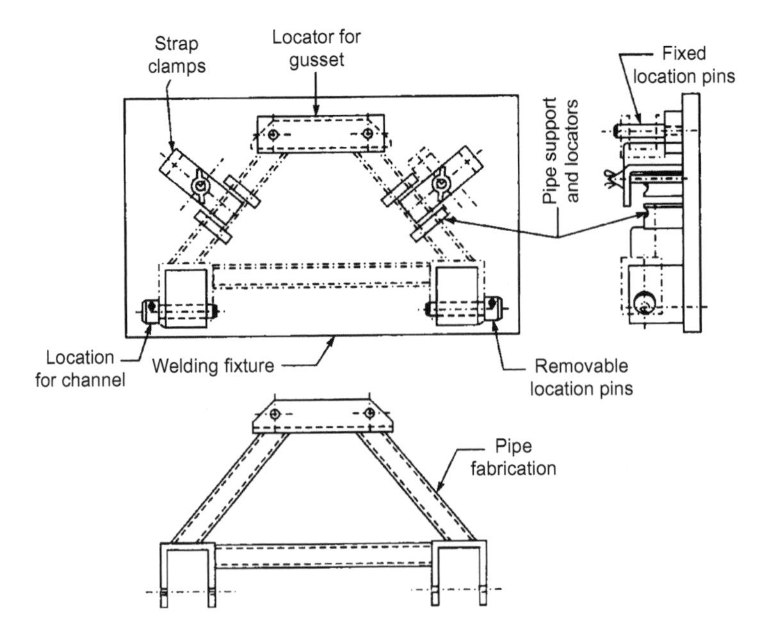

Fig. 10.4a *Welding fixture for pipe fabrication*

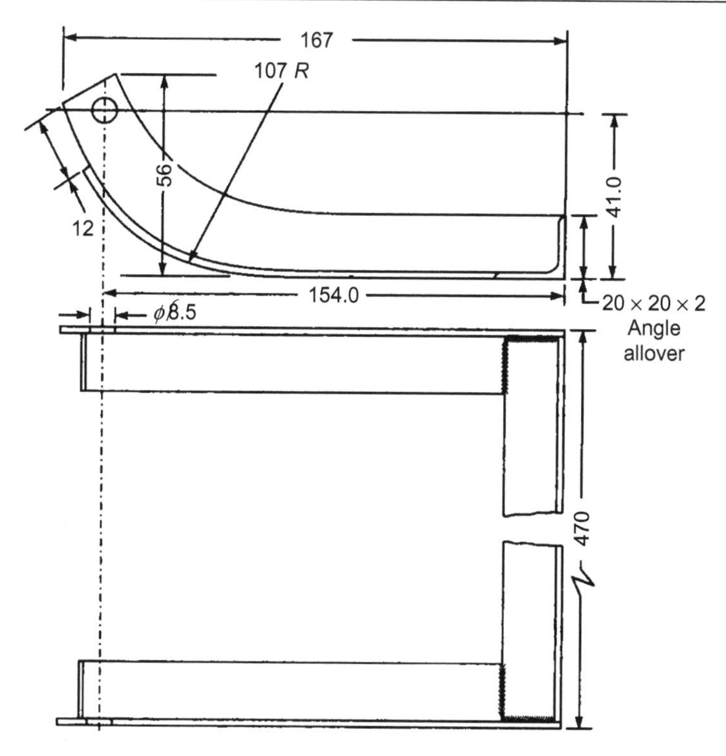

Fig. 10.4b *Machine cover: workpiece for welding fixture in Fig. 10.4c*

semicircular cutouts and clamped by strap clamps actuated by fly nuts. The channels and gussets are located and supported by suitable brackets and aligning pins.

Figure 10.4b shows a fabricated cover for an agricultural machine. Dimensions 154.0 and 41.0 for 8.5 ϕ holes indicate that the holes in the curved end angles should align precisely after welding.

Figure 10.4c shows a welding fixture for the cover shown in Fig. 10.4b. The curved end angles of the cover are located by pins with recesses equal to the angle width for longitudinal location of the curved angles (Sect *BB*). The recessed diameter also provides rest for the angles. The unrecessed pins at the top are removable to allow unloading of the welded cover from the top. The key in the long base and the mating key-way in the end brackets (housing the location pins) facilitate alignment of the end-brackets to ensure that 8.5 ϕ holes near the unwelded ends of the curved angles are aligned properly. The longitudinal angle connecting the curved end angles is located by a step in the rest on one side and by location pins on the other. The rests near the curved angles are far enough from the weld joint to avoid the welding spatter from falling on the rests or the location pins.

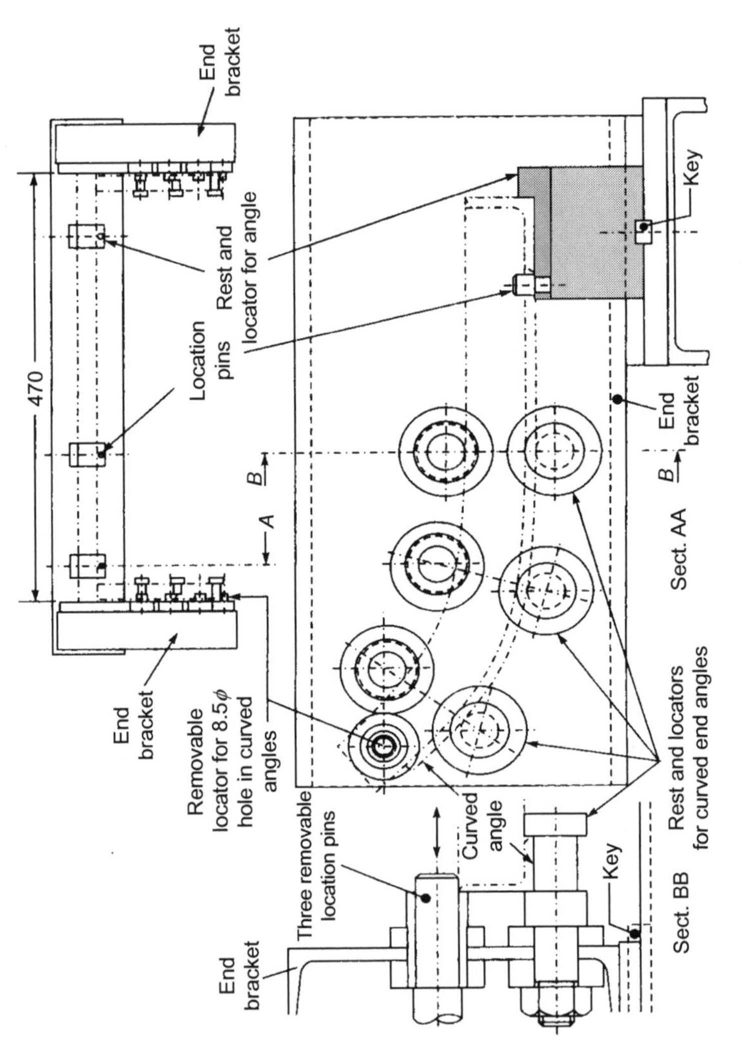

Fig. 10.4c *Welding fixture for cover in Fig 10.4b*

Most of the welding fixtures are used mainly for tack-welding the constituents together. After tack-welding, the fabrication can be removed from the fixture for full welding without the fixture.

Pressing Fixtures

Assembly operations often involve pressing interference fit pins, bushes and other parts in the housings. The pressing fixtures used for these operations consist of:

1. Location arrangement for housing.
2. Locator for the part to be pressed.
3. System for alignment of the part to be pressed with the housing.
4. Arrangement for application of press force to drive the part into the housing.

Figure 10.5(b) shows a bush pressing fixture. The housing is located by a slide fit locator in the hole mating with the outside diamater of the bush. The

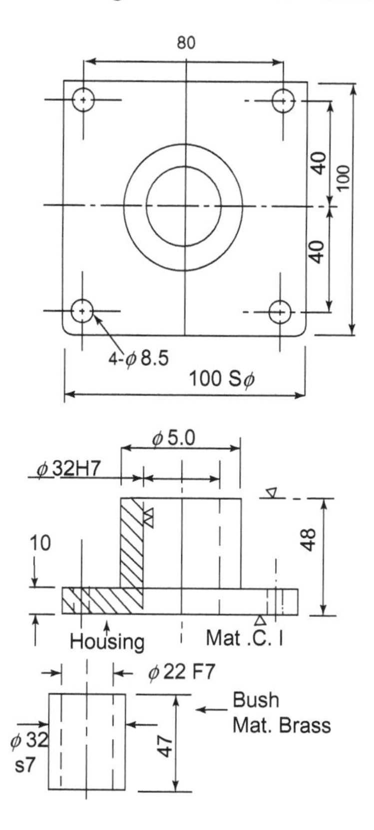

Fig. 10.5a *Workpiece for Fig. 10.5b*

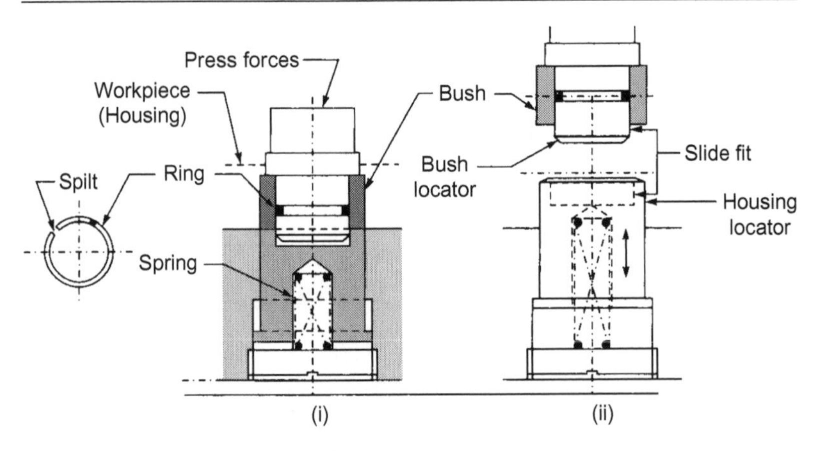

Fig. 10.5b *Bush pressing fixture*

housing locator has a smaller alignment bore at the top. This hole is slide fit with another locator which engages with the bush bore. As the bush locator is longer than the bush, the protruding length below the bush engages with the alignment hole in the housing locator. This aligns the bush outside the diameter with the mating bore in the housing. The bush locator houses a split ring of spring steel. The ring acts like a piston ring in an engine cylinder or like an internal circlip. The outside diameter of the ring is bigger than the bush bore. The split ring holds the bush from within the bore with spring action and prevents it from falling down due to gravity.

Press force is applied at the top of the bush locator. The bush locator enters the slide fit hole in the housing locator and aligns the outside diameter of the bush with the bore in the housing. Further downward movement drives the bush into the housing as the housing locator is pushed downwards against the spring.

During upstroke of the press, the spring pushes the housing locator and the bush locator upwards to the position shown in Fig. 10.5b(ii).

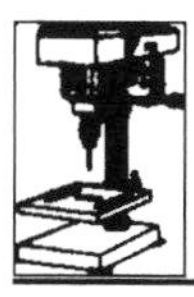

CHAPTER 11

Developments in Jigs and Fixtures

Advent of Numerically Controlled (NC) Machines and Computerised Numerical Control (CNC) has enhanced precision and reduced need for manual human skill. Competitive prices have made the machines affordable to medium size organizations. Built-in precision and easy repeatability has eliminated the need for guide bushes in jigs and necessity for variety of milling cutters.

Modular construction has decreased drastically the time as well investment for jigs and fixtures. Mass produced standard clamps, locators, fixture bases, guide bushes etc.—and commercial marketing—have decreased their costs substantially. Sub-assemblies of modules like swinging and toggle clamps, pump jigs, even adjustable jigs for cylindrical and standard rolled sections have simplified design and manufacture of jigs and fixtures.

 Tooling for NC Machines

Drill Jigs used on NC machines do not require guide bushes. The machine spindle can be moved precisely, automatically, along the three major axes. In fact the accuracy in the centre distances between the drilled holes depends upon the motion precision of the machine. As there are no guide bushes, there is no question of a drill wandering due to wear of the bushes, hence the better precision. Drilling tooling comprises just a fixture with workpiece locating and clamping arrangement. However, we have to provide means for locating (aligning) the drilling fixture on NC machine table. Two adjacent square edges of fixture base serve as X and Y axes. The fixture axes should be parallel to the workpiece axes—specified or assumed. The fixture axes must be ground square with each other (Fig. 11.1). Furthermore there should be provision for setting the spindle position at the starting point of the proposed NC/CNC program cycle. The program should reckon the zero disposition—fixed zero/full shift zero/fully floating zero—of the NC machine to be used.

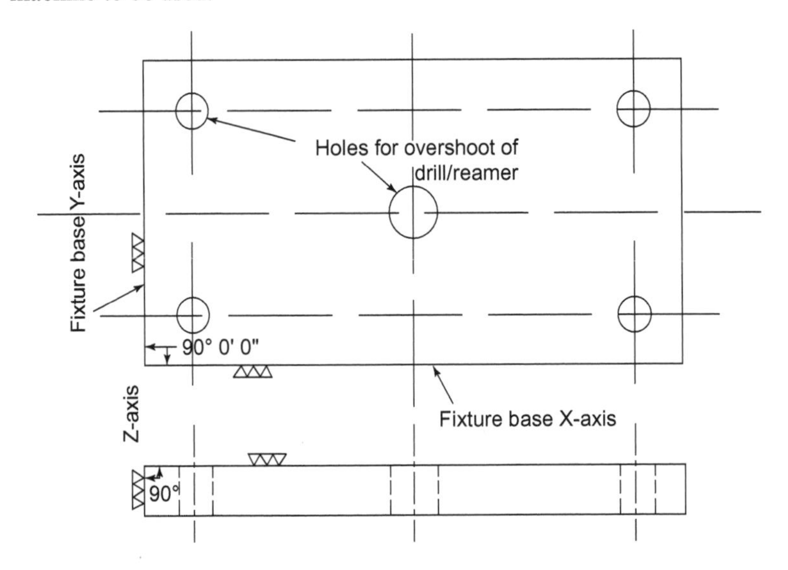

Fig. 11.1 *Grinding base edges tp provide X-Y-axes*

NC/CNC machines use *set point* for setting fixture with respect to machine spindle. Point-to-point drilling programs use *set point* as the datum for the program cycle.

For fixed zero and full shift zero type machines, the workpiece must be placed in the first quadrant: the X and Y axes motions can only be positive. So, the *set point* should be on the left and operator side of workpiece (Fig. 11.2a).

Workpiece hole as a set point

Sometimes *set point* is placed at the workpiece hole nearest to the origin (Fig. 11.2 b). For rectangular workpieces with holes' positions in Cartesian coordinates, this is convenient. In any case it is necessary to provide drill overshoot holes in fixture base. By machining the one closest to the origin precisely, we can use it as the *set point.* When zero is adjustable, the origin is placed at the *set point.* However, in fixed zero machines, the *set point* is given some tentative co-ordinates (X = 30, Y = 30 in Fig. 11.2b); naturally positive only since the workpiece must be placed in the first quadrant. The tentative coordinates should reckon the fixture overall dimensions. The fixture base should rest properly on the m/c table.

When we use a workpiece hole for the *set point* position, the overshot drill will enter the setting hole. If the over-travel hole is same size as the drill, the

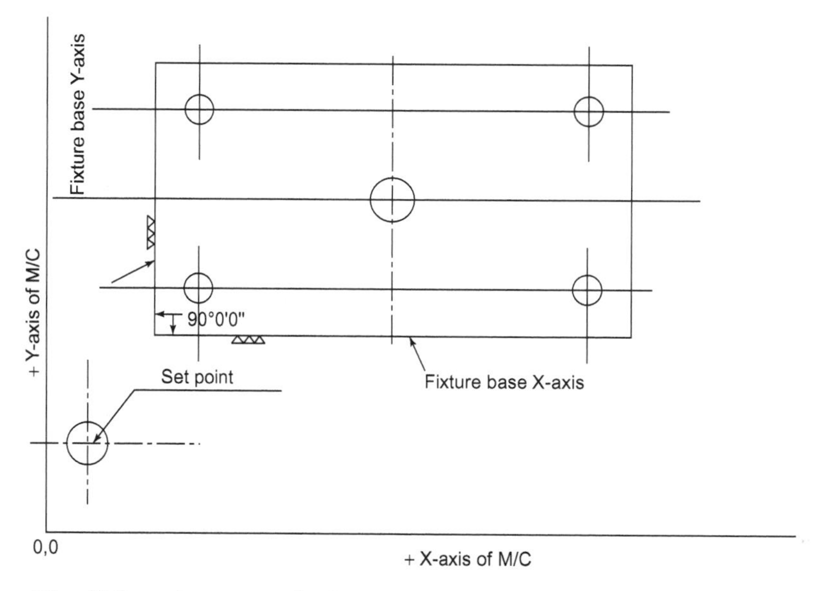

Fig. 11.2a *Set point in the first quadrant for fixed zero and zero shift m/cs*

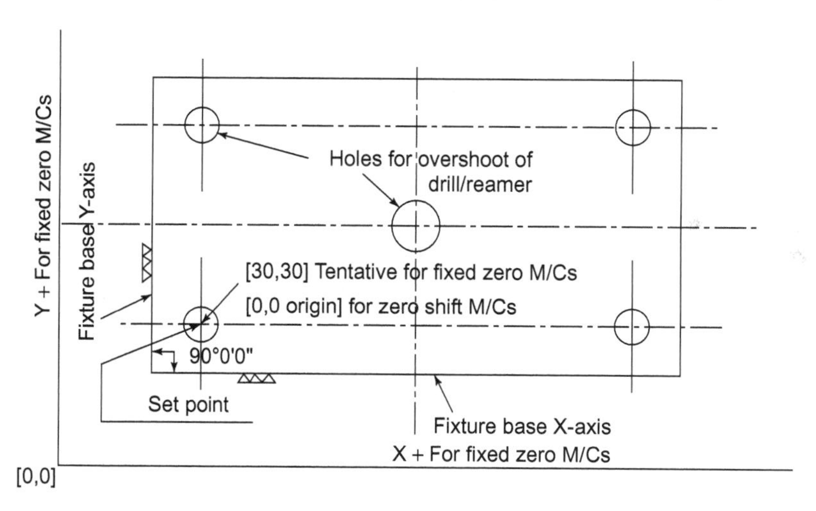

Fig. 11.2b *Set point at workpiece hole nearest to origin of fixed zero m/cs*

cutting tool might rub the hole surface and damage it. So the *set point* hole should be at least 1 mm bigger than the drill size. It would be even more convenient to make the hole size equal to the next bigger size aligning plug available. Some use a hardened bush as the locating hole at *setting point.*

Fully floating zero allows placement of zero anywhere. This is advantageous in cylindrical workpieces with concentric holes (Fig. 11.3), or workpieces in which the holes' positions are specified from a geometrical

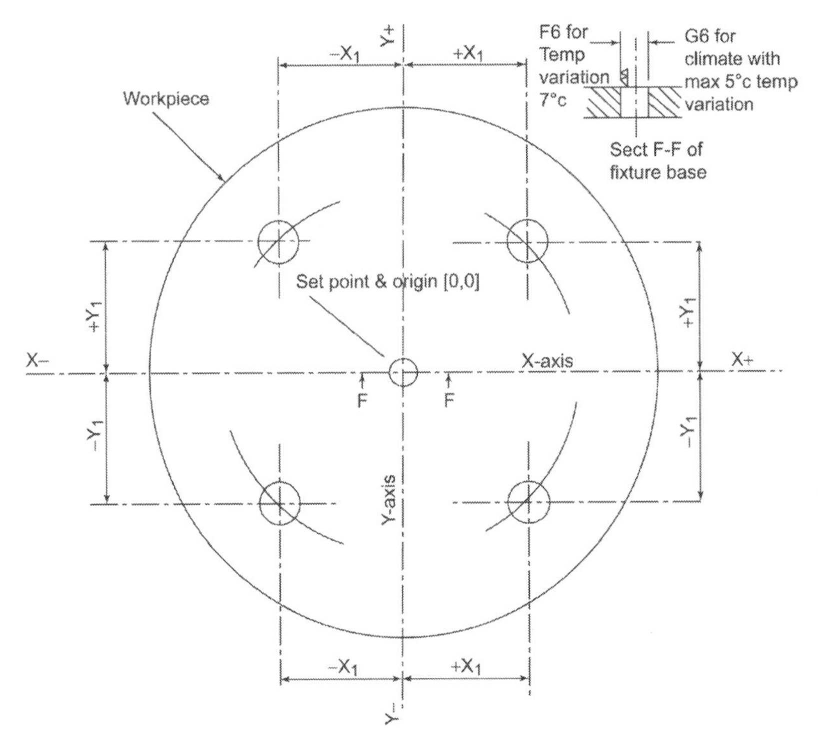

Fig. 11.3 *Placing zero at centre of a cylindrical workpiece (only for zero full float m/c)*

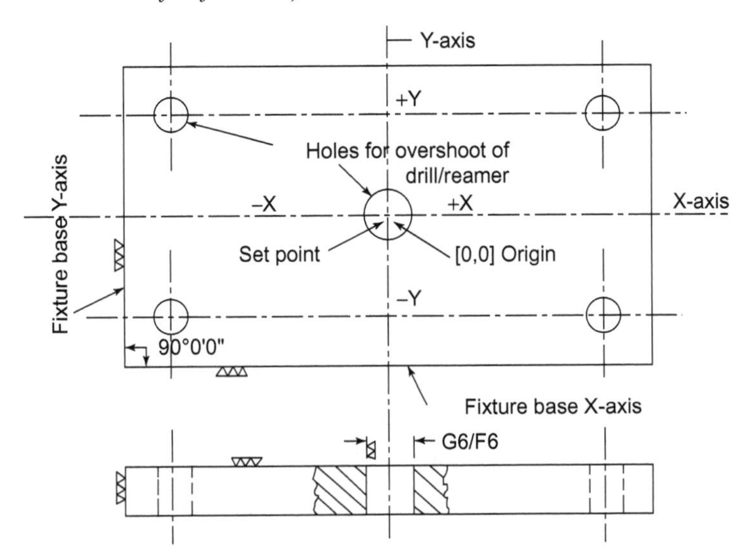

Fig. 11.4 *Set point at important datum of workpiece (only for fully floating zero m/cs)*

centre or some important point, which serves as the workpiece datum (Fig. 11. 4). In such cases zero can be placed at the centre/datum point of the workpiece. Naturally X and Y axes motions will be negative as well as positive.

Set point can be a precisely (G6/F6) machined hole with good surface finish (reamed or ground), or a ground cylindrical plug press fit in the base. When a precise hole is used, it can be aligned sooner with the m/c spindle by using a close fit (h6) locating plug held in spindle collet (Fig. 11.5). Good alignment can be effected by jogging (inching) the m/c spindle (table). When a plug is used to define the *set point*, the location diameter can have wide (h11–16) tolerance, since it will be made true (concentric) with the spindle by using a dial gauge (Fig. 11.6).

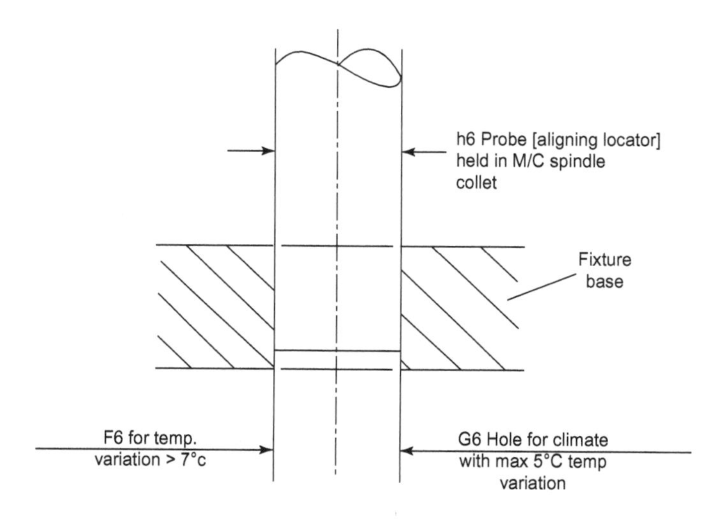

Fig. 11.5 *Aligning set pt. hole with m/c spindle*

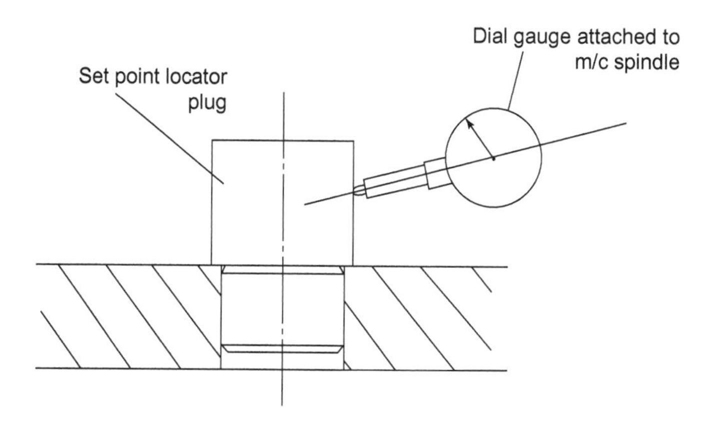

Fig. 11.6 *Aligning set point plug with m/c spindle*

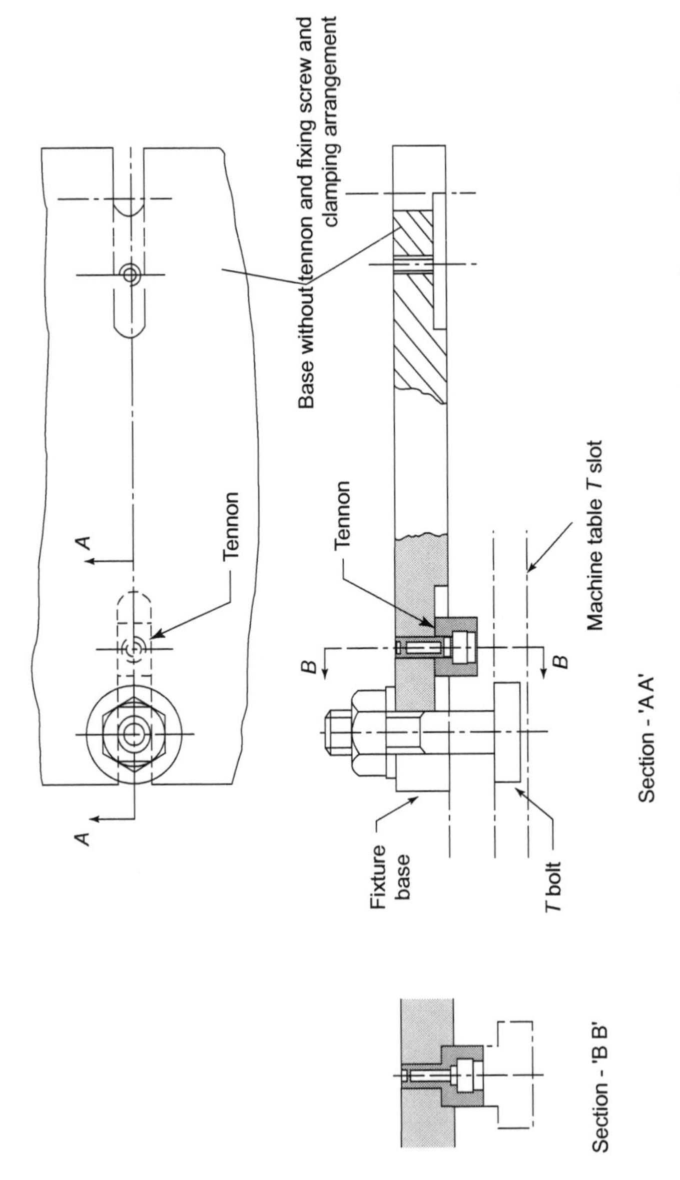

Fig. 11.7 *Providing close fit tennons on CNC fixture base for quick alignment of axes of base with axes of m/c*

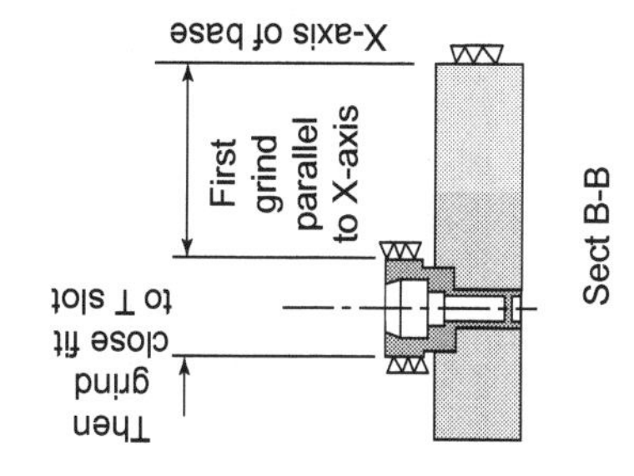

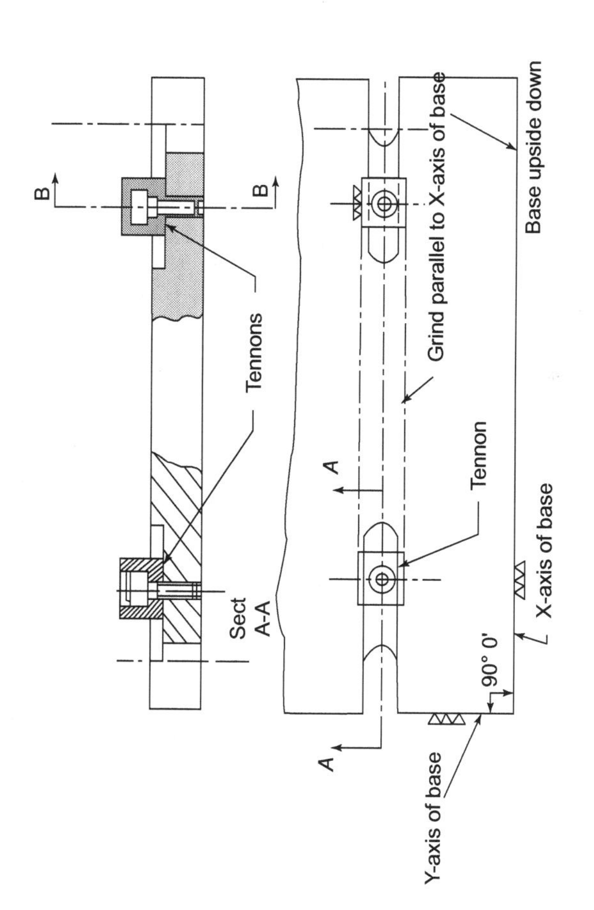

Fig. 11.8 *Grinding tennons parellel to X axis of fixture base*

For setting NC/CNC fixture the ground X and Y edges of the fixture base must be made parallel to the machine (table) X-Y axes. This can be accomplished quickly and precisely by providing close fit (f6/g6) tennons on the fixture base (Fig. 11.7). However the tennons should be finish ground, parallel to the X-edge of the fixture base, to f6/h6 size *after assembling on the fixture base* (Fig. 11.8). Some people prefer using dial gauge for making X and Y edges of the base parallel to the table motions. They fear that tennons that are close fit in one T slot of m/c may not be equally close fit in the neighboring T slot. We can syntheSize both methods by using tennons for quick positioning the fixture and checking the resulting parallelism with motions of m/cs X and Y by running dial gauge on the ground X and Y edges of the fixture base.

After finish machining one hole the spindle is withdrawn well clear of the workpiece and the fixture before moving to the next hole. Before commencing cutting feed for the next hole, the spindle is brought rapidly down closer to the workpiece, maintaining a safety gap of 2–3 mm only between the workpiece surface and the cutting end of the drill/reamer. The withdrawal and rapid approach strokes (the non-cutting time) can be minimised by reducing the retraction distance.

The simplest way of doing it is to keep the heights of clamping and locating elements at the minimum necessary—*ala* face milling fixtures. At the same time, the withdrawal stroke of m/c spindle must provide enough clear space for easy, obstacle-free, loading/unloading of workpiece and cutting tools.

Figure 11.9 shows an NC m/c fixture for drilling three holes in the workpiece, shown at smaller scale, above the fixture. The workpiece is located on its edges by six location pins and clamped by two knurled-head screws. Two close fit tennons align the X–Y motions of the m/c table with the fixture. The slots at both ends of the fixture base facilitate securing it onto m/c table. with 'T' bolts, nuts and washers. The *set point* is placed on the left and operator side of the workpiece to enable use of any type of m/c: fixed/shiftable/fully floating zero. It is desirable to draw the m/c table in red/blue/green chain-dotted line to make sure that the fixture is resting well on the m/c table. Figure 5.12 in Chapter 5 shows plate type jig for the same workpiece. Both jigs use the same location and clamping systems. Only that the jig plate in Fig. 5.12 becomes the fixture base in Fig. 11.9. However, as the base has to accommodate *set point* hole too, the base is bigger than the jig plate. There are no drill guide bushes in the NC/CNC fixtures; and the base has square, ground X–Y axes edges.

Z-axis coincides with the m/c spindle axis. The zero of the Z-axis is usually set on the top face of workpiece, whence cutting commences. The reading is positive (+) upwards i.e. for all spindle withdrawal strokes and negative (–) downwards. The Z coordinate of the set point should provide ample clearance for loading/unloading cutting tools and workpiece. Fixtures in which milling cutters are plunge fed also set Z-axis zero at top face of workpiece.

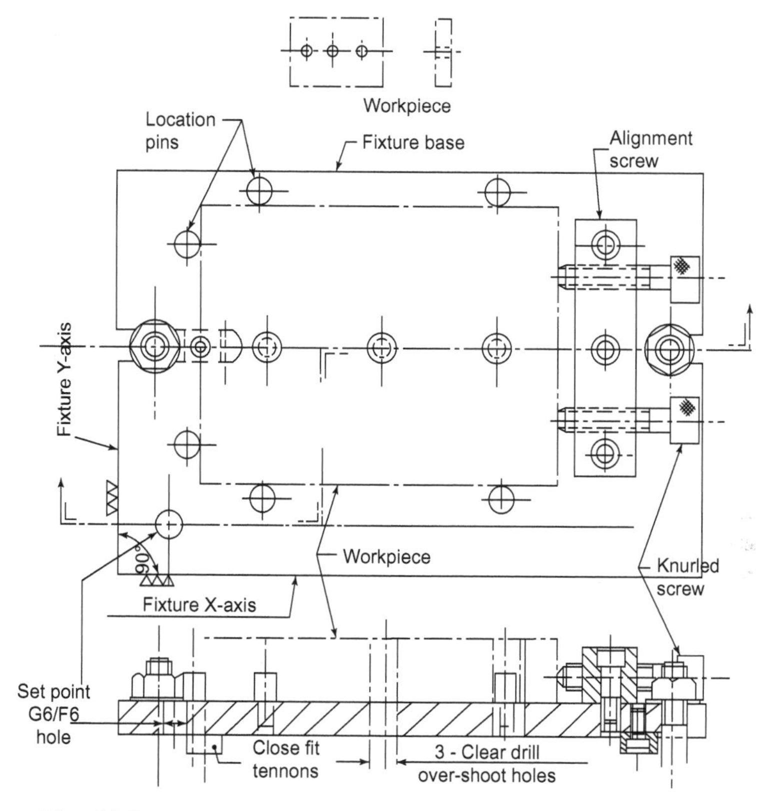

Fig. 11.9 *Fixture for drilling workpiece on NC/CNC machines*

Usually there are three reference levels of vertically fed cutting tool in NC/CNC programs (Fig. 11.10).

1. Initial position I of the tool with cutting end of the tool in retracted position.
2. Position R at which the cutting tool is brought forward rapidly before commencing slow cutting feed. To reckon the variation in workpiece position R should be about 1–3 mm from the workpiece surface whence cutting commences.
3. Level Z, where cutting ends. This position should reckon the length of the conical cutting end of a drill and 1–3 mm drill overshoot.

In profile milling fixtures like one illustrated in Fig. 11.11, zero of Z-axis is set 1.5–2 mm below the lower profiling level. This provides cutter overlap on the workpiece lower edge and ensures that the entire width (thickness) of the workpiece edge is machined.

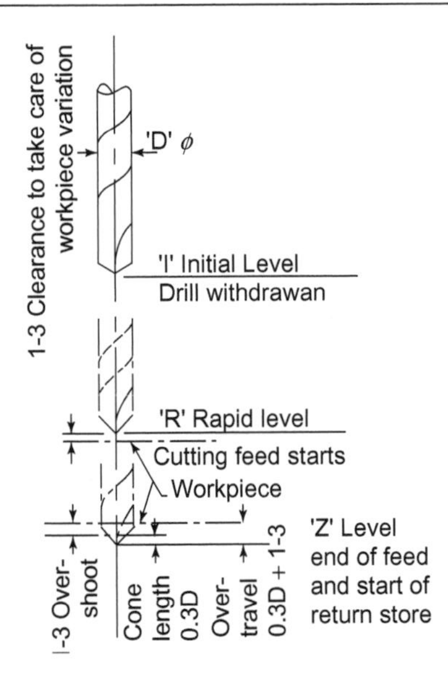

Fig. 11.10 *Three levels of m/c spindle*

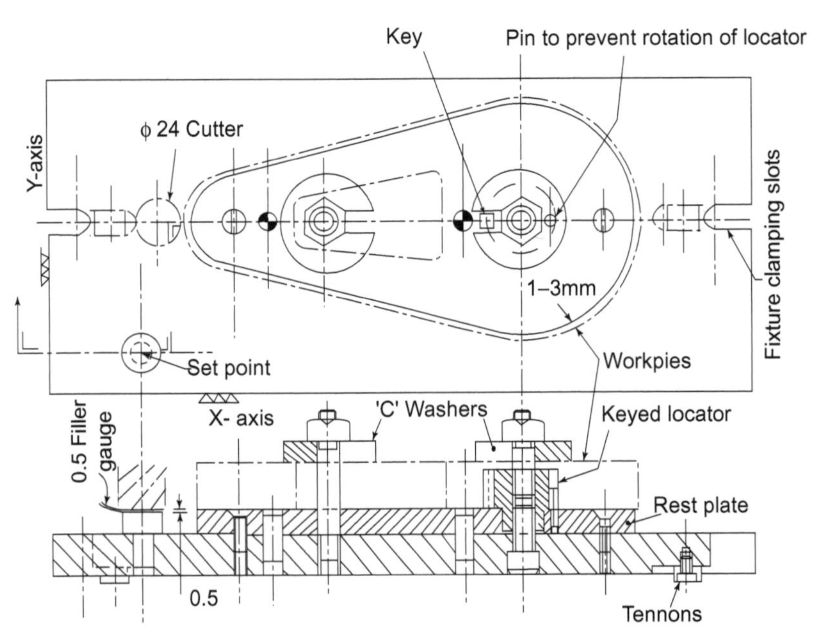

Fig. 11.11 *Profile milling fixture for NC/CNC m/c s*

In Continuous Path Programs used for profile milling *set point* is placed well clear of the workpiece, at a place with ample clearance for changing the cutting (milling) tools (Fig. 11.11). Profiling fixtures usually have a locating plug at the *set point*. Because milling cutters are manufactured oversize to provide sharpening allowance on the cutter diameter, a new cutter might be 0.0 76–0.125 oversize. Moreover after many re-sharpening grinds, the cutter may even become undersize. It is impossible to provide a hole close fit for a cutter with so much diametrical variation. The plug at the *set point* is aligned perfectly with the machine spindle axis by using a Dial Gauge (Fig. 11.6). The cutting end of the tool (end-mill) must also be set vertically (Z axis). The top surface of the plug can be used as the reference—Z-axis zero—for vertical setting of spindle. A 0.5 mm filler gauge can be used for vertical placement of the cutter. After placing the cutter at the *set point*, operator has only to press 'Start' button to commence the profiling program.

Note that the workpiece resting plate in the cam profile milling fixture in Fig. 11.11 is also profiled like the workpiece. However, the profile of the resting plate is about 1.5–3 mm (per side) smaller than the workpiece profile. This prevents the cutter machining the rest plate. It also provides space for the vertical overlap (overshoot) of the cutter below the workpiece edge to be machined.

The key-wayed hole in the workpiece is used for location and clamping with a simple 'C' washer. Rotation of the locator during operation is prevented by a pin anchored in the rest plate. The pin engages with a slot provided in the locator. A cutout in the workpiece is used for an additional 'C' washer clamp. The *set point* is well clear of the workpiece and the clamping mechanism to provide ample tool loading/unloading clearance. Needless to say that two edges of the fixture base are ground square to each other to serve as X and Y axes of the base; nor that the fixture base is provided with two tennons for quick positioning of the fixture on m/c.

The size of the cutter is an important parameter in contriving the program. The cutter size should be specified in the fixture drawing. It is also a good practice to draw the locus of the cutter on the drawing to check that locators and clamps do not obstruct the path of the cutter

Note that the (0.076–0.125) oversize of a new cutter will machine 0.038–0.062 (per side) underrsize workpieces. As the cutter becomes underrsize after re-sharpening grinds the profiled workpieces would become oversize. Most profiling programs have provision for reckoning cutter size variation.

Drilling and milling fixtures for CNC machines are similar to the fixtures for NC machines. However, most CNC fixtures, including those for drilling, have a separate *set point* well clear of the workpiece and the locating and clamping elements. Most CNC programs commence machining programs from the *set point*.

Existing drill jigs and milling fixtures can be modified for usage on NC/CNC machines. This entails:

1. Grinding two edges of the jig base parallel to workpiece X–Y axes (usually the two edges of rectangular workpieces). Consider provision of tennons.

2. Providing a *set point* for setting the m/c spindle to 'Start' position.
3. Provide clamping slot for securing fixture to m/c table.
4. Remove drill bushes.

Modification of a conventional milling fixture usually involves addition of a bigger base/adaptor plate. For the NC/CNC, milling fixtures need a *set point,* which is usually a plug.

The *set point* must have enough clear space around it to allow usage of Dial Gauge for making the setting plug concentric with the m/c spindle.

The conventional milling fixture in Fig. 6.6 has not got such space. So, it is necessary to use a bigger base as an adaptor (Fig. 11.12). The bigger base has two square ground edges to serve as X and Y axes. Furthermore, the base has got tennon locating slots on top as well as bottom. Both top and bottom slots should be parallel to the X edge of the base. The top tennon slots are close fit with the tennons of the existing conventional fixture (Fig. 6.6), while the tennons in the bottom slot should be close fit with the Tee slots of the table of NC/CNC machine to be used. The existing fixture is secured to the bigger base with Allen screws and dowels.

A common base can be used as an adaptor for using many conventional milling fixtures on NC/CNC machines. Even a common *Setting Point* can be used. The top face of the setting plug will then be at the lowest Z level among all the fixtures to be used. Naturally the Z axes zero positions from the setting plug top face will be different for different fixtures.

The conventional milling fixture in Fig. 6.6 used a gang of cutters to machine nine surfaces of the workpiece simultaneously. A NC/CNC m/c will, however, use a single (20 mm Dia.) cutter suitable for machining the central slot in one pass. The cutter will be moved suitably along all three axes automatically by the m/c program. The right-hand portion of Fig. 11.12 shows the program cycle. The cutter is rapidly brought within 1–3 mm from the workpiece before starting cutting feed. The gap is necessary to reckon variation in workpiece size. It is also necessary to provide some over-travel to ensure that the required face is machined completely, without leaving any undesired step. Thus, the cutter (m/c table) travel will be:

Machine stroke = (1–3 + Cutter Radius) + Length to be machined + (1–3 + Cutter Radius)

When the surface to be machined is bigger than cutter diameter, it is necessary to use number of passes to machine the entire face. Every following cut must ensure that there is some overlap over the surface machined in the previous cut, so that there are no projections on the machined surface.

The plan of the program layout in Fig. 11.12 gives the co-ordinates of the centre of the cutter on the cutting face. The elevation of the layout shows the cutter at the beginning and the end of the machining stroke and the three cutting levels Z1, Z2 and Z3.

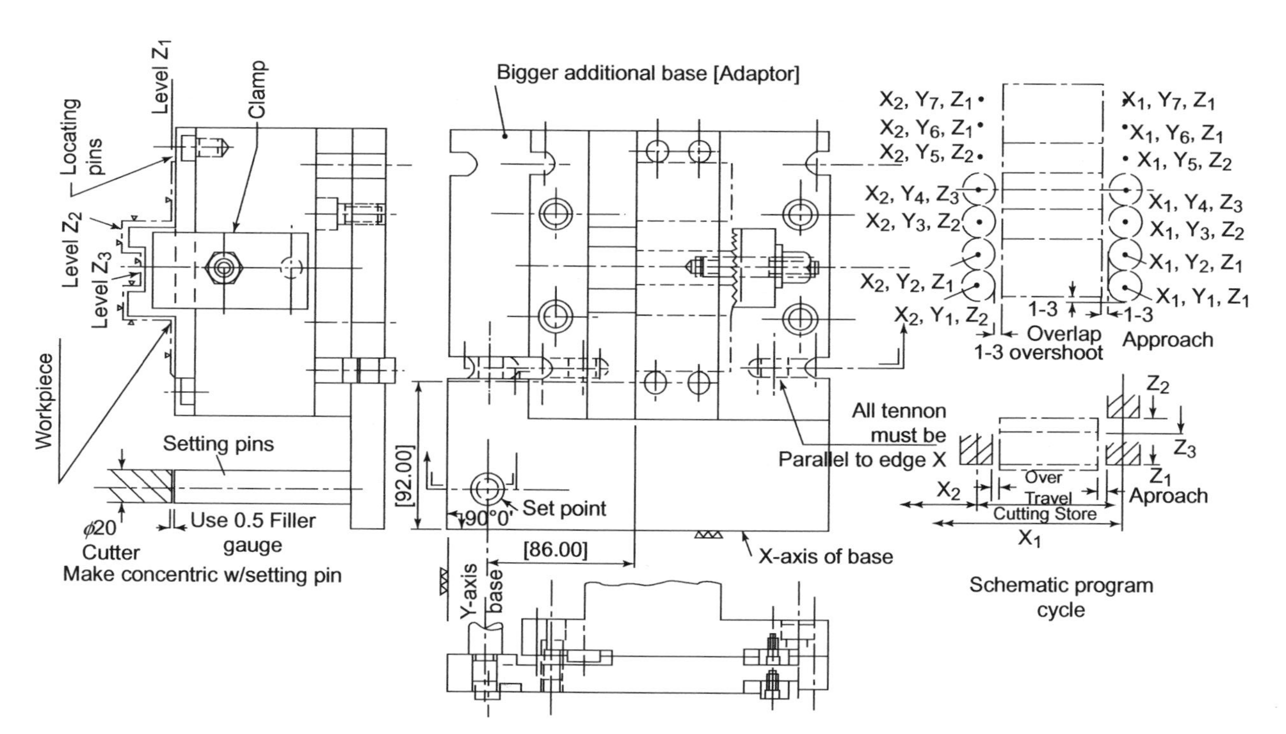

Fig. 11.12 *Modification of conventional milling fixture [Fig. 6.6] for usage on NC/CNC m/c s*

NC/CNC Turning Centres

Programmable turning machines almost eliminate need for form tools. For any profile can be turned by programming the tool motions suitably. There are only two axes: Z-axis coinciding with the machine axis and X-axis for the radial position of the tool (centre of the radius at the cutting point). The apex of centre mounted in m/c spindle is taken as the origin (X = 0; Z = 0). It is necessary to provide a *set point* well clear of the workpiece loading/ unloading and tool changing(for re-sharpening) paths. Fig.11.13 shows the *set point* for the program illustrated in the figure.

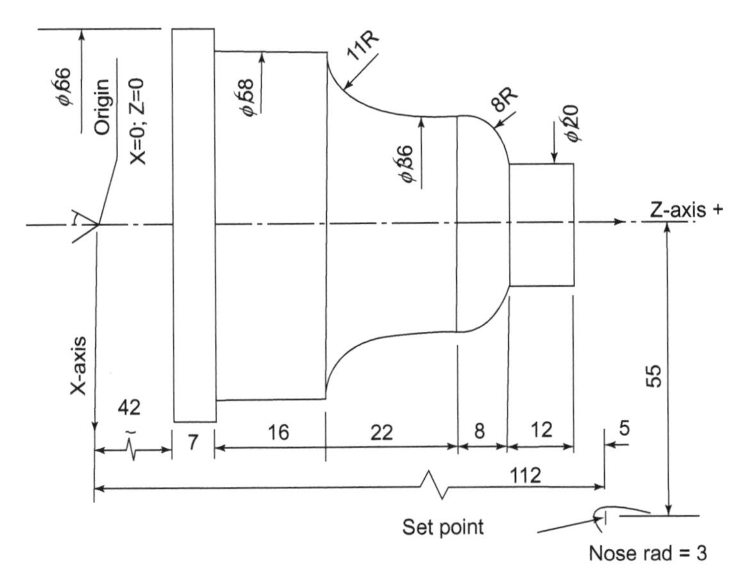

Fig. 11.13 *Set point and origin on NC/CNC turning machines*

Modular Jigs and Fixtures

Module: A standard self-contained unit. The term is used widely in electronics industry. It is jargon for standardised, easily connectable/replaceable, sub-assembled unit like a timer or a contactor. Modular construction implies assembling standardised sub-assemblies. For example, in a hydraulic system the pump, a self-contained unit comprising many parts, is a module. Similarly various control valves, actuators like cylinders and hydraulic motors—each a self-contained integral unit—are all modules. Likewise spark plugs, carburetors, fuel pumps and anti-friction bearings are modules used in modular automobiles. Modules usually have many applications.

Toggle clamps comprising links, pivots and adjustment screws are modules. Swinging hook clamp (Fig. 15.6) with all the constituents like spring, stud and nut is a module. Assembled floating pad (Fig. 15.14a) is a module. Pump jigs (Fig. 5.21), rotary (Fig. 6.8) and indexing (Figs 4.9 and 4.10) tables, lathe chucks (Figs 7.3–7.10), vises (Fig. 6.3), jigs in Figs 5.24 and 5.25 and milling fixture in Fig. 6.12 are modules. Some manufacturers consider interchangeable hard and soft chuck jaws, standardised fixture bases (horizontal, angular, cubical) with 'Tee' slots (Fig. 11.14) or tapped and/or reamed holes (Fig. 11.15), even jig feet, modules. By this reckoning, all standardised parts in Chapter 15 of this treatise can be considered modules; and all jigs and fixtures constructed from these as modular. Personally, I feel that we should call only subassemblies with more than one parts as modules. By this definition slotted (Fig. 15.7) and swinging strap clamps (Fig. 15.10) can be called modules only if they are supplied with clamping studs, heel pins, washers and the nuts.

Modular construction assembles the commercially available modules in an arrangement suitable for the required applications. Modules are bought from specialist manufacturers. So, the quality is better than a do-it-yourself thing. Ready availability reduces designing (no need to draw details), manufacturing (no need to machine standard parts) and repairing time. On the other hand number of parts—particularly the fasteners—far exceed those required for non-modular construction. For each module must be secured by fasteners and connected mechanically/electrically/hydraulically/pneumatically to other modules.

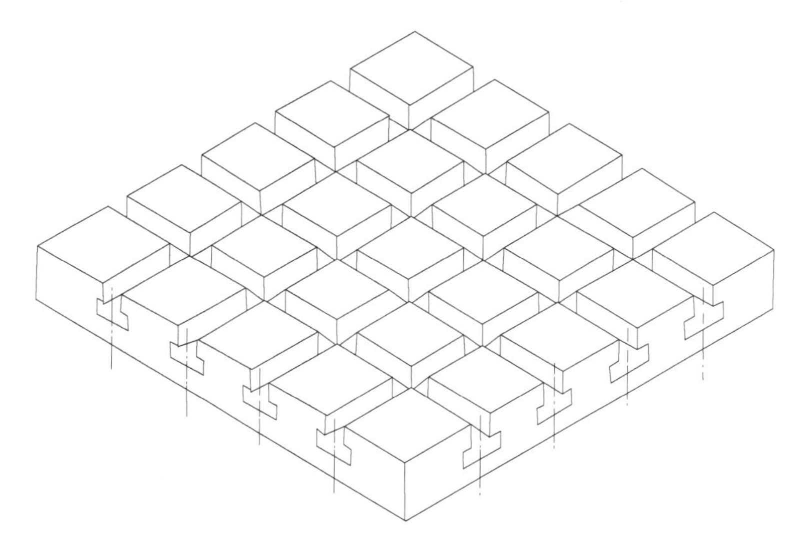

Fig. 11.14 *Tee-slotted fixture base for modular fixture (off m/c assy)*

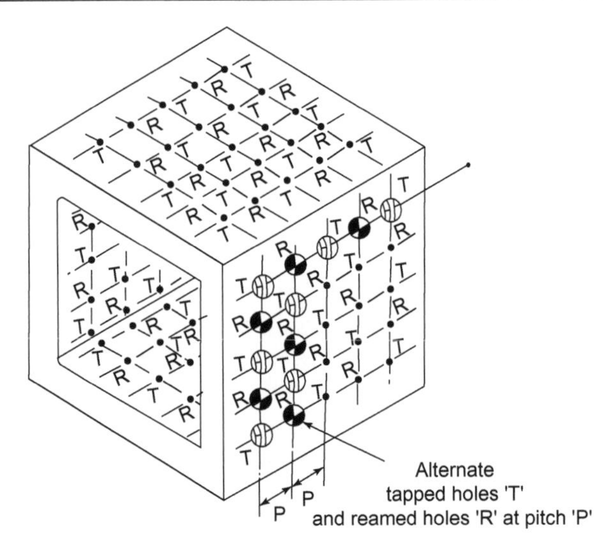

Fig. 11.15 *Square tubular base for modular jigs and fixtures*

Non-modular construction, on the other hand, attempts to combine number of constituents in fewer sophisticated parts. In a non-modular hydraulic press, a single fuselage of a casting/forging will accommodate hydraulic cylinder and some valves. Furthermore the valves and cylinder might be connected internally by suitable holes. So, minimum external piping and connecting joints; or the externally mounted valves with securing fasteners and the connecting piping with inevitable joints. Non-modular construction makes machines sturdy—fewer joints—and compact. However, the manufacture is tougher. Even if bore of built in cylinder or the valve becomes oversized the entire casting/forging must be discarded. This will waste all the work done in preceding operations, which is not a small loss of money and *time*. You may also compromise quality for expediency. You might make do with grinding—even finish boring—the cylinder inside instead of honing it like a specialist manufacturer. After all, the usage will improve the surface finish, one reasons.

Modular construction is like a shop setup (Chapter 13). In a shop set up you build, *on machine table,* a temporary make do fixture quickly and economically for machining samples or small batch production. However, the machine to be used remains idle while you assemble a set up *on machine table*. In modular fixture, this idle time of a machine is eliminated almost altogether by using a modular base. Modular fixture base can have 'T' slots (Fig. 11.14) or number of threaded or/and reamed holes (Fig. 11.15). Depending on application, the base might be an angle plate, a cubical block or an angular structure (Fig. 11.16). A standard lathe face

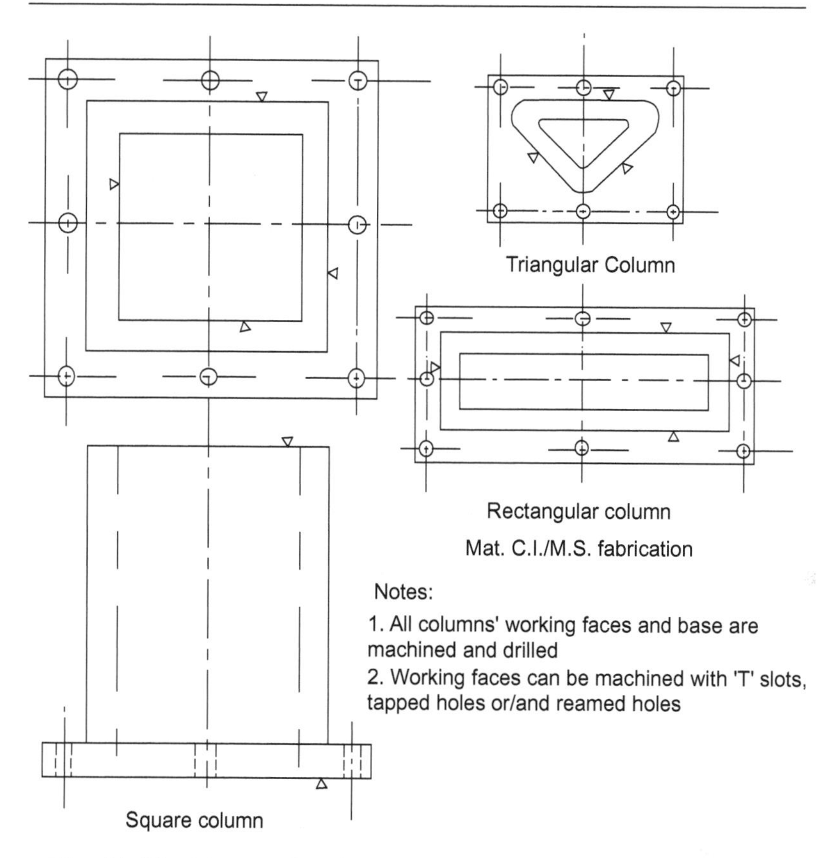

Fig. 11.16 *Variety of modular column shapes available comercially*

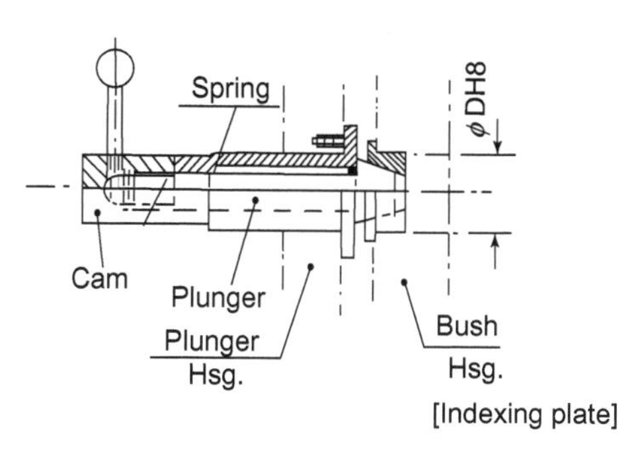

Fig. 11.17 *Modular indexing arrangement*

plate is a module when a temporary fixture comprising standard locators and clamps is built on it *off the machine*—without keeping the machine idle. The *Setup* in Fig. 13.8 can be considered modular fixture when assembled off the machine to be used.

Figure 11.17 shows sub-assembly of modular indexing arrangement. You have only to machine the housings to mount the arrangement. Figure 11.18 shows ball lock location pin—a removable dowel which can be clamp into a dowel hole like a miniature expanding mandrel. Versions of locating dowels with 'L', 'T' or ring shaped handles for quick removal or rapid locking rotation are available.

Modular tooling eliminates need for manufacture/procurement of standard parts or the necessary accessories like fasteners, springs, washers, etc. You only have to machine the mounting surfaces and threaded mounting holes. This reduces cost and time and enhances quality through specialist manufacture.

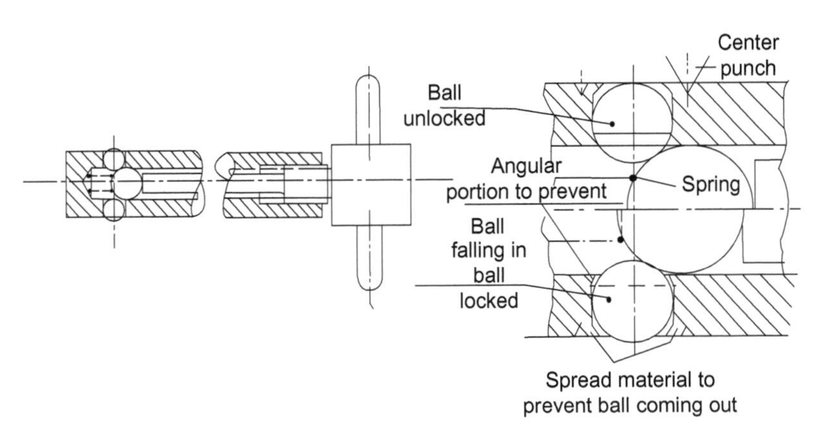

Fig.11.18 *Ball lock location pin*

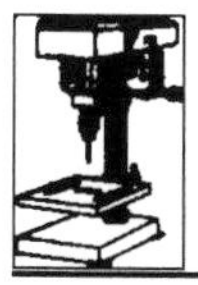

CHAPTER 12

Inspection Devices

Along with the manufacturing, the inspection of the components must also be speeded up in the mass production. The skills required for inspection must be reduced to lower the labour costs. This is achieved by replacing standard measuring instruments such as the vernier and micrometer by gauges. The gauges do not measure the actual size of the manufactured component but merely check if the dimensions of the component fall within the high and low limits specified on the drawing. They ensure the desired fit in assembly.

Standard Gauges

Cylindrical holes can be inspected by simple plug gauges (Fig. 12.1). A plug gauge consists of two hardened plugs with a connecting handle. The longer *go* plug is passed through the hole to ensure that the hole size is bigger than the low (minimum) limit. The shorter *not go* plug should not pass through the hole, if it is lesser than the high (maximum) limit specified on

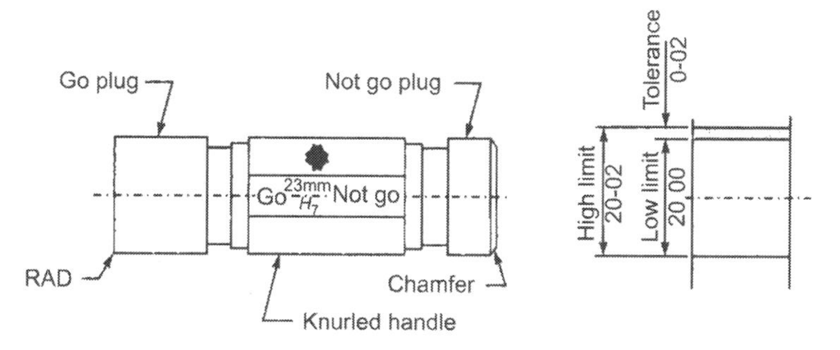

Fig. 12.1 *Plug gauge*

the drawing. Thus, an unskilled inspector can pass the component merely by checking that the *go* plug enters the component and the *not go* plug does not.

Similarly, outside diameters can be inspected by caliper or snap gauges. (Fig. 12.2). Length gauges are also used in a similar manner. For the male parts in all the gauges, *go* gap through which the component must pass would be bigger than the *not go* gap into which the component should not enter.

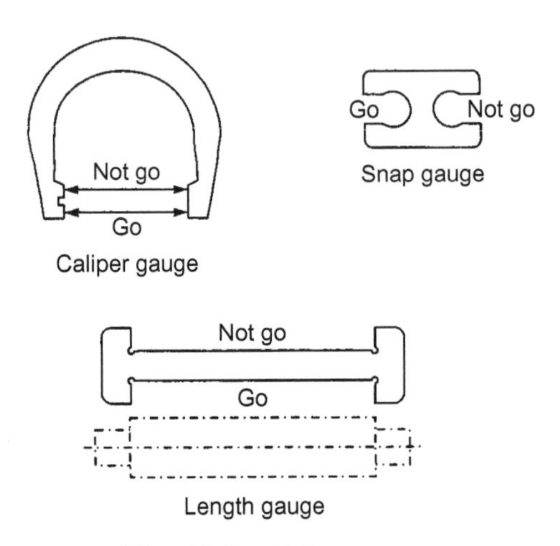

Fig. 12.2 *Caliper gauges*

Plug gauges and outside diameter gauges (caliper and snap gauges) have been standardised by the Indian Standards Institution and are readily available in the market. Length gauges must, however, be manufactured to suit the components.

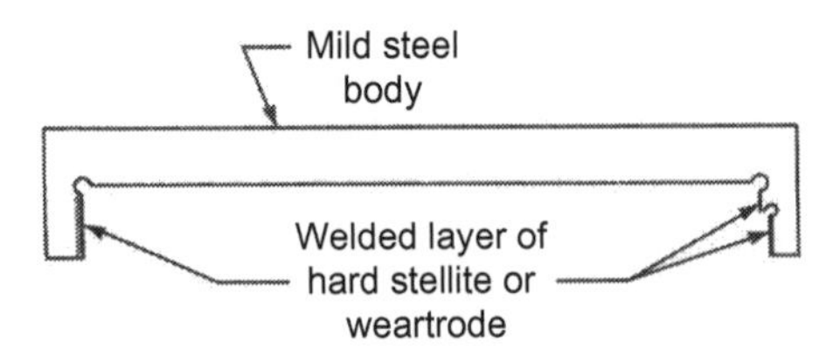

Fig. 12.3 *Large caliper gauges*

Special Gauges

Slots, gaps and key-ways are checked by gauges which function like plug gauges. They are made from plates and are rectangular in section (Fig. 12.4).

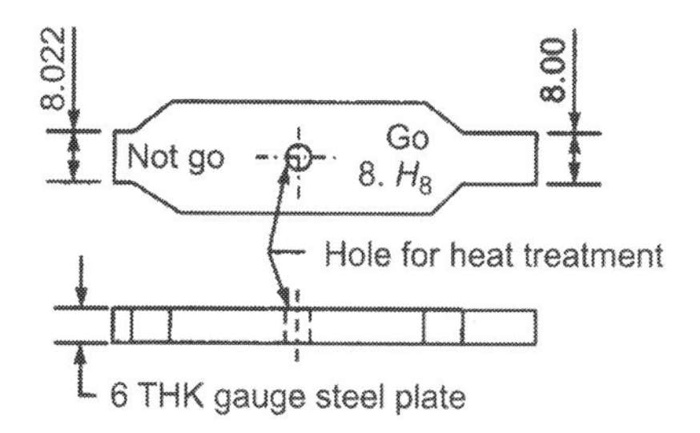

Fig. 12.4 *Key-way and slot checking gauge*

Tapered holes are inspected for the diameter of the bigger end by a tapered plug with a step at big end. The lower face of the step corresponds to the low limit of the hole size and the upper face with the higher limit. If the face of the workpiece falls within the upper and lower faces of the step, the workpiece is within the limits (Fig. 12.5). The inspection is carried out by seeing or by the feel of the finger.

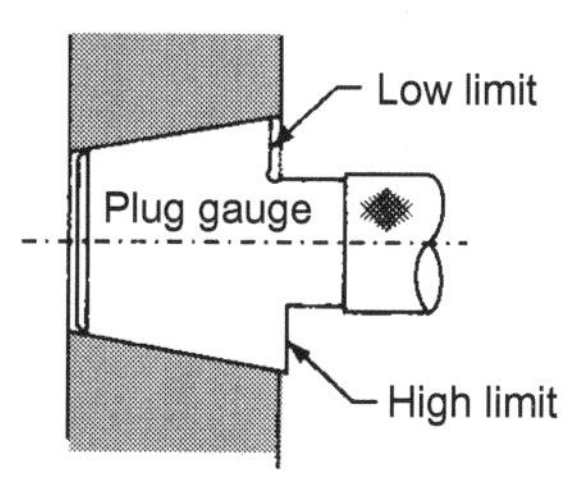

Fig. 12.5 *Flush surface guage for tapered hole*

A similar method is used for checking distances between parallel faces of the workpieces. Figure 12.6 shows a flush surface gauge for checking the shoulder to end face length of the pin. If the length is within the limits, the small end of the pin falls between the two limiting faces of the gauge. Flush surfaces are sometimes built in a pin. Then, the gauge is called a flush pin gauge (See Fig. 12.7). Flush pin gauges can be used conveniently for inspection of the distance between two conical bores.

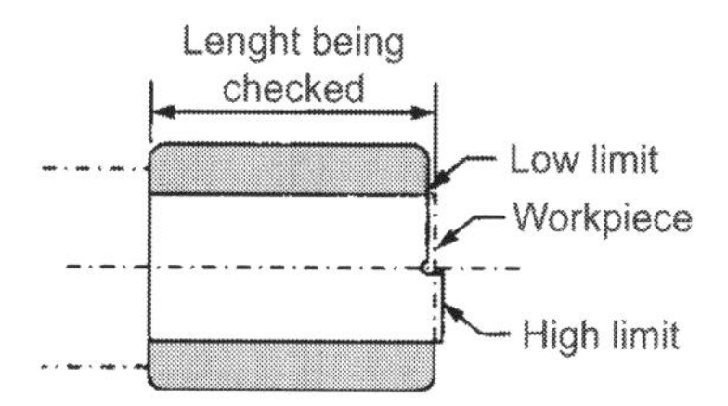

Fig. 12.6 *Flush surface length guage*

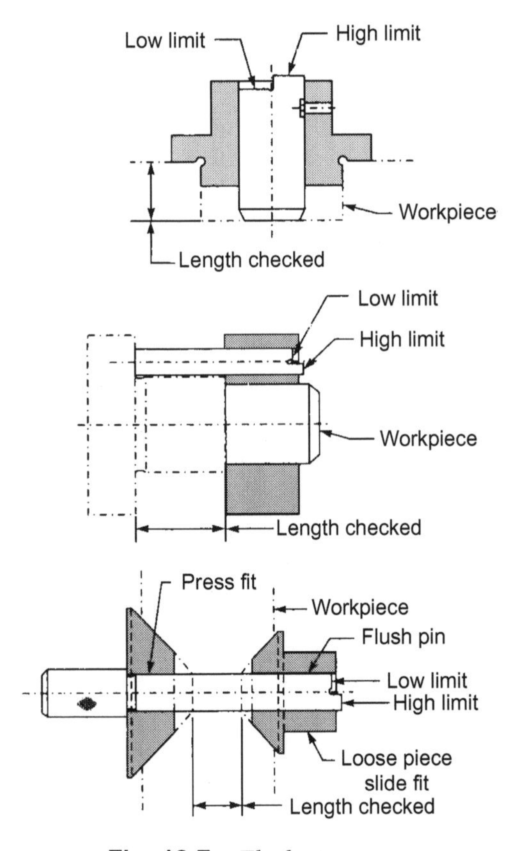

Fig. 12.7 *Flush pin gauges*

The centre distance between two cylindrical holes can be inspected with a snap gauge (Fig. 12.8). The holes should be first inspected individually for

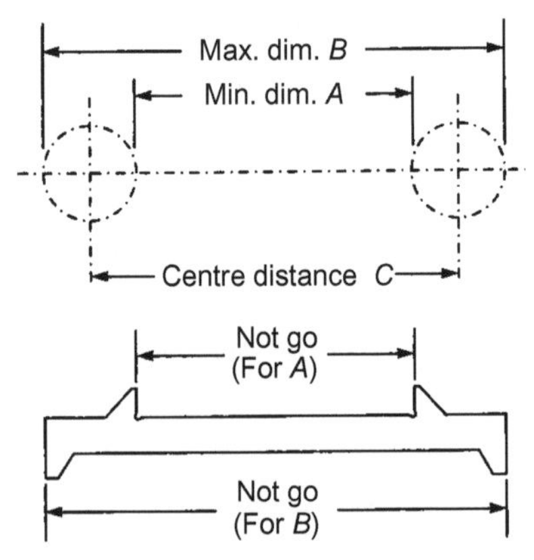

Fig. 12.8 *Snap gauge for checking centre distance*

accuracy of the diameters before the centre distance is checked. In this type of centre distance gauge, there is no *go*. Instead, there are two *not gos*. One inspects dim. *A* for the minimum centre distance limit and the other dim. *B* for the maximum centre distance. If none of the *not go* enter the workpiece, the centre distance is within the limits specified on the drawing.

Receiver Gauges

The centre distance as well as the diameters of the holes can be inspected at one go by using a receiver gauge. These are used for checking the suitability of the workpiece for assembly with other mating parts. If a receiver gauge accepts a workpiece, it can be assembled easily in the final product. A receiver gauge does not measure the extent of inaccuracies in the workpiece. The gauge just checks the possibility of easy assembly.

Figure 12.9a shows a receiver gauge for a gear box cover. Centre distance C between the shafts *A* and *B* is exactly equal to the centre distance of the

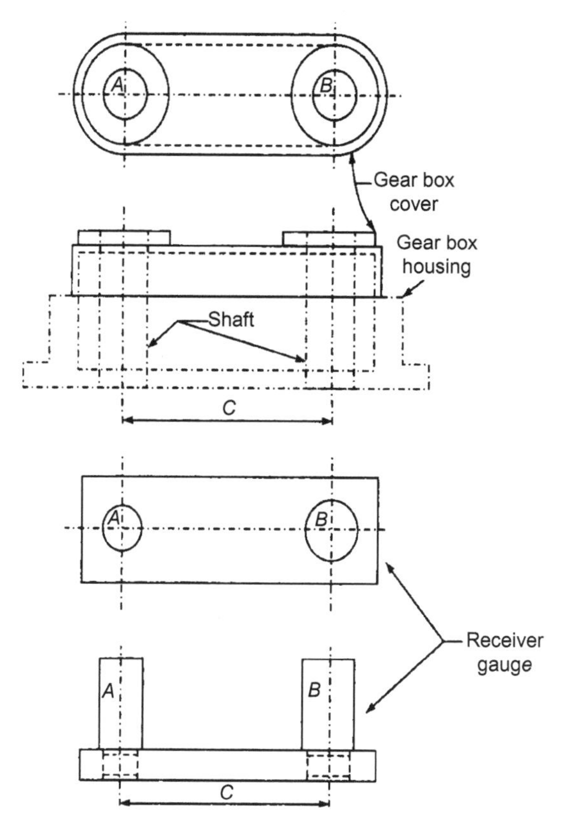

Fig. 12.9a *Receiver gauge for gear box cover*

shaft holes in the corresponding gear box housing. The diameters of the posts *A* and *B* are manufactured to the maximum limit of the shafts mating with the holes in the gear box cover. Thus, the receiver gauge is a plate fitted with two plugs *A* and *B*. If the gear box cover to be checked enters both plugs *A* and *B* we can be sure that the hole sizes as well as the centre distance between the holes are suitable for easy assembly of the gear box cover with the mating shafts and gear box housing. If the receiver gauge does not accept the workpiece, it cannot be assembled with the corresponding mating parts.

Checking keyway centrality of shafts and hubs

Checking centrality of a keyway *precisely* is rather tricky. According to the prevailing practice the shaft is kept on 'V' blocks and rotated slowly, inched, to make the keyway horizontal. This is checked by a dial gauge. But the keyway depth is usually very small: only 3–4 mm only for a 8 wide X7 deep key. So small a face, even after truing by a dial gauge, cannot be considered precisely horizontal.

After making the face horizontal the centrality is checked by measuring the distance from the keyway face and the external diameter of the shaft, on the both sides (Fig. 12.9b). The difference between the readings on both the sides gives the error in the centrality of the keyway.

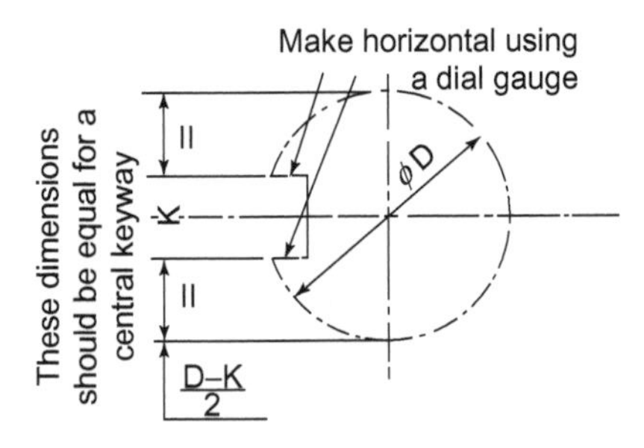

Fig. 12.9b *Checking centrality of a keyway in a shaft*

Figure 12.9c shows keyway dimensions for a 24 diameter shaft and the keyway centrality checking gauge. The segmental construction facilitates the precise machining and accurate measurement. The two halves (1 A and B) can be held together face to face—their radii aligned—to grind the seating surface for the key (2) and the segments alignment key (3). Even the bore can be finish ground after screwing the two halves together ,along with the aligning key (3).

The edges of the segments are ground parallel to the keyway faces. They provide a resting face during finishing of the keyway face and measuring the dimension 8.00 between the keyway face and the 24 G6 diameter: the distances shown by equal marks in Fig. 12.9b. Such faces machined to

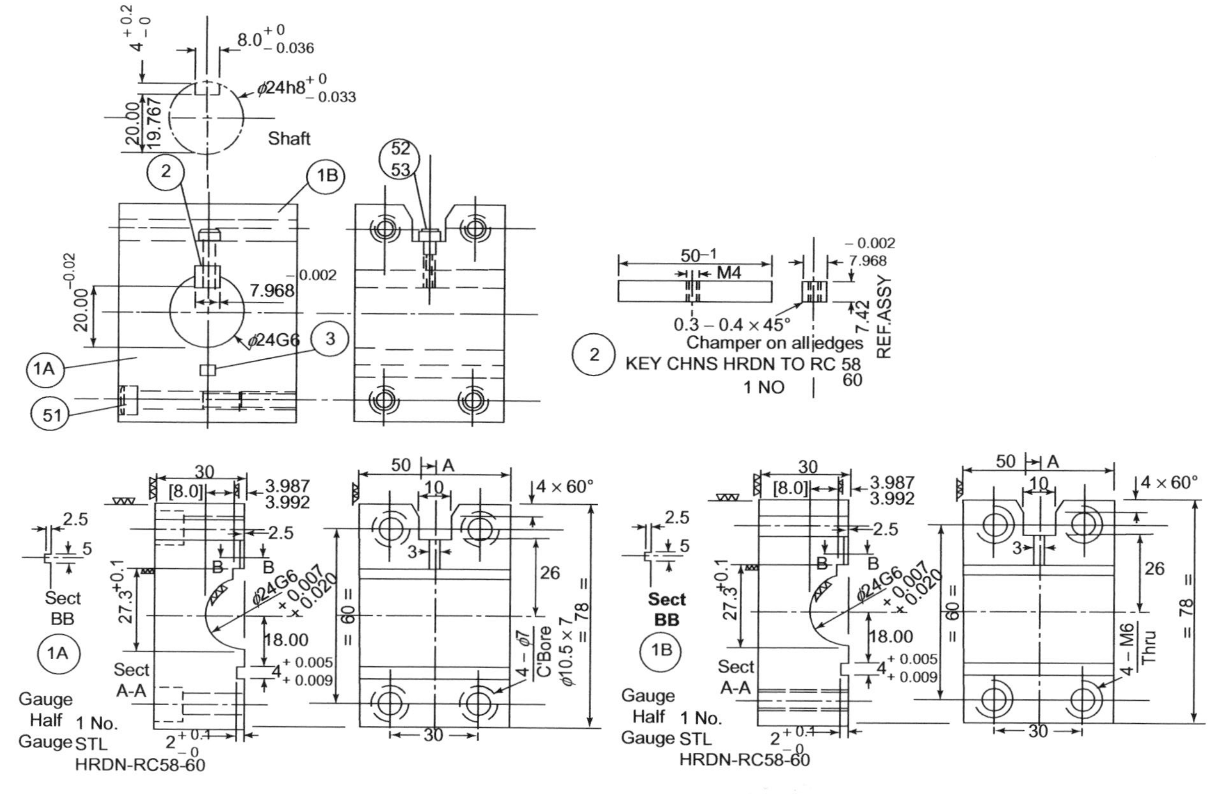

Fig. 12.9c *Receiver gauge for keyway centrality [shaft]*

facilitate accurate machining and measurement are called **Tooling face**. The 78 long tooling face allows more precise truing for horizontality than much smaller (3.3 long) face of the keyway. Consequently, the gauge is a better and faster method of checking centrality of the keyway.

A receiver gauge should admit the biggest size of shaft; hence the 24 G6 tolerance. The keyway size, on the other hand should suit the minimum size of the keyway: 24.00 – 0.036 = 23.964. Furthermore, the key insert should have a wear allowance: 10% of the workpiece tolerance of 0.036. Even this should have a manufacturing tolerance of 0.002; hence the size 7.968 – 0.002. Like all new gauges, this one too will not pass the workpieces within the tolerance but differing very, very marginally from the minimum size (range 23.968–23.964) due to the wear allowance.

Fig. 12.9d shows a gauge for checking the centrality of a keyway in a hub. The plug mounted with the key is made suitable for the minimum bore of the hub :24.00 – 0.004 = 23.996. The key insert is made suitable for the minimum (8.00 – 0.018 = 7.982) keyway size, with the added wear allowance of 0.004 and manufacturing tolerance of 0.002. Keeping the gauge body square, with two edges parallel with the keyway depth face, facilitates accurate manufacture and measurement of the keyway faces from the 23.996 diameter. Due to the wear allowance, the gauge will not pass the keyways in the width range 7.982–7.986, despite being within the workpiece tolerance range.

Receiver gauges can be used conveniently to simultaneously check a number of dimensions in a workpiece in a single handling. A multi-dimensional receiver gauge holds a number of locators which engage simultaneously with the workpiece to check its suitability for assembly.

Figure 12.10 shows an inspection device for checking the various dimensions of a workpiece. The workpiece is inserted into the flush surface gauge and a plug is inserted into the gauge and workpiece cross hole C. If these three can be assembled together we can be sure that:

1. Workpiece diameter *d* is less than the high limit;
2. Cross hole diameter C is more than the low limit, the plug acts as a *go* gauge; and
3. Cross hole C is at the centre of diameter *d* within the given centrality limits and the mating parts in the crosshole can be assembled without any trouble.

Thus, the flush surface gauge and the plug together act as a receiver gauge.

After the plug, flush surface gauge and the workpiece have been assembled together, the distances of cross-hole C from collar (l_1) and end face of the small diameter (l_2) can be checked. The end face of diameter *d* should be within two flush steps of the gauge. The distance of crosshole C from collar (l_1) can be checked by checking the gap between the collar and the unstepped face of the flush surface gauge with *go, not go* snap gauges. During this inspection, the assembly serves as an inspection fixture.

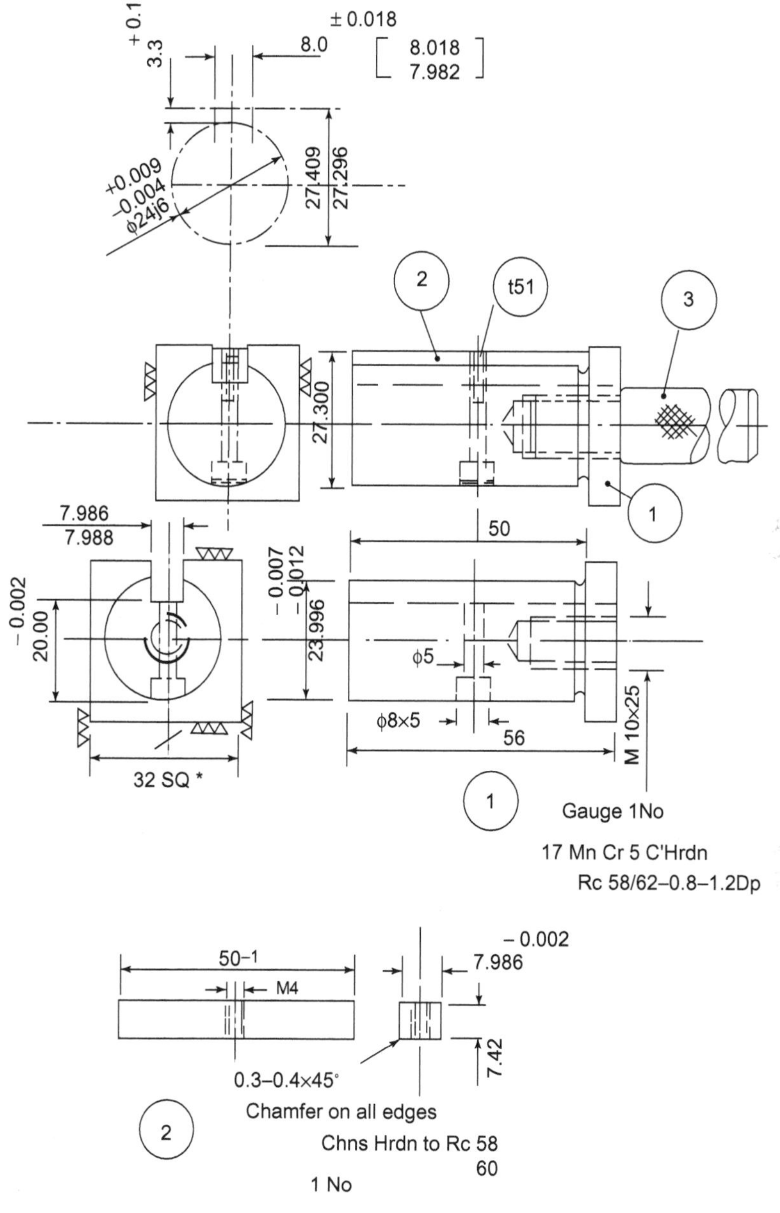

Fig. 12.9d *Receiver Gauge for keyway centrality in hub*

Inspection fixtures often have workpiece holding and moving arrangement for convenience. Figure 12.11 shows an inspection fixture for checking the concentricity of the angular seat of the valve with respect to its stem. The stem is guided in a hardened bush, and there is an arrangement for

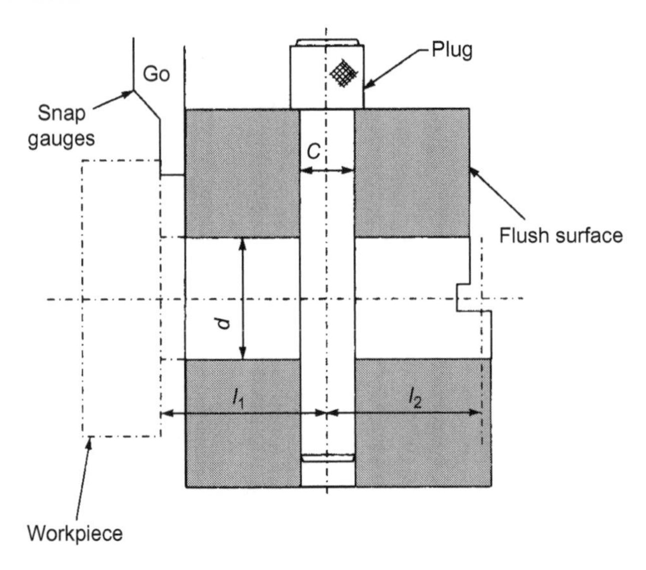

Fig. 12.10 *Inspection device for checking four sizes*

mounting a dial gauge in the suitable position. The valve has to be simply loaded in the guide bush and rotated around the stem axis to measure the concentricity of the angular seat with the dial gauge. Thus, the inspection fixture simplifies and speeds up the inspection of the valve.

Workpiece Marking and Setting Gauges

Machining allowances on castings and forgings often vary considerably. Consequently, the amount of material to be machined away must be varied in such a manner that the holes in the workpiece would be at the centres of the

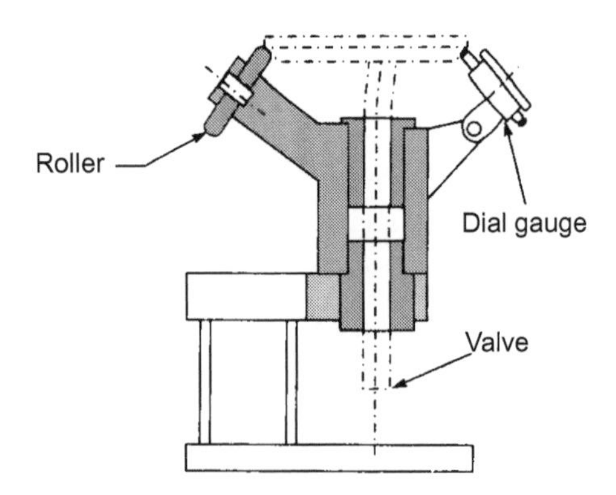

Fig. 12.11 *Valve concentricity inspection fixture*

corresponding bosses. So, we have to locate on the bosses while machining reference faces, which would later be used as locations while making holes in the bosses. This can be done by using marking and setting gauges.

Figure 12.12 shows a marking gauge for a casting with two bosses *P* and *Q*. The casting is levelled with wedges and its height is adjusted in such a way that the pointers for bosses *P* and *Q* top and bottom are more or less symmetrical with respect to the bosses. The casting can be marked in this position by two markers for the top and bottom faces to be machined. The marking can be used for levelling the workpiece during machining operation. Furthermore, if there is insufficient machining allowance on either of the faces, the fact would be discovered before commencing costly machining operation, which might turn out to be wasteful at a later stage when the workpiece is rejected due to insufficient machining allowance.

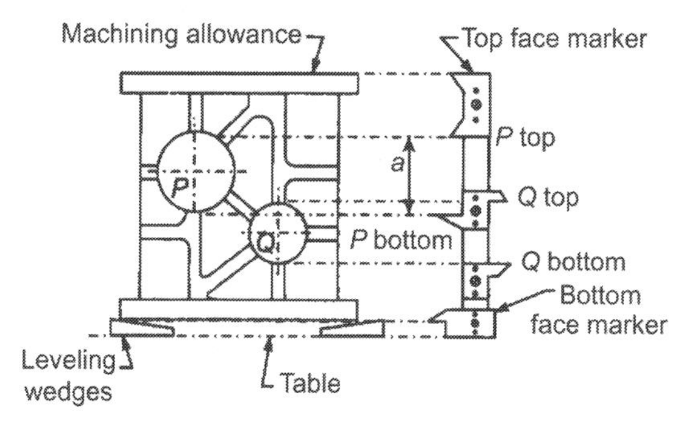

Fig. 12.12 *Marking gauge for casting*

Figure 12.13 shows a setting gauge for the workpiece shown in the fixture. The fixture has got two location pins *A,* which can be engaged with guide bushes *B* in the loose setting gauge. The gauge *has four small circular discs which serve as templates for positioning* the workpiece in the fixture. After engaging pins *A* in bushes *B* of the setting gauge, the workpiece is moved in the fixture to align the workpiece bosses with the circular disc templates on the gauge. After alignment, the workpiece is clamped in position in the fixture by four hexagonal headed bolts.

The gauge can then be removed and the end face of the workpiece can be machined. The loose setting gauge is used mainly to position (locate) the workpiece correctly in the fixture.

Materials and Wear Allowance

Since gauges might be used hundreds of times in every shift, they are subjected to abrasion and wear. This is countered by hardening the working surfaces of gauges to 60–65 HRC. Over and above this, plug gauges are

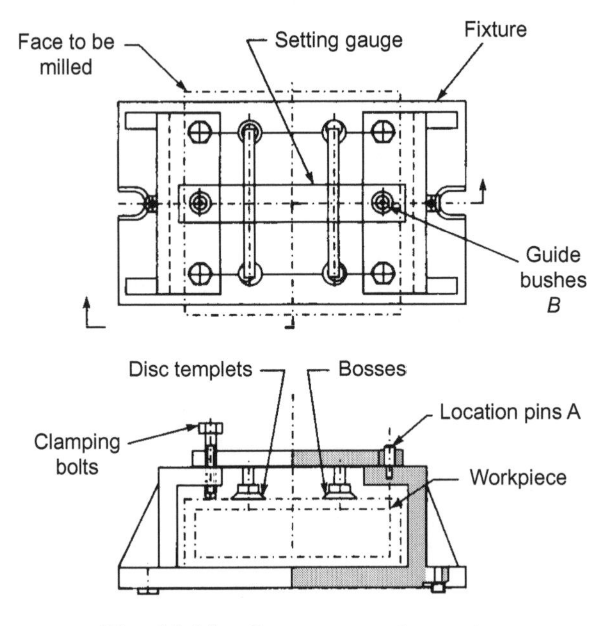

Fig. 12.13 *Setting gauge for casting*

made slightly oversized and gauges for male parts are made slightly underrsize to provide wear allowance. The allowance is generally 10% of the tolerance on the component. For example, a 70 mm ϕ *H7* hole has got a tolerance of + 0.03 mm. So, the *go* size plug would have wear allowance of 0.003 mm. The plug diameter would be 20.003 mm when new, so that it can be used till the gauge wears by 0.003 mm.

The steel used for gauges should be suitable for hardening to 60–65 HRC. Moreover, it should have low coefficient of thermal expansion so that the gauge size does not change much due to climatic temperature variations. Many types of commercial gauge steel are readily available in the market. Most of them contain about 1% carbon.

For economy in material as well as hardening costs, gauges are designed such that only the parts subjected to wear are made of hardened steel. Handles and unimportant constituents are made of cheaper mild steel. In bigger gauges, the entire body is made of mild steel and only the surfaces subjected to wear are deposited with a welded layer of hard material such as stellite or weartrode (Fig. 12.3).

Gauges are often handled a large number times in every shift. Consequently, they should be made as light in weight as possible to reduce handling fatigue.

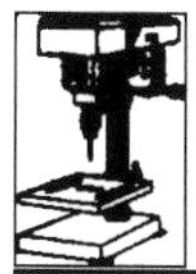

CHAPTER 13

Shop Setups

The manufacture of sophisticated fixtures entails considerable machining, heat treatment, precision finishing and skillful assembly. The more sophisticated the fixture, the higher its manufacturing cost and longer its manufacturing time. On the other hand, prototype samples must be produced as fast as possible to procure orders for jobbing work. Small enterprises engaged mainly in jobbing work, use ingenious methods to manufacture samples without manufacturing a costly sophisticated fixture. These temporary low cost arrangements are called shop setups. Even big organizations with ample resources, use shop setups, to produce a small number of sample pieces for checking their suitablity in assembly.

A wide variety of standard setup elements have been developed for repeated usage in different shop setups. One of the principles of a good shop setup is to use a machine table as a base for resting a workpiece and avail the machine *T* slots for clamping.

The *T* bolt or the combination of a *T* nut and a stud (Fig. 13.1) is used widely. The combination of *T* nut, a heel pin and a lock nut can be used conveniently for heel support. Figure 13.2 shows a swinging hook clamp with a special sleeve for mounting onto a *T* slot. Figure 13.3a shows a

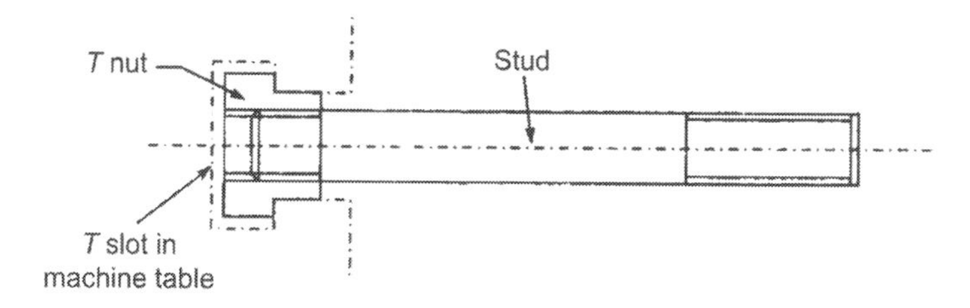

Fig. 13.1 *Combination of T nut and stud as T bolt*

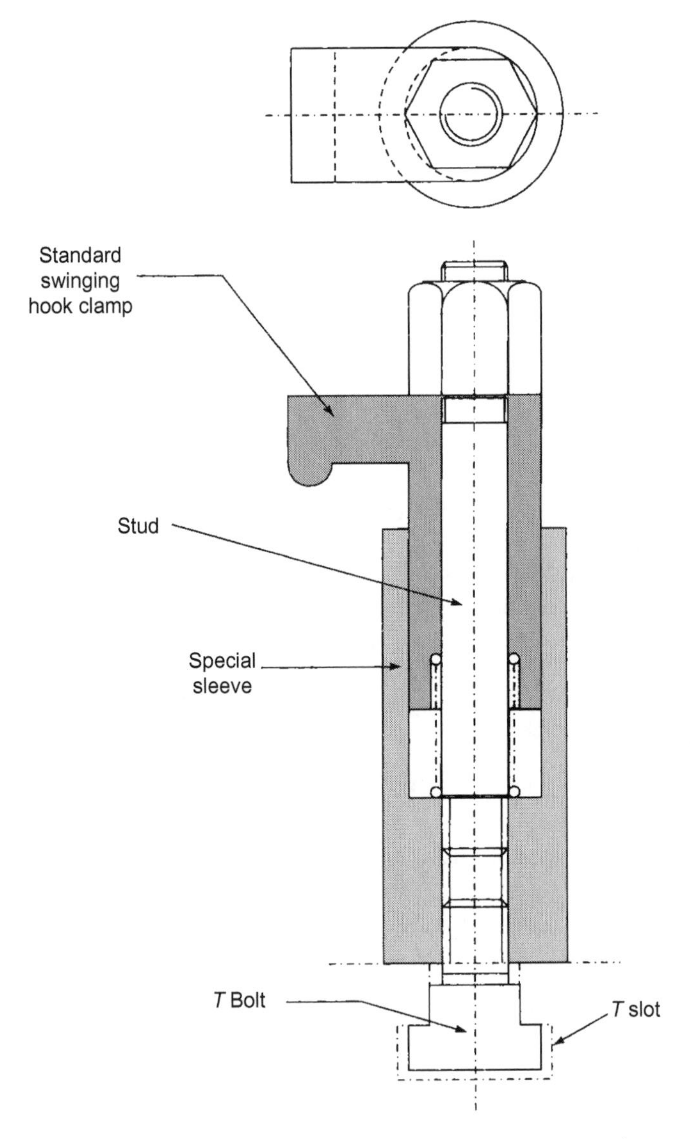

Fig. 13.2 *Mounting of swinging hook clamp on a T slot*

cam-operated edge clamp suitable for a *T* slot. Most of the screws actuated clamps can be fixed onto the *T* slots.

Figures 13.3b–d show some other standard clamps found convenient in shop set-ups. The curved universal clamp in Fig. 13.3b does not require any heel packing. The curved shape facilitates positioning in such away that one end of the clamp serves as a heel. The screw actuated wedge clamp in

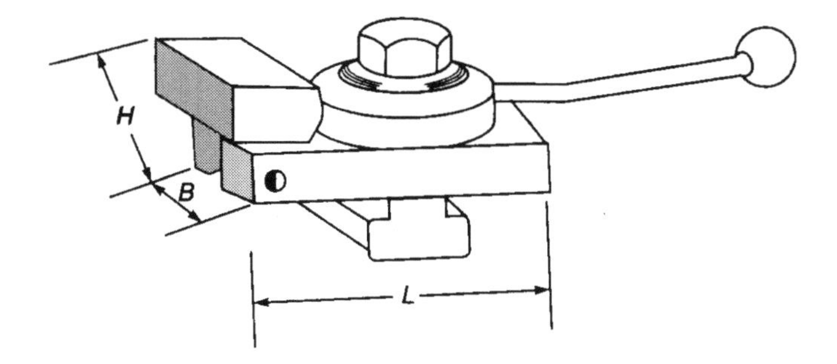

Fig. 13.3a *Cam operated edge clamp*

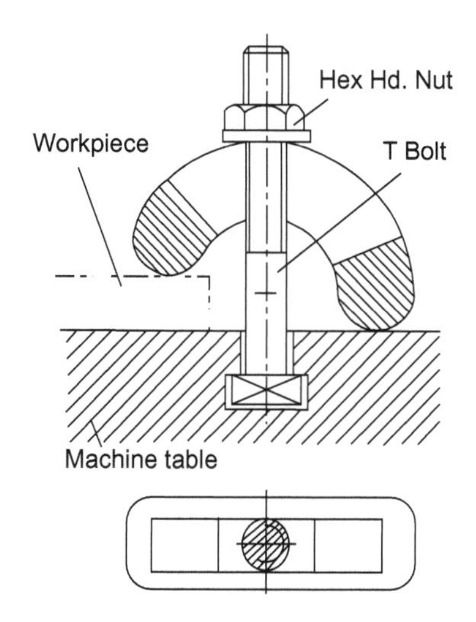

Fig. 13.3b *Universal clamp*

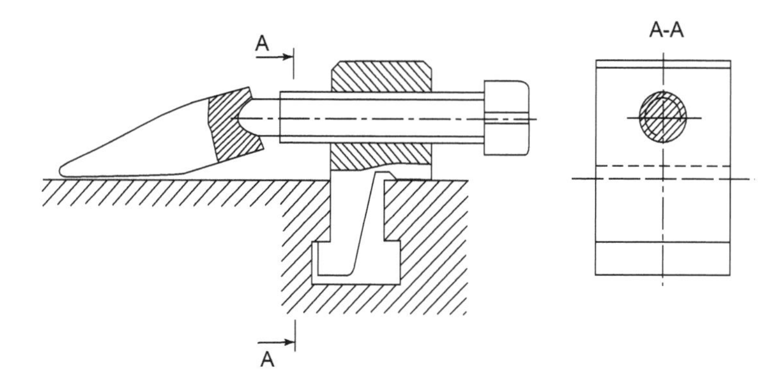

Fig. 13.3c *Edge clamp*

Fig. 13.3c is very convenient in clamping workpiece edges in face milling setups. The clamp shown in Fig. 13.3d is supplied as an accessory with many jig boring machines. The curved stepped serrated heel facilitates the heel height adjustment; although the height can be adjusted only in steps.

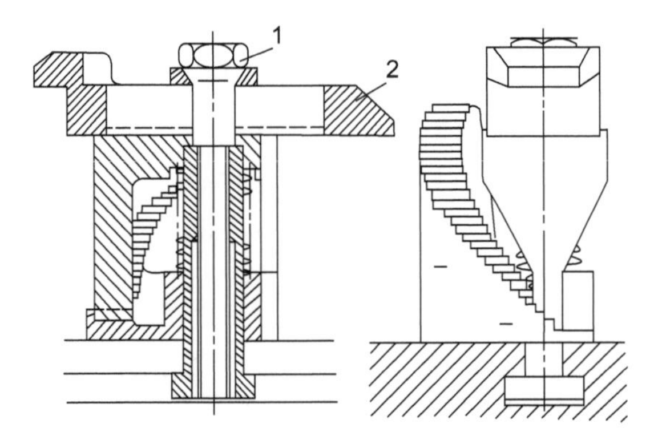

Fig. 13.3d *Stepped spiral heel*

In turning machines, such as lathes, the standard face plate (Fig. 13.4) can be used as a fixture base. The slots in the plate serve as an anchorage for the clamping elements.

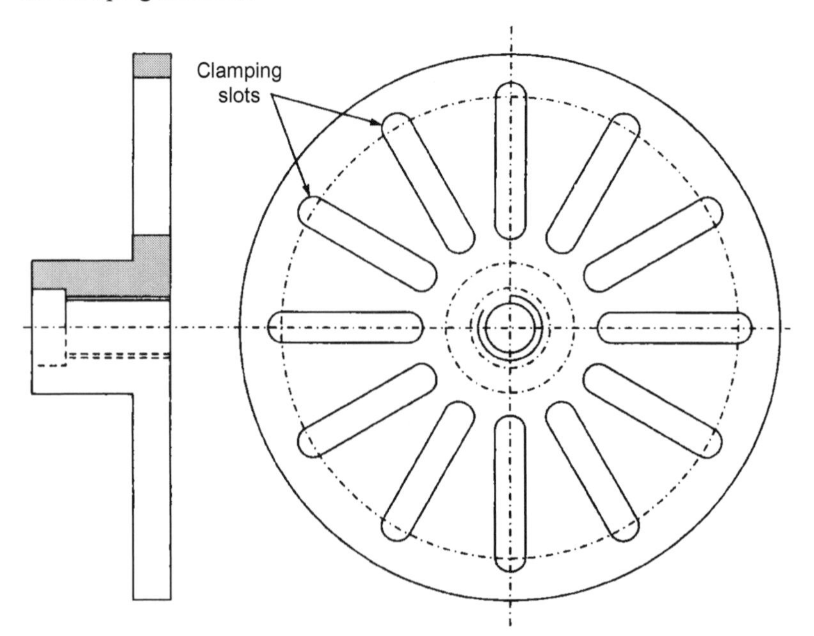

Fig. 13.4 *Face plate of a turning machine*

The slots are also used for securing location elements. Figure 13.5a shows a shop setup for boring a pedestal on a lathe. A slotted plate is used to locate the base of the pedestal. A special nut anchorable in the *T* slot is used to house the clamping screw. The nut itself is clamped on the face plate by two standard slotted clamps and hexagonal bolts, nuts, and washers. A tenoned *V* block transmits the clamping force to the pedestal.

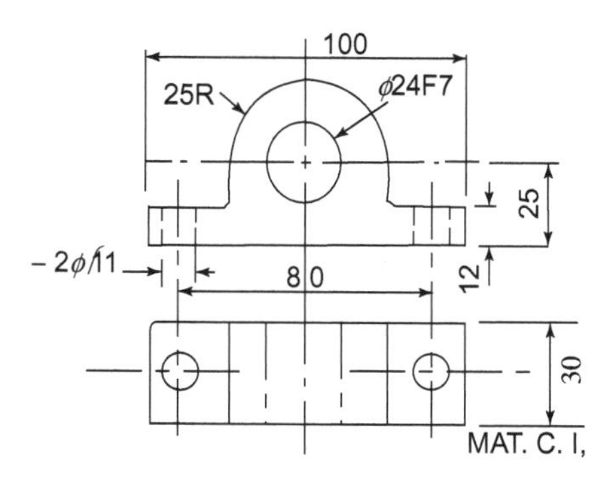

Fig. 13.5a *Workpiece for boring and facing set-up in Fig. 13.5b*

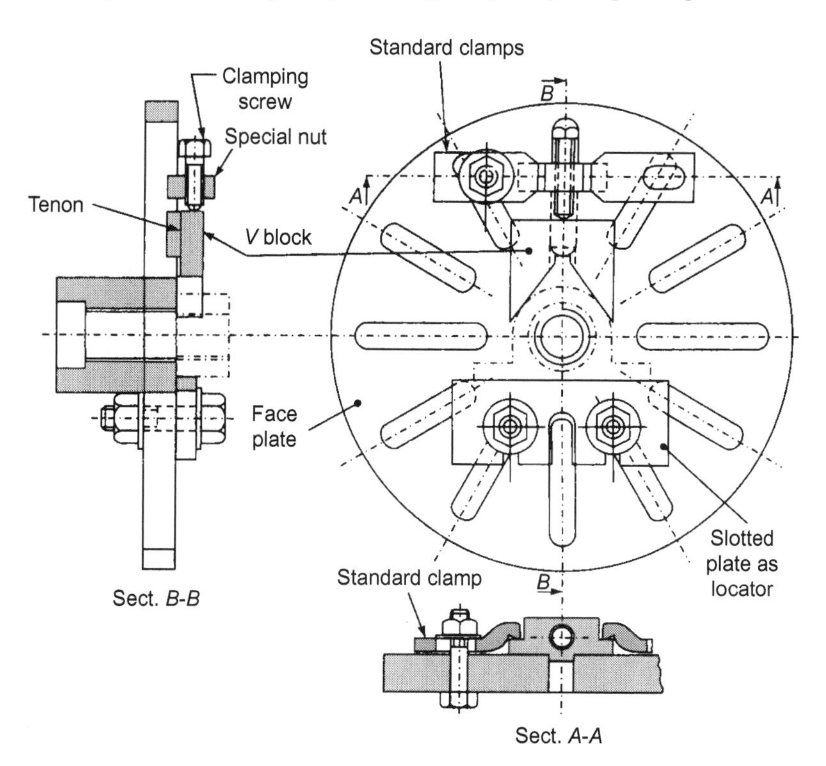

Fig. 13.5b *Shop setup for boring a pedestal on lathe*

Figure 13.6 shows various elements used in shop setups. The V blocks are provided with slots at the bottom to enable fitting of a suitable tenon. Figure 13.7 shows another type of special nut used for housing adjustable location screws. The integral tee simplifies clamping onto the *T* slot. The tee also prevents rotation.

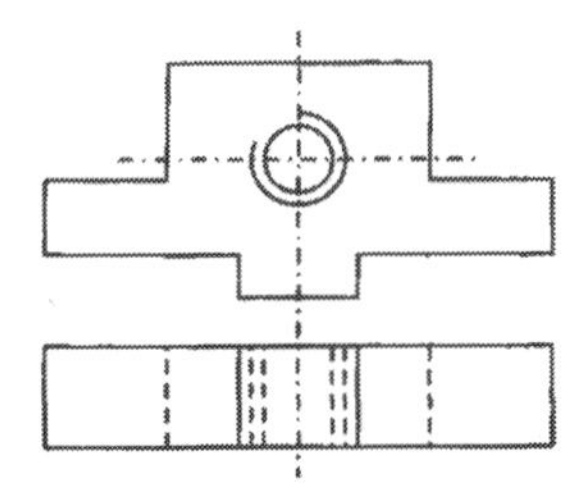

Fig. 13.6a *Special nut for setup in Fig. 13.5*

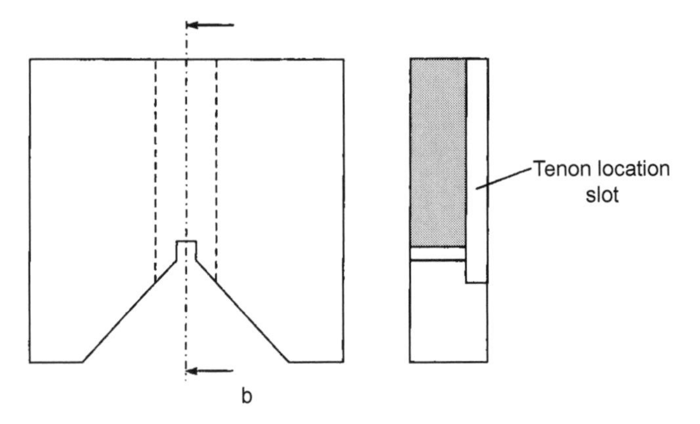

Fig. 13.6b *V block for setup in Fig. 13.5*

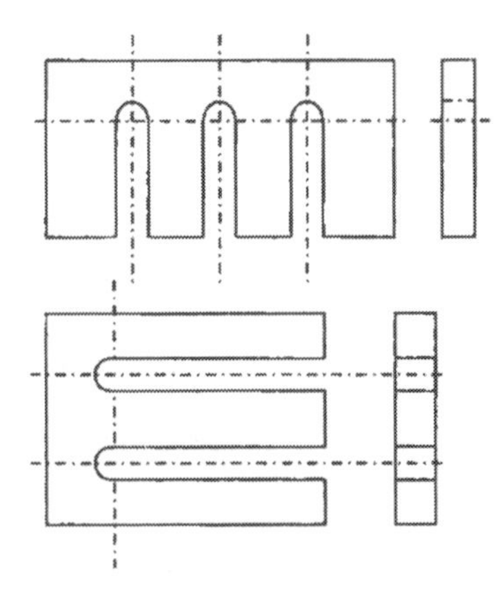

Fig. 13.6c *Slotted plates for shop setups*

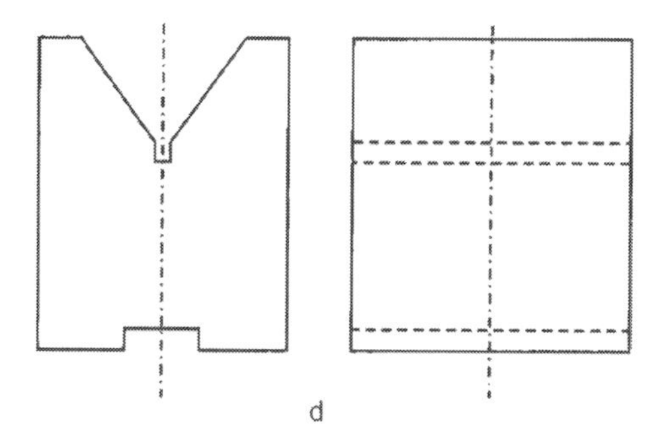

Fig. 13.6d *Tenoned V block for shop setups*

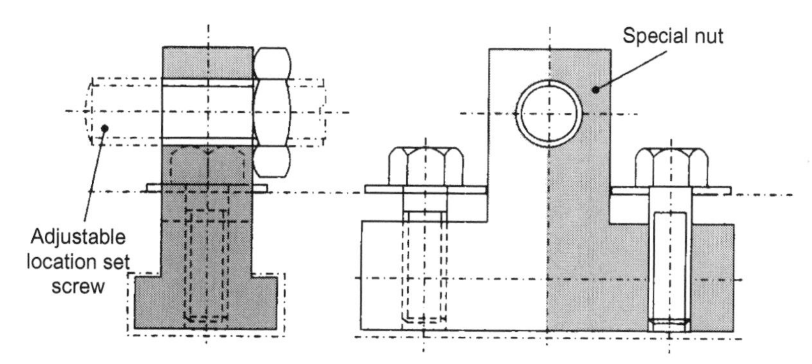

Fig. 13.7 *Special nut for adjustable location screws in shop setups*

Figure 13.8b shows a shop setup for straddle milling of a workpiece shown in Fig. 13.8a. The setup also requires a locator for the bore in the

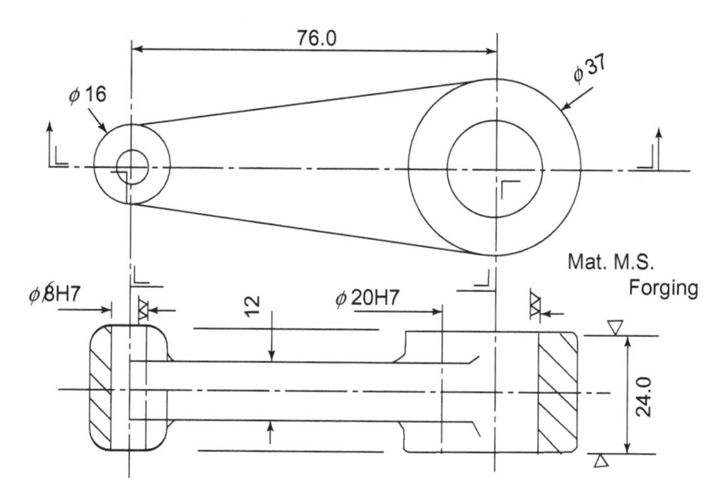

Fig. 13.8a *Workpiece for straddle milling shop setup in Fig. 13.8b*

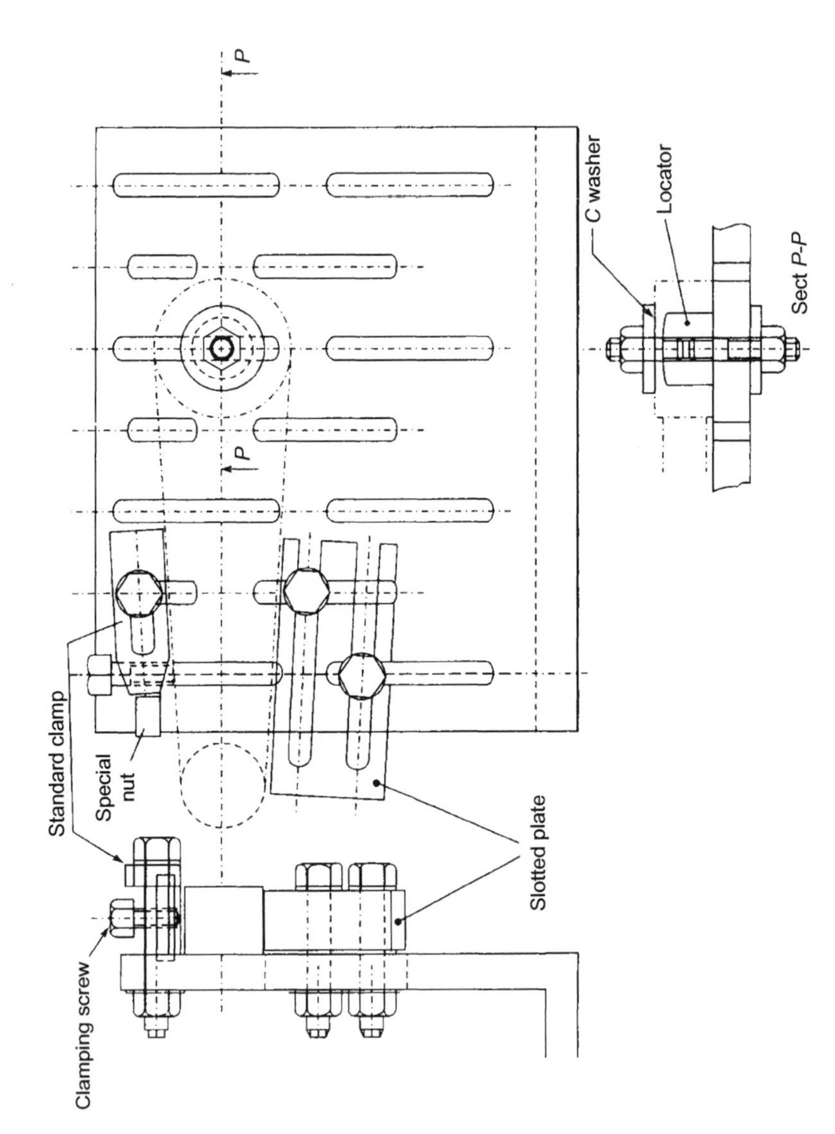

Fig. 13.8b *Shop setup for straddle milling*

bigger boss of the workpiece. The internal threads in the locator are used for anchoring and fixing workpiece clamping studs. All other elements in the setup, such as slotted plate, special nut, standard clamp and C washer, can be used for other shop setups too.

A pair of *V* blocks shown in Fig. 13.6d can be used in setups for milling keyways on cylindrical shafts. The *V* blocks are used for location only. Clamping is affected by *T* nuts, studs and standard slotted clamps.

Compound tables, easily available as an accessory, facilitate jig drilling (within 0.05 mm), milling and many other operations on a drilling machine. The table has two mutually perpendicular guide-ways with lead screws and hand-wheels with vernier scales. These help precision motion within 0.05. The precision can be enhanced further by using slip gauges and dial gauges. The table top is provided with '*T*' slots for clamping the workpiece directly on the table. There is a precise central location hole too.

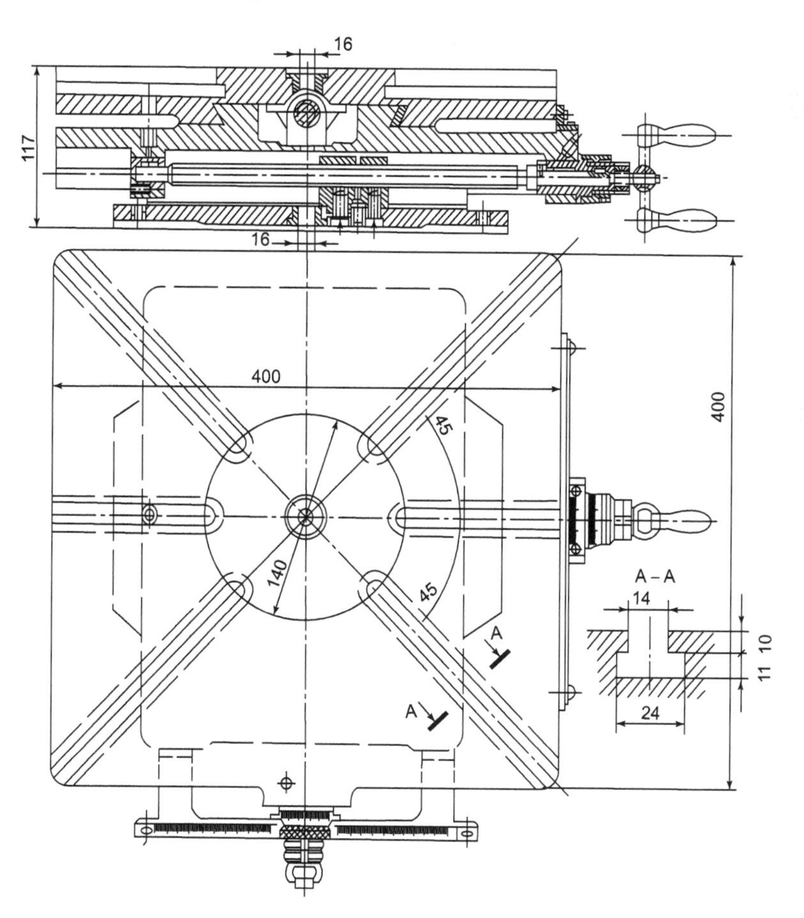

Fig. 13.9 *Compound table*

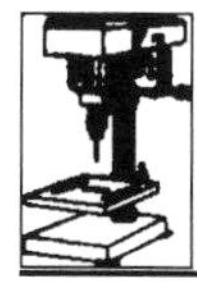

CHAPTER 14

Estimation

In small enterprises, draughtsmen are, sometimes, told to estimate the cost of the designed jig/fixture. The cost comprises the following constituents:

1. Material costs
2. Machining cost
3. Heat treatment expenses
4. Assembling and try-out cost.

Material Costs

Material costs are estimated by finding out the volume of the raw material required. By multiplying the volume with the specifc gravity, the weight of the raw material is obtained. Tables giving weight/metre length of cylindrical, hexagonal/square bars and flats are readily available. Similarly, tables stating weight/sq. metre of the various plate thicknesses can be used for finding out the weight of the raw material. Table 14.1 gives weight/metre of the standard sizes of rolled steel—round, square, hexagonal bars and plates. The weight of cast iron is nearly the same as that of steel. Brass weighs about 10% more, while aluminium weighs only one third (33%) of the weight of steel.

The costs of raw materials also differ a lot. medium-carbon steel (RC 45–55) costs 1.5–2 times more than mild steel while high-carbon steel may cost four times the cost of mild steel.

Non-shrinking tool steel can be 5–6 times costlier than mild steel. Furthermore, casting also involves pattern costs.

Inflation increases the costs as time passes. The cost of steel might be 10% higher after an year. So, it is advisable to find out the latest prices of the materials at the time of estimation.

Table 14.1 *Weights of rolled steel (7.843 gm/cc)*

Size S	*Round S ϕ (kg/metre length)*	*Square (S Sq.)*	*Hexagonal SA/F*	*Sheet S Thick (kg/sq. metre)*
5	0.154	0.20	0.170	39.2
5.5	0.19	0.24	0.206	
6	0.222	0.28	0.245	
7	0.302	0.38	0.333	55
8	0.395	0.502	0.435	
9	0.50	0.64	0.551	
10	0.62	0.785	0.68	78.5
11	0.75	0.95	0.823	
12	0.89	1.13		94.2
14	1.21	1.54	1.33	109.9
16	1.58	2.01		125.6
17			1.96	
18	2.00	2.54		141.3
19		2.83	2.45	
20	2.47	3.14		
22	2.98	3.80	3.29	172.7
25	3.85	4.91		196.2
27		5.72	4.96	
28	4.83	6.15		219.74
32	6.31	8.04	6.96	251.14
35				274.67
36	7.99	10.17	8.81	
38				298.22
40	9.86	12.56		
41			11.4	
45	12.49	15.90		313.92
50	15.41	19.62	17.0	331.36
55	18.7	23.7	20.6	364.46
56	19.34	24.62		
60	22.2	28.3	24.5	397.63
63	24.47	31.16		
65	26.0	33.2	28.7	430.77
70	30.2	38.5	33.3	463.9
71	31.08	39.57		
75	34.7	44.2	38.2	497.04
80	39.46	50.24	43.5	530.18

Machining Costs

Machining costs depend upon the type and size of the machine required. The hourly rates of bigger machines can be 2–3 times the rate of a smaller machine. The hourly rate for milling would be higher than that for turning. The rates for precision grinding machines are even more.

Furthermore, harder materials can be machined only with smaller cuts and require much more machining time than mild steel or aluminium. The range of cuts possible with the grinding machine are very small fraction of the cuts possible with lathes or milling machines. The cuts made with grinders usually range from 0.005 to 0.025, while the cuts of the range of three is common with a lathe, shaping or milling machine.

Computing precise machining time itself can be a costly affair. It is a must in mass production when a large number or similar pieces are produced. However, a jig/fixture is usually manufactured only once. So, accurate computation of the machining costs is not warranted. A rough estimate is enough.

Graphs and tables come handy in quick estimation of machining time.

Heat Treatment Expenses

Heat treatment cost depends upon the weight of the jig/fixture part at the time of heat treatment. It can cost as much as the cost of the material.

Assembling and Try-out Costs

Assembling and try-out costs comprise drilling and fitting costs. These are usually estimated on hours/shifts basis. As the required time depends upon the number of parts, precision and sophistication necessary in a jig/fixture, good judgement based on experience is necessary.

Small enterprises have small all round staff. So, the industry relies more on thumb rules than elaborate calculations for estimation.

Provided below are the thumb rules used by a small, competent, thriving tool room. The total cost of a part is taken as a multiple of the raw materials cost. The cost depends upon the operations involved. The following table encapsules the rules:

Table 14.2 *Thumb rules for estimation*

Group no.	*Operations involved*	*Total costs*
1.	Only shaping, turning drilling and fitting.	Three times the raw materials cost.
2.	Shaping/turning, drilling, fitting and milling.	Four times the raw materials costs.

(contd.)

Group no.	*Operations involved*	*Total costs*
3.	Above operations plus heat treatment.	Five times the raw materials costs.
4.	Above operations plus precision grinding or lapping.	Six times the raw materils costs.

Although, the above method gives a very subjective estimate, the organisation finds it satisfactory.

As manufacturing of the tools often entails rectification/adjustments after a try-out, the margin of profit in the manufacture of jig/fixture should be higher than mass production work.

The profit is rarely less than 30% of the manufacturing cost. It can be as high as 100% of the manufacturing cost.

Example 14.1: Find the manufacturing cost of 14ϕ bore collared bush shown in Fig. 15.11. The bush is to be manufactured from 28ϕ × 35 long alloy steel bar which costs Rs. 80/kg. After rough turning, the bush is to be hardened and finished by grinding.

Solution: Referring to Table 13.1, we note that 28 ϕ steel bar weights 4.83 kg/metre.

$$\therefore \text{ Wt. of a 35 long piece} = \frac{35}{100} \times 4.83$$

$$= 0.169 \text{ kg.}$$

$$\text{Cost of material at Rs. 80 per kg} = 0.169 \times 80$$

$$= \text{Rs. } 13.52$$

Machining involves turning, hardening and grinding.

Referring to Table 13.2, we notice that the bush falls in Group 4, for which the total cost is approximately six times the raw material cost.

$$\therefore \quad \text{Total cost} = 13.52 \times 6$$

$$= \text{Rs. } 81.12$$

If the bush is to be sold, profit should be added.

$$\text{Selling cost at 30\% profit} = 81.12 \times 1.3$$

$$= \text{Rs. } 105.5 \text{ (min.)}$$

$$\text{Selling cost at 100\% profit} = 81.12 \times 2$$

$$= \text{Rs. } 162.24 \text{ (max.)}$$

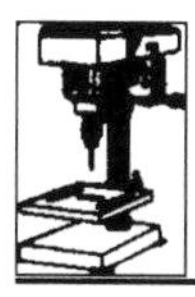

CHAPTER 15

Reference Tables

Tolerance limits for selected holes (hole basis)

Nominal sizes		*H*7		*H*8		*H*9		*H*11	
Over (mm)	up to and incl. (mm)	ul +	ll	ul +	ll	ul +	ll	ul +	ll
6	10	15	0	22	0	36	0	90	0
10	18	18	0	27	0	43	0	110	0
18	30	21	0	33	0	52	0	130	0
30	50	25	0	39	0	62	0	160	0
50	80	30	0	46	0	74	0	190	0
80	120	35	0	54	0	87	0	220	0
120	180	40	0	63	0	100	0	250	0
180	250	46	0	72	0	115	0	290	0

ul = Upper limit; II = Lower limit; Unit = 0.001 mm.

Fig. 15.1 *Hole tolerance for common fits*

Tolerance limits for selected shafts

Nominal sizes		*c*11		*d*10		*e*9		*f*7		*g*6		*h*6		*k*6		*n*6		*p*6		*s*6	
Over (mm)	to (mm)	ul −	II −	ul −	II −	ul −	II −	ul −	II −	ul −	II −	ul −	II −	ul +	II +	ul +	II +	ul +	II +	ul +	II +
6	10	80	170	40	98	25	61	13	28	5	14	0	9	10	1	19	10	24	15	32	23
10	18	95	205	50	120	32	75	16	34	6	17	0	11	12	1	23	12	29	18	39	28
18	30	110	240	65	149	40	92	20	41	7	20	0	13	15	2	28	15	35	22	48	35
30	40	120	280	80	180	50	112	25	50	9	25	0	16	18	2	33	17	42	26	59	43
40	50	130	290																		
50	65	140	330	100	220	60	134	30	60	10	29	0	19	21	2	39	20	51	32	72	53
65	80	150	340																	78	59
80	100	170	390	120	260	72	159	36	71	12	34	0	22	25	3	45	23	59	37	93	71
100	120	180	400																	101	79
120	140	200	450																	117	92
140	160	210	460	145	305	85	185	43	83	14	39	0	25	28	3	52	27	68	43	125	100
160	180	230	480																	133	108
130	200	240	530																	151	122
200	225	260	550	170	355	100	215	50	96	15	44	0	29	33	4	60	31	79	50	159	130
225	250	280	570																	169	140

ul = Upper limit; II = Lower limit; Unit = 0.001 mm

Fig. 15.1(contd.) *Shaft tolerance for common fits*

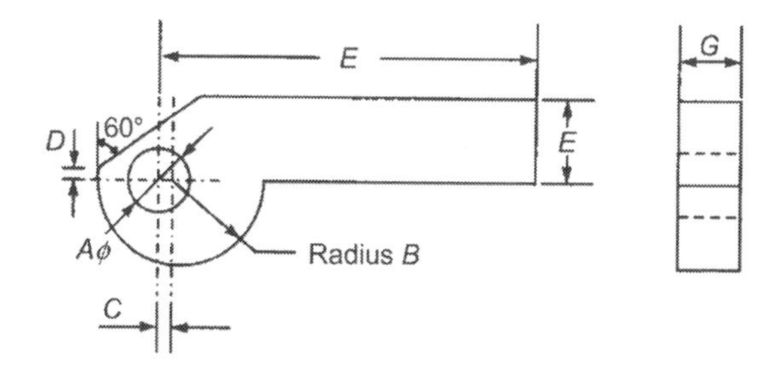

Material: mild steel

A	B	C	D	E	F	G
10	13	1.5	3	12	60	10
12	16	2	4	15	70	12
16	20	2.5	5	18	90	16
20	25	3	6	24	110	20

Fig. 15.2 *Cam clamps*

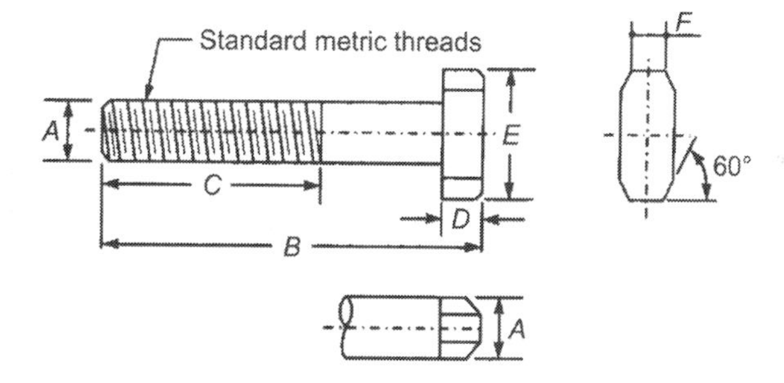

A	B	C	D	E	F
M 10	50	35	12	28	5
M 12	62	38	15	32	6
M 16	82	47	20	35	6
M 20	100	60	22	40	10

Fig. 15.3 *Quarter-turn screw*

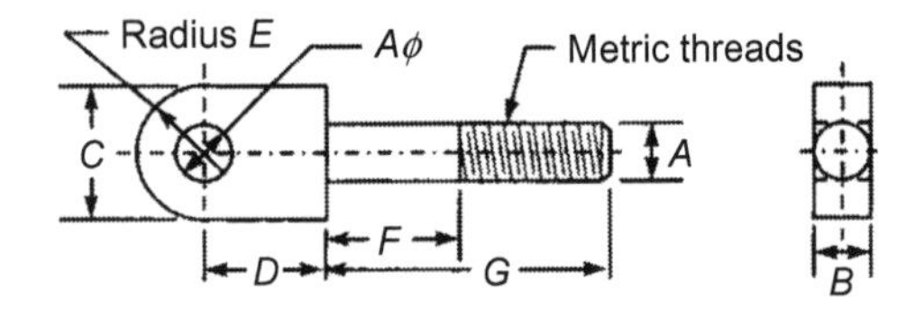

A	B	C	D	E	F	G
10	13	20	13	10	12	32
10	13	20	13	10	25	62
12	16	25	16	12	16	50
12	16	25	16	12	25	75
16	20	32	20	16	20	90
20	22	38	22	20	22	75

Fig. 15.4 *Eye bolts*

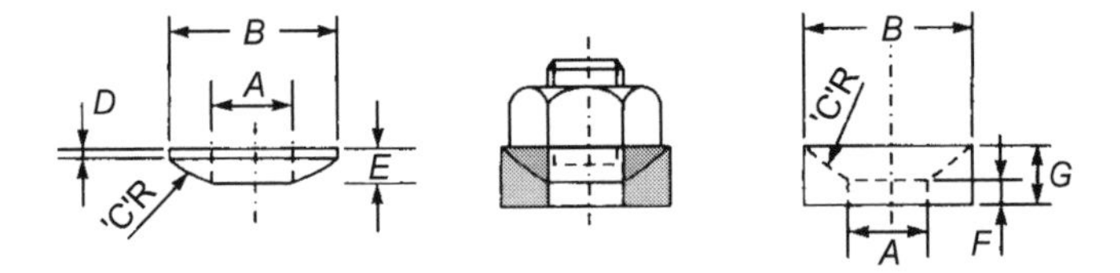

Material: mild steel

A	B	C	D	E	F	G
9	20	20	2.5	4.5	2.5	5
11	22	22	2.5	6	2.5	6
14	28	28	2.5	6.5	2.5	6.5
18	40	40	3	7	3	7

Fig. 15.5 *Spherical washers*

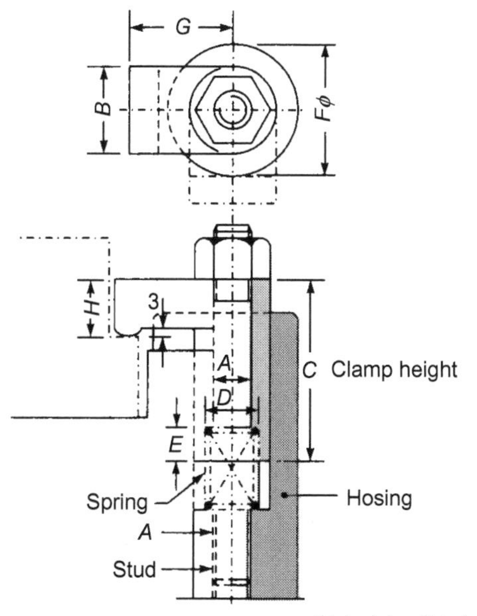

A	*B*	*C*	*D*	*E*	*F*	*G*	*H*
M8	14	44	11	6	26	24	11
M12	21	66	16	9	40	34	16
M16	28	88	22	12	52	44	22
M20	35	96	26	15	65	55	28
M24	42	106	32	18	80	68	32

'C' R = Radius *C*

Fig. 15.6a *Swinging hook clamps*

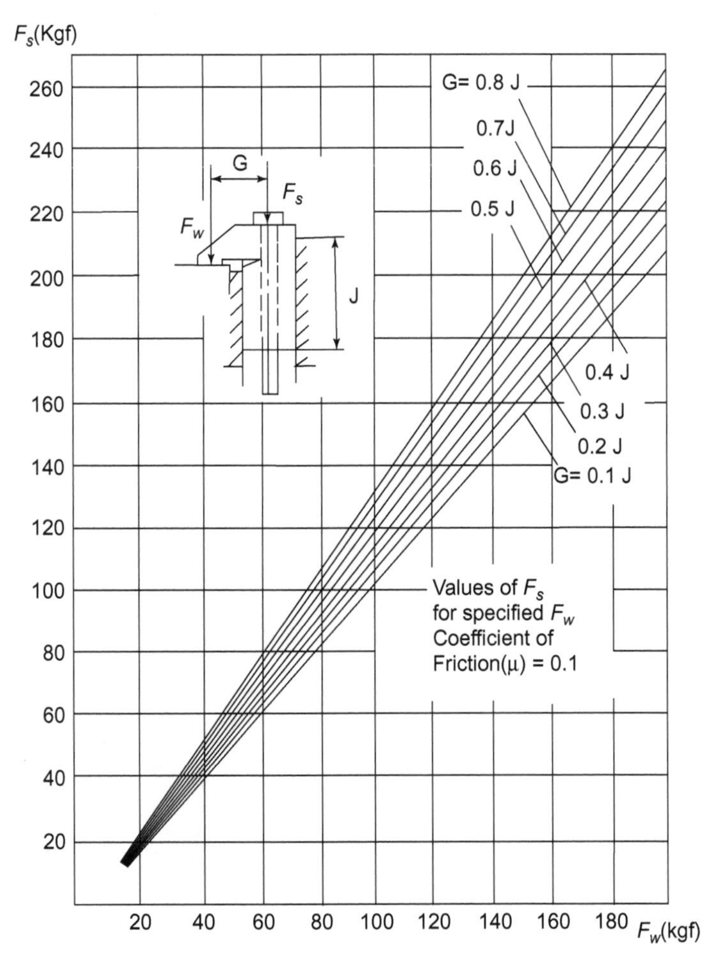

Fig. 15.6b *Clamping force for hook clamps*

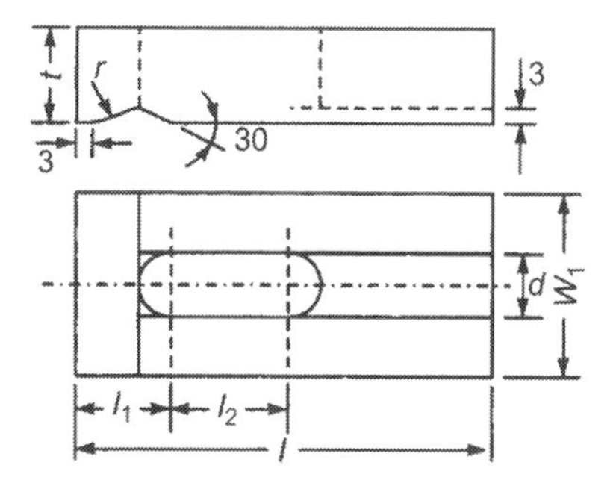

Material: mild steel

dH 13	*l*	l_1	l_2	*r*	W_1	*t*	Screw size
6.6	60	13	13	12	20	12	*M* 6
9	68	15	15	14	25	14	*M* 8
11	75	18	20	16	30	16	*M*10
14	90	20	25	20	40	20	*M*12
18	110	23	30	25	50	25	*M* 16
22	125	25	35	30	60	30	*M* 20
26	150	30	40	30	70	35	*M* 24
33	200	35	50	35	80	40	*M* 30

Fig. 15.7 *Slotted strap clamps*

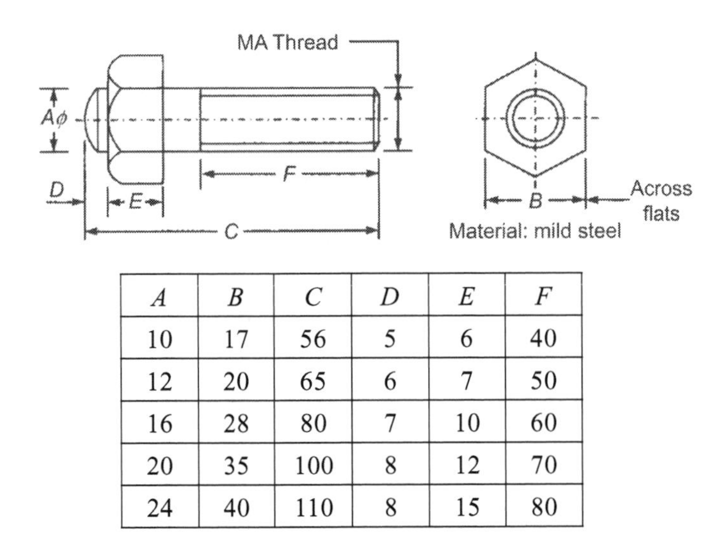

A	B	C	D	E	F
10	17	56	5	6	40
12	20	65	6	7	50
16	28	80	7	10	60
20	35	100	8	12	70
24	40	110	8	15	80

Fig. 15.8 *Adjustable heel pins*

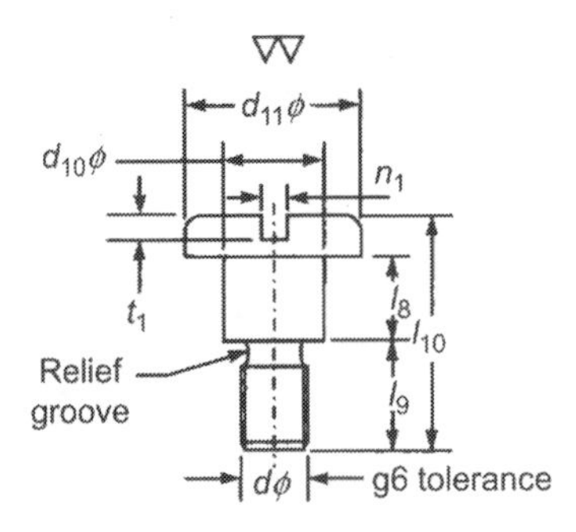

d g_6	l_8	d_{10}	d_{11}	l_9	l_{10}	n_1	t_1
M5	5	7.5	12	8	15.5	1.6	2
M6	6 / 7.5	10	16	10	19.5 / 21	2	2.5
M8	10	13	20	12	27	2.5	3

Fig. 15.9 *Shoulder screws*

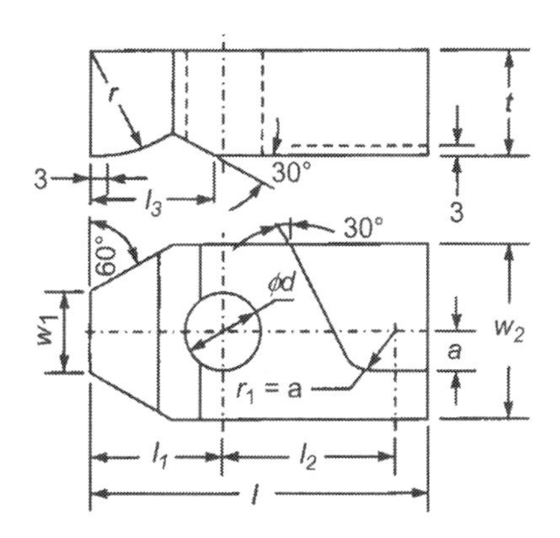

Material: mild steel

d H_{13}	w_2	w_1	t	l	l_1	l_2	l_3	a	r	Size of screw
6.6	20	7	12	52	20	25	14	4	12	M_6
9	25	9	14	60	22	30	18	5	14	M_8
11	30	11	16	70	24	35	20	6	16	M_{10}
14	40	15	20	80	26	40	22	7	20	M_{12}
18	45	18	25	90	32	45	28	9	25	M_{16}
22	60	23	30	100	38	50	32	11	30	M_{20}
26	60	26	30	125	50	60	32	13	30	M_{24}
33	70	34	35	150	60	70	40	17	35	M_{30}

Fig. 15.10 *Swinging strap clamps*

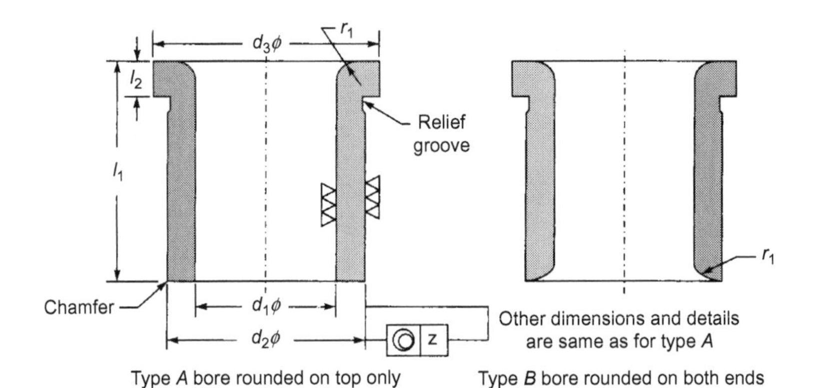

Material: steel hardened to 62-65 HRC

<table>
<tr><th colspan="2">$F_7 d_1$</th><th colspan="2">l_1</th><th rowspan="2">l_2</th><th>d_2</th><th rowspan="2">d_3</th><th rowspan="2">r_1</th><th rowspan="2">z</th></tr>
<tr><th>Over</th><th>Up to</th><th>Short</th><th>Long</th><th>n_6</th></tr>
<tr><td>–</td><td>1</td><td rowspan="3">6</td><td rowspan="3">9</td><td rowspan="3">2</td><td>3</td><td>6</td><td rowspan="3">1.2</td><td rowspan="6">0.005</td></tr>
<tr><td>1</td><td>1.8</td><td>4</td><td>7</td></tr>
<tr><td>1.8</td><td>26</td><td>5</td><td>8</td></tr>
<tr><td>2.6</td><td>3.3</td><td rowspan="3">8</td><td rowspan="3">12</td><td rowspan="3">2.5</td><td>6</td><td>10</td><td rowspan="2">1.6</td></tr>
<tr><td>3.3</td><td>4</td><td>7</td><td>11</td></tr>
<tr><td>4</td><td>5</td><td>8</td><td>12</td><td rowspan="3">2</td></tr>
<tr><td>5</td><td>6</td><td rowspan="2">10</td><td rowspan="2">16</td><td rowspan="2">3</td><td>10</td><td>14</td><td rowspan="7">0.01</td></tr>
<tr><td>6</td><td>8</td><td>12</td><td>16</td></tr>
<tr><td>8</td><td>10</td><td rowspan="2">12</td><td rowspan="2">20</td><td rowspan="2">4</td><td>15</td><td>19</td><td rowspan="2">2.5</td></tr>
<tr><td>10</td><td>12</td><td>18</td><td>22</td></tr>
<tr><td>12</td><td>15</td><td rowspan="2">16</td><td rowspan="2">28</td><td rowspan="2">4</td><td>22</td><td>26</td><td rowspan="2">4</td></tr>
<tr><td>15</td><td>18</td><td>26</td><td>30</td></tr>
<tr><td>18</td><td>22</td><td rowspan="3">20</td><td rowspan="3">36</td><td rowspan="3">5</td><td>30</td><td>35</td><td rowspan="3">6</td></tr>
<tr><td>22</td><td>26</td><td>35</td><td>40</td><td rowspan="7">0.02</td></tr>
<tr><td>26</td><td>30</td><td>42</td><td>47</td></tr>
<tr><td>30</td><td>35</td><td rowspan="2">25</td><td rowspan="2">45</td><td rowspan="2">5</td><td>48</td><td>55</td><td rowspan="5">8</td></tr>
<tr><td>35</td><td>42</td><td>55</td><td>62</td></tr>
<tr><td>42</td><td>48</td><td rowspan="2">30</td><td rowspan="2">56</td><td rowspan="2">6</td><td>62</td><td>69</td></tr>
<tr><td>48</td><td>55</td><td>70</td><td>77</td></tr>
<tr><td>55</td><td>63</td><td>35</td><td>72</td><td>6</td><td>78</td><td>85</td></tr>
</table>

Fig. 15.11 *Collared bushes*

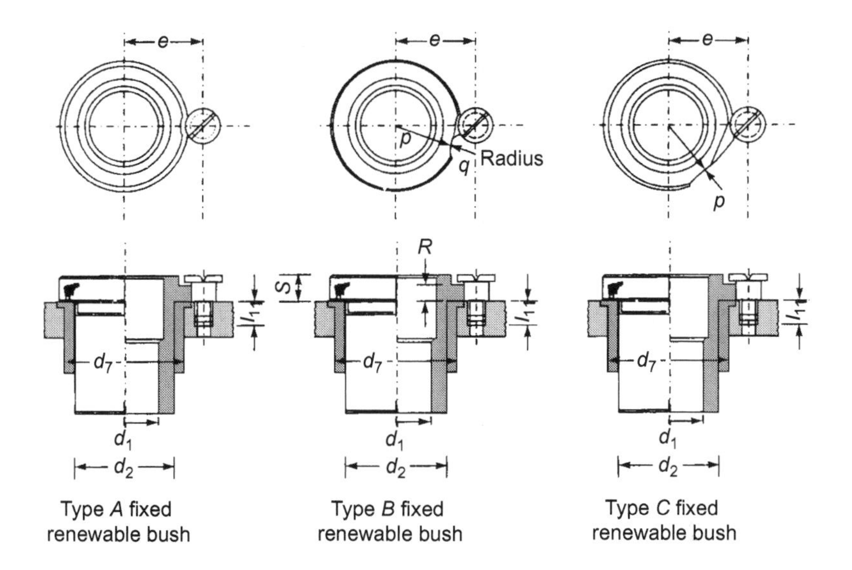

Type *A* fixed renewable bush

Type *B* fixed renewable bush

Type *C* fixed renewable bush

Material: steel hardended to 62–65 HRC

Renewable drill bush			Liner bush		e	l_{11}	Locking screw	P	q	R	S
d_1 G_7		d_2	d_2	d_7		Min.					
Over	Up to	h_6	H_7	m_6							
—	2.65	8	8	12	11.5	10	M5 × 5	5	7	4	7
2.65	4.75	10	10	15	13			6.5	7	4	7
4.75	8.5	15	15	20	17.5	12	M6 × 6	9	9	5	9
8.5	14	22	22	28	21.5			13	9	5	9
14	19	28	28	36	25.5		M6 × 7.5	17	9	7	11
19	25	35	35	46	31			22.5	9	7	11
25	33.5	46	46	56	37	15	M8 × 10	26	11	9	14
33.5	45	58	58	70	44			33	11	9	14

Fig. 15.12 *Renewable and slip bushes*

Material	Ref. No.		Important constituents (%)						Max. hardness (RC)	Applications
	Indian	British	C	Mn	Cr	Ni	W	V		
High speed steel 18%	T75W18 Co6Cr4V1	—	0.75	0.35	4.3	—	18	1.6	65	Metal cutting tools: drills
High speed steel 22%	—		0.8	0.35	4.3		22	1.6	66	High stress cutting tools: milling cutters
Cold working die steel (high carbon, high chromium; HCHC)	T160Cr12	—	1.6	0.35	12			0.8	62	Cold working high impact press tools, threading rolls
Die steel (hot working)	T35Cr5 Mo100	—	0.32	0.35	5.0		1.4	0.3	48	Forging, extrusion and hot working dies
Carbon steel			0.85	0.87					61	Standard cutting tools
Spring steel	50Cr1V23	En44	1.0	0.5	1.2				47	Collets, springs
Medium carbon steel	C45	En8	0.45	0.75					45	Bolts, shafts, bigger gears
High tensile steel	40Ni2Cr1	En24 Mo28	0.4	0.55	1.1	1.5			50	Highly stressed parts: piston rods, gears, shafts
Oil hardening non-shrinking tool steel [OHNS]	T110W2 Cr1	—	1.1	1.1	1.1		1.5			Fine engraving tool, taps, reamers, cutters, knives, gauges
Nickel chrome steel	13Ni3Cr80	En36	0.14	0.5	0.9	3.3			62	Gears, case hardened parts

Fig. 15.13a *Ferrous materials for jigs, fixtures and tools*

(Contd.)

Carbon chromium bearing steel	103Cr1	En31	1.05	0.35	1.15				62	Cold forming tools, knurling tools, ball bearings
Carburising steel	17MniCr95	—	0.17	1.15	0.95				59 [case]	Shafts, gears, spindles
Carburising steel	15Ni2Cr1 M015	En354	0.15	0.8	1.00	1.75			59 [case]	Heavy duty components: gears
Nitriding steel	40Cr2AI1	En41b	0.4	0.55	1.65	0.3			66 [case]	High abrasion, high fatigue, low distortion, low stress parts: boring bars
Free cutting	14Mn1	En202	0.14	1.4					can not be hardened	Parts needing good machinability and finish: threaded fasteners
Mild steel	S14									

Fig. 15.13a (contd.) *Ferrous materials for jigs, fixtures and tools*

Castings

Class	General	Malleable		Nodular	Grey	Mechanite										
Grade	GCI	MCI		SG		Heat resistant				Wear resistant				Corrosion resistant		
	15-25	A	B	370-800	30-40	HR	HS	HSV	HE	W1	–	4	VSH	CC	CR	CRS
Tensile strength (kg/mm^2)	15–25	36	28	37–80	30–40	28	42	70	17	35	–	42	70	28	17	38

Mechanite General

Grade/	GM	GA	GC	GE	GF	AQ	SF	SP	SH	AQS
Class	60	50	40	30	20		60	80	100	
Tensile strength (kg/mm^2)	38	35	28	21	14	35	42	56	63	56

Fig. 15.13a (contd.) *Ferrous materials for jigs, fixtures and tools*

1. Aluminium	Tensile strength 6.5–43 kg/mm^2. It is used for low stress parts needing light weight, corrosion resistance and good thermal and electrical conductivity.
2. Brass	Alloy of copper (54–73%) and zinc (remaining), tensile strength 28–68 kg/mm^2. It is used for parts needing corrosion resistance, fine surface finish and bearing properties: bushes for low speed shafts.
3. Bronze	Tensile strength 20–55 kg/mm^2. It is used for low speed bearings and parts calling for corrosion resistance. Phospher bronze is used widely for replaceable nuts mating with lead screws in machine mechanisms.

Fig. 15.13b *Non-ferrous materials*

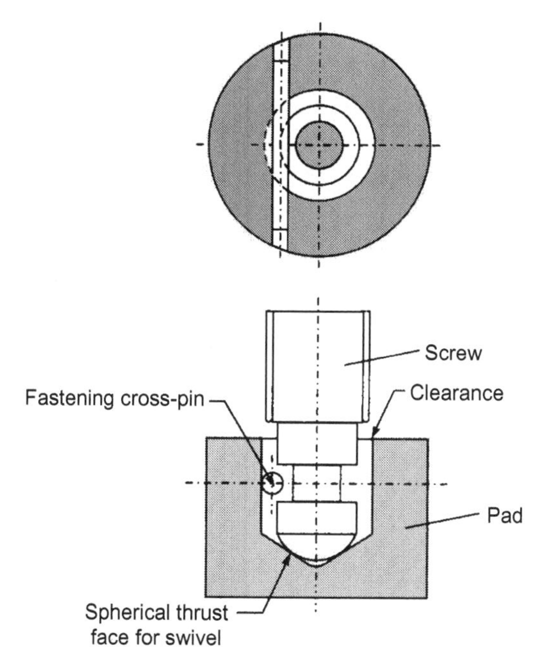

Fig. 15.14a *Floating pad assembly*

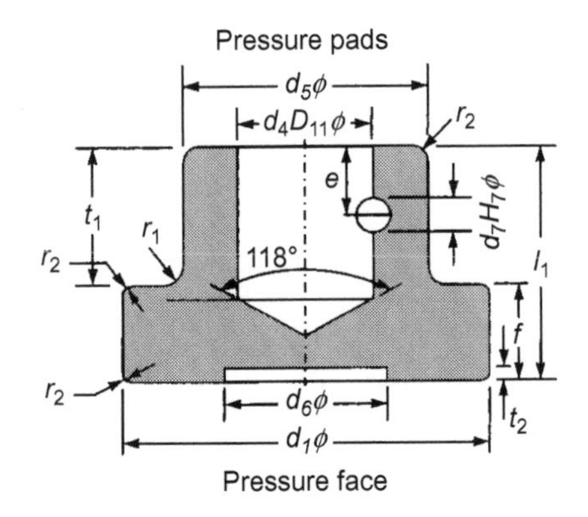

Dimensions												For screw with threads	Fastening pin
d_1	d_4	d_5	d_6	d_7	e	f	h	r_1	r_2	t_2	t_1		
10	3.8	8	4	1.5	2.5	2.5	7	1.2	0.3	0.5	4.5	M5	1.5m 6 × 6
12	4.8	10	5	1.5	2.5	2.5	8	1.5	0.3	0.5	5	M6	1.5m 6 × 8
16	6.4	12	7	2	3	3.5	9.5	2	0.4	0.5	6	M8	2m 6 × 8
20	7.4	15	8	2	3.5	5	12	2	0.4	1	7	M10	2m 6 × 14
25	9.5	18	10	3	4.5	6	15	3	0.6	1	9	M12	3m 6 × 14
32	12.5	22	14	3	6	7	19	3	0.6	1	12	M16	3m 6 × 16
40	15.5	28	18	4	7.5	9	24	4	0.8	1	15	M20	4m 6 × 20

Fig. 15.14b *Floating pressure pads*

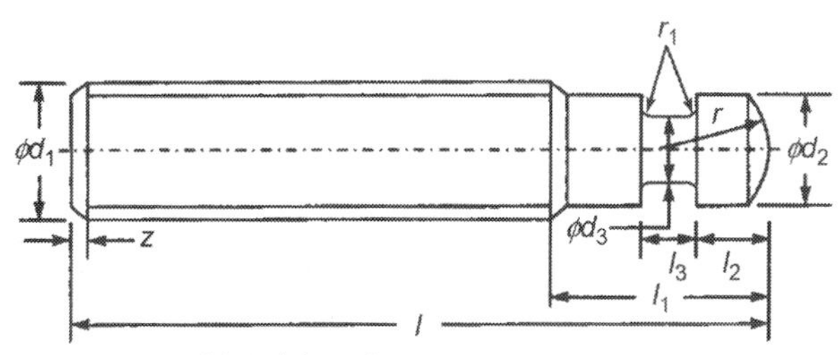

Material: surface hardening steel

d_1	d_2	d_3	r	r_1	l_1	l_2	l_3	l	Z
M6	4.5	3	3	0.6	6.5	2.2	2.2	30,50	1.0
M8	6	4	5	0.8	8.5	2.8	3	40,60	1.25
M10	7	5	6	0.8	10.0	3.2	3	60,80	1.50
M12	9	6	6	1.0	13.0	4.3	4.5	60,80,100	1.75
M16	12	9	9	1.0	17.0	6.3	4.5	80,100,125	2.0
M20	15	10	13	1.5	21	7.4	6	100,125,150	2.5

Fig. 15.14c *Screws for floating pressure pads*

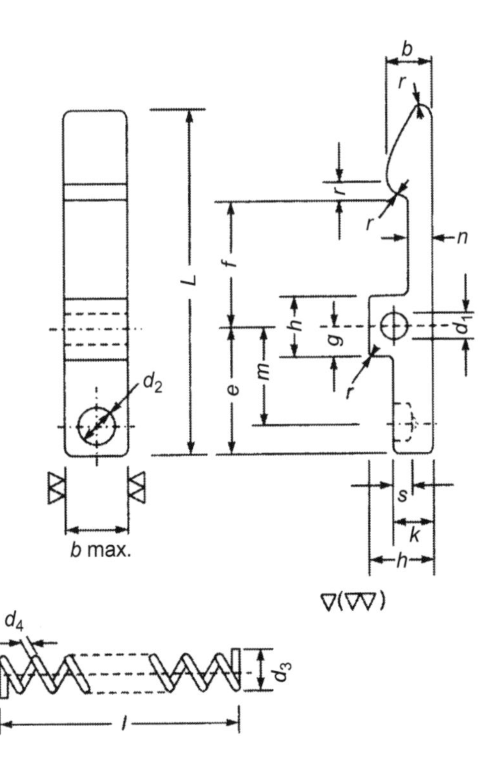

Springs Steel (IS: 727-1964) for Springs

Length					Locking dog									Spring effective coils
L	b	d_1 E_9	d_2	e	f -0.2	g	h	s	k	m	n	r	d_3	d_4	l (Free-length)
45	8	4	5.5	15	15	4	9.5	2	5.5	11	4	1.6	4.6	0.6	16
60	10	5	7.0	20	20	5	12.0	3	7.0	15	5	2.5	5.8	0.8	18
80	14	6	9.0	30	30	6	15.0	5	9.0	23	7	4.0	7.4	1.0	22

All dimensions in mm

Fig. 15.15 *Locking dogs*

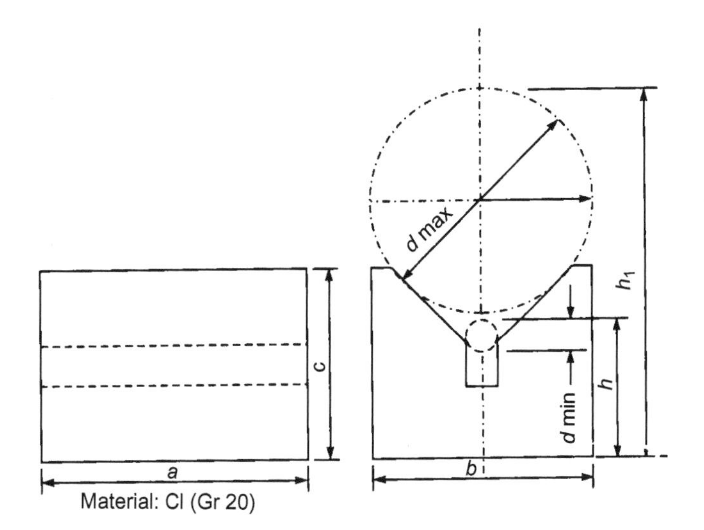

a	b	c	d_{max}	d_{min}
50	40	40	40	5
63	50	50	50	5
80	63	63	63	7
100	80	80	80	7
200	200	200	200	10
300	300	300	300	12

Fig. 15.16a *V locator for long cylinders*

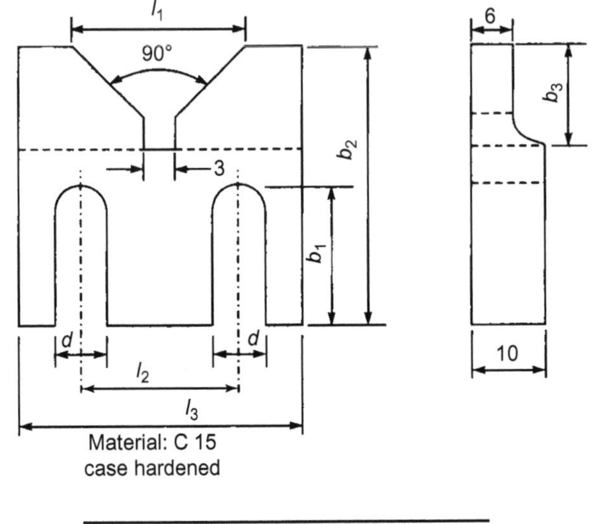

(a)

l_1	l_2	l_3	b_1	b_2	b_3	d
25	30	45	15	32	15	7
36	25	50	20	45	25	9
50	32	60	22	55	30	11

(b)

Fig. 15.16b *V locator for short cylinders*

CHAPTER 16

Exercises

The introduction of new products or modifications in the existing ones calls for the manufacture of new jigs, fixtures, etc. In mass production, the method of manufacture is worked out carefully, long before the production commences. In fact, the equipment, jigs, fixtures and gauges required for the product are purchased/ manufactured well before manufacture of products begins. This calls for careful planning of the manufacturing process. Generally, method engineers prepare a process plan called operations sheet, which is used as reference data by tool designers, tool room planners and workshop engineers.

Process Planning

Planning means thinking ahead of time. Process planning involves detailed planning of the operations necessary to convert the raw material into finished products. Process planning is done before commencing manufacture to achieve economy.

The work to be carried out at each stage is specified along with the details of equipment, tooling methods and procedures, number of personnel required and degree of skills necessary for the operation. Estimated operation time and machine/tool setting time are also computed. The operations are arranged in a sequence, which is logical, economical and practical. The operations sheet serves as a medium of communication among the members of the production team.

In a big organisation, process planning is entrusted to the methods department, which compiles the process planning (operations) sheet. A copy of the process planning sheet is sent to the tool designer who designs the toolings or tools enlisted in the sheet and enters the corresponding numbers on the process planning sheet.

In smaller organisations, a tool designer might be assigned the task of preparing the operations sheet. He plans the process before commencing designing of the jigs, the fixtures, gauges and other tools necessary for manufacturing the product. The following principles should be taken into account while planning the manufacturing process.

Principles of Process Planning

1. **Establish Reference Datum Surfaces at Early Stage.** For cubical parts, the first operation is generally machining the resting face, which can be used as datum for the subsequent operations. In cylindrical workpieces, the first operation is generally turning. The turned portion can be used as datum for the subsequent operations.
2. **Choose Cheapest Machining Process which can Accomplish the Tolerances Specified on Drawing.** Turning is cheaper than grinding, cylindrical workpieces having manufacturing tolerances above 0.05 mm should be finished on lathes rather than on cylindrical grinders. Similarly, unimportant faces can be machined cheaply on shaping machines. It might be necessary to use milling for better finish and flatness. For perfect parallelism and high degree of surface finish, it is necessary to use a costlier surface grinding operation.

   The size of the machine should also be commensurate with the size of the workpiece. It would be uneconomical to machine a small workpiece on a large machine.
3. **Finishing Operations should be Carried out at Later Stages.** This prevents damage to finished surfaces in transit.
4. **Sequence of Operations should be Logical and Practicable.** For example, lighting a stove would precede cooking whereas cleaning utensils generally follows eating.

Similarly, for the pivot pin shown in Fig. 16.1,

a. Turning to $12f^{-0.1}_{-0.02}$ must precede milling to $5^{+0}_{-0.1}$ flats so that the turned diameter can be used as location for centrality of the flats. Radius 6 at the end can also be formed during turning.
b. Face *B* must be machined to length 44 mm before milling, so that it serves as location face for maintaining dimension 31 mm for milled flats.
c. Flats $5^{+0}_{-0.1}$ must be milled before drilling 4f hole so that the milled flats can be used for location during drilling. This would ensure that the drilled hole is square with the milled faces.

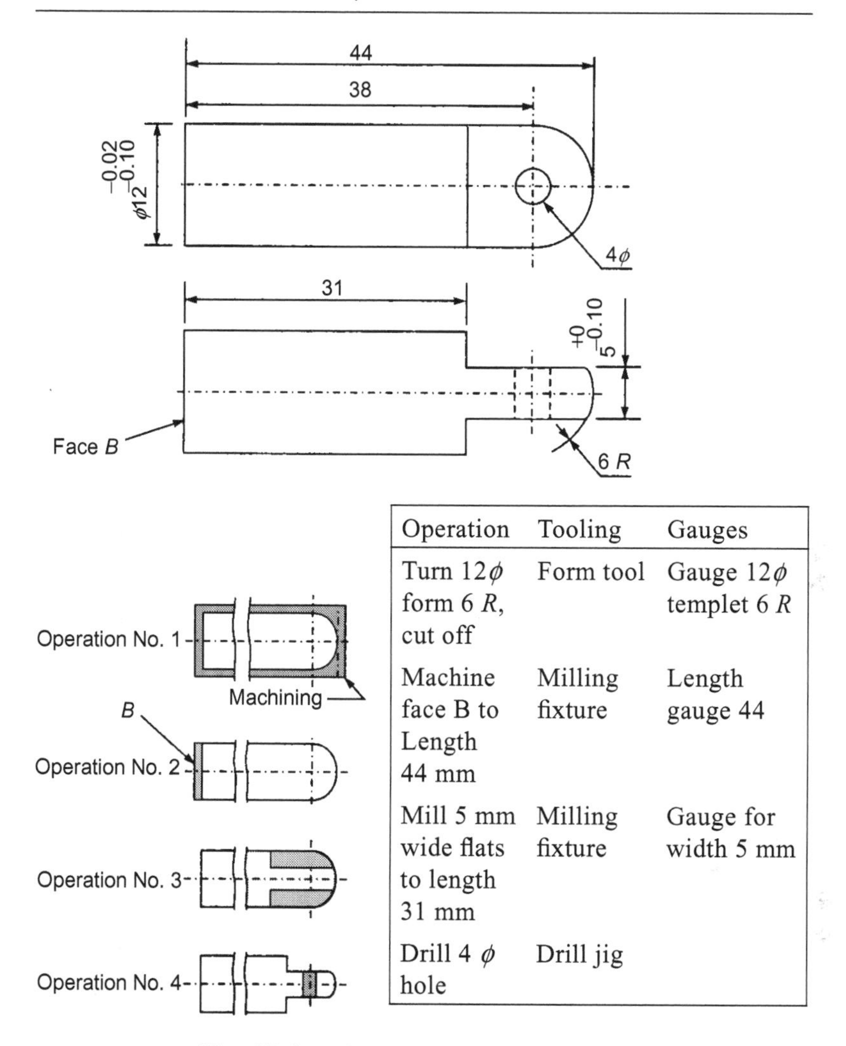

Operation	Tooling	Gauges
Turn 12ϕ form 6 *R*, cut off	Form tool	Gauge 12ϕ templet 6 *R*
Machine face B to Length 44 mm	Milling fixture	Length gauge 44
Mill 5 mm wide flats to length 31 mm	Milling fixture	Gauge for width 5 mm
Drill 4 ϕ hole	Drill jig	

Fig. 16.1 *Clamping variable workpieces*

Workpieces for Practice

The following pages contain drawings of a number of engineering components for practising jig/fixture designing (Figs. 16.2–16.25). The reader is advised to work out a tentative process plan with operations arranged in a proper sequence. The designer should take into consideration the operations carried out on the workpiece, before it reaches the stage for which the jig/fixture is being designed. The chaindotted workpiece represented in the jig/fixture drawing should show the workpiece in the state it is when the

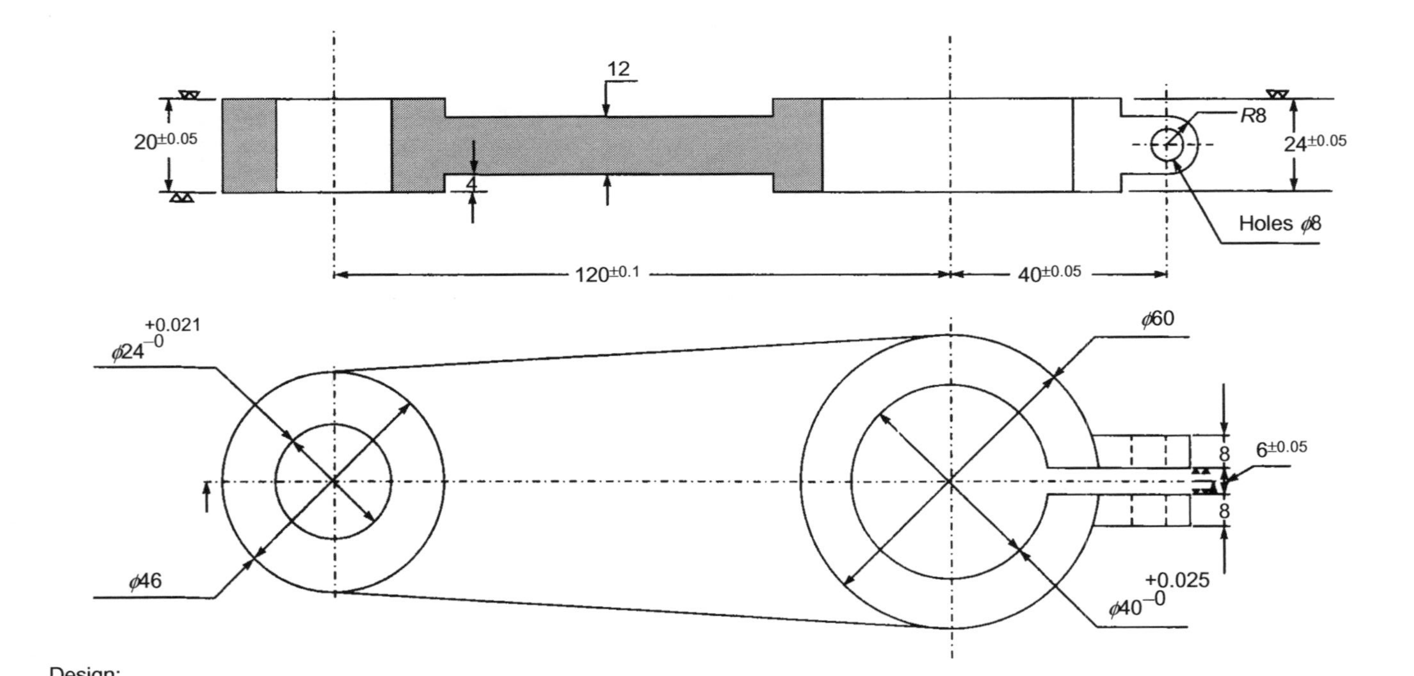

Fig. 16.2 *Workpiece for jigs and fixture design practice*

operation is taken up. For example, the workpiece in the milling fixture for the pivot pin shown in Fig. 16.1 should be drawn as after turning (operation No. 2). Note the absence of 4ϕ hole which is drilled after milling. Similarly, the workpiece in the drill jig for the pivot pin should be shown as it would appear after milling (operation No. 3). Naturally, the surfaces which would be machined later cannot be used for location in the jig/fixture meant for an earlier operation.

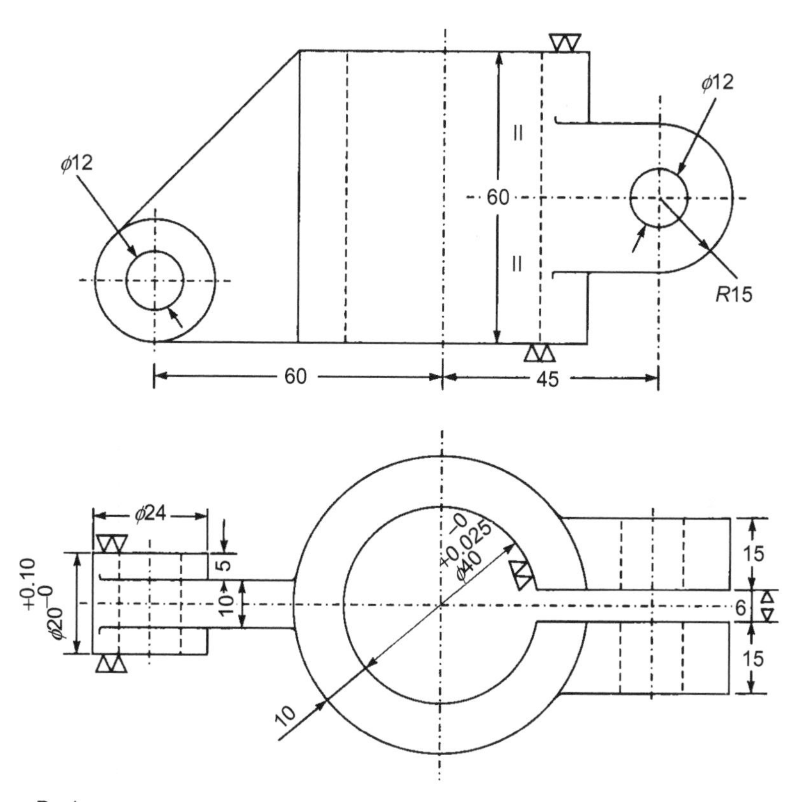

Design:

1. Turning fixtures (a) bore 40ϕ, face 60ϕ boss (b) Face other side of 60ϕ boss
2. Milling fixtures (a) Face 24ϕ bosses (b) Mill 6 wide slot
3. Drill jig 12ϕ holes

Fig. 16.3 *Workpieces for jigs and fixtures design practice*

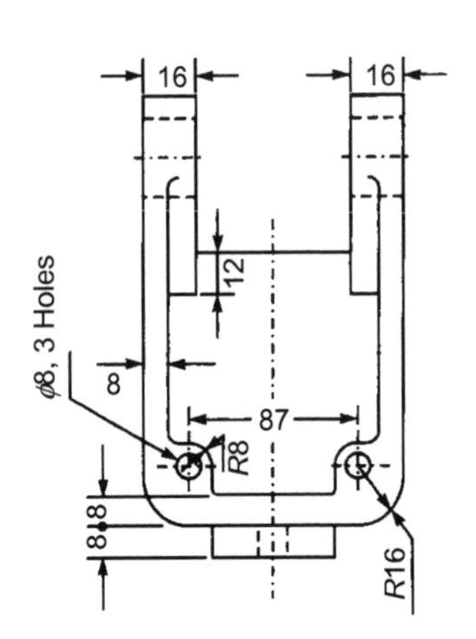

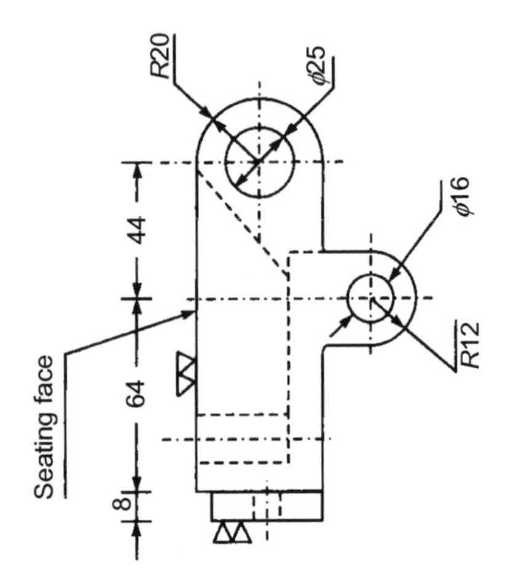

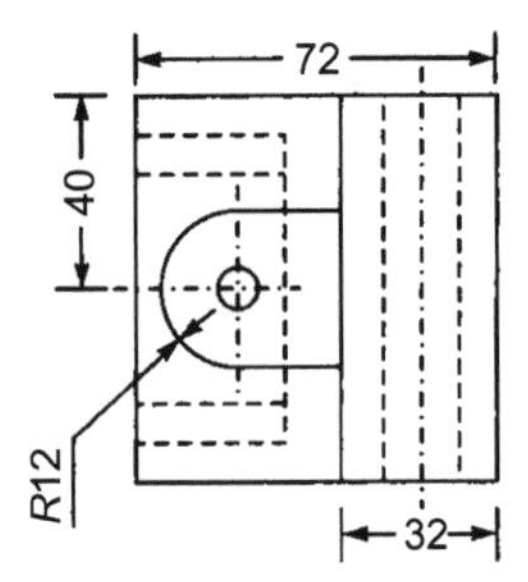

Design:

1. Milling fixtures (a) Seating face (b) 12 *R* boss
2. Drill jig (a) 25ϕ,16ϕ holes (b) 8ϕ holes

Fig. 16.4 *Workpieces for jigs and fixtures design practice*

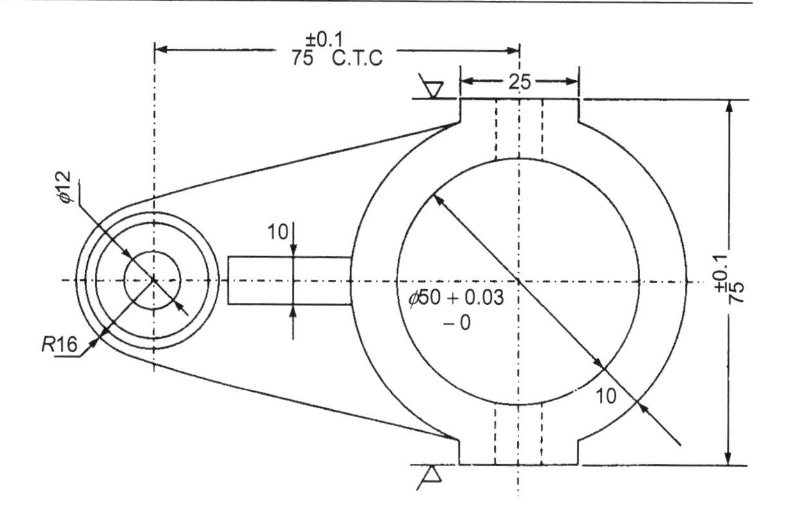

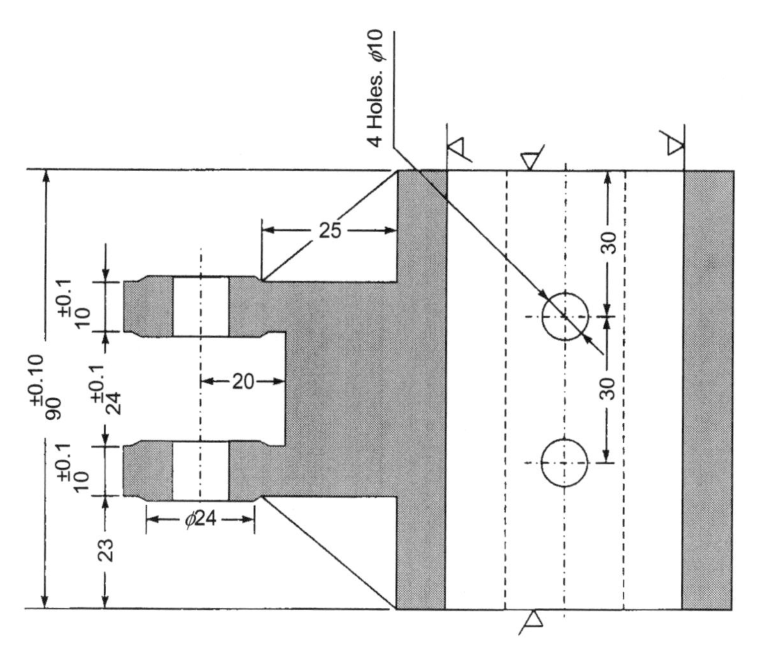

Design:

1. Turning fixture for 50ϕ bore and 70ϕ face
2. Milling fixture for (a) 24ϕ bosses (b) 25 × 90 pads
3. Drill jig for 10ϕ, 12ϕ holes

Fig. 16.5 *Workpieces for jigs and fixtures design practice*

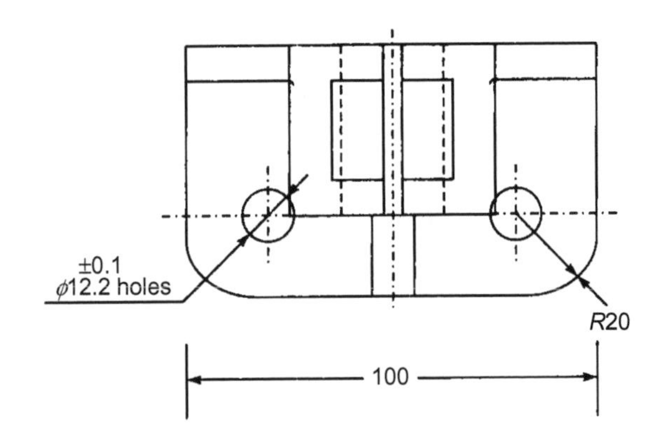

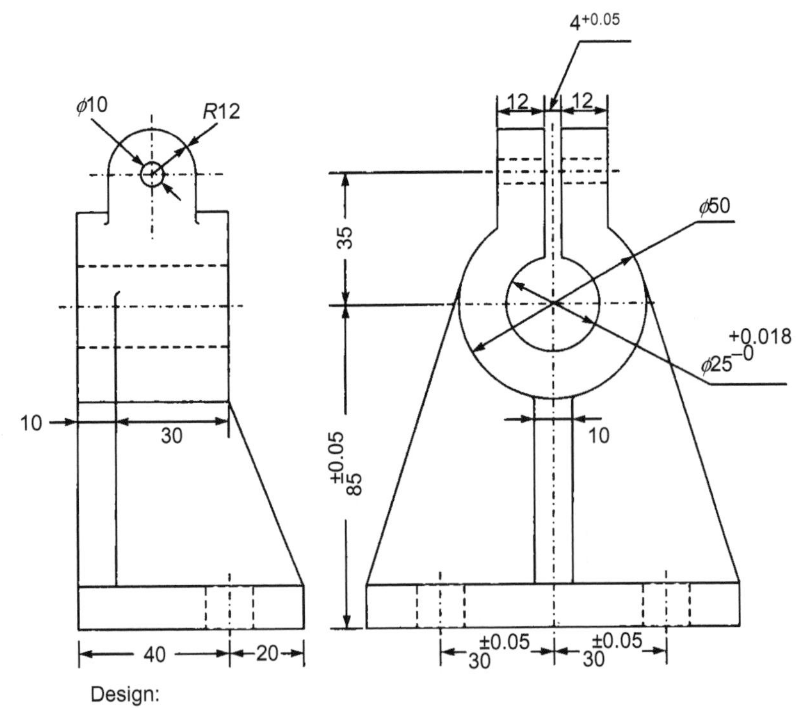

Design:

1. Milling fixture (a) 60 × 100 base (b) 4 wide slot
2. Turning fixture 25 ϕ bore and vertical face
3. Drill jig 12.2ϕ, 10ϕ holes

Fig. 16.6 *Workpieces for jigs and fixtures design practice*

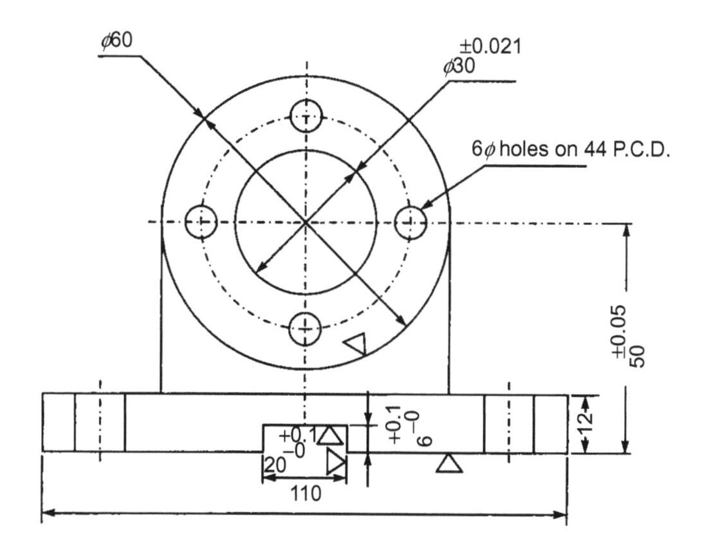

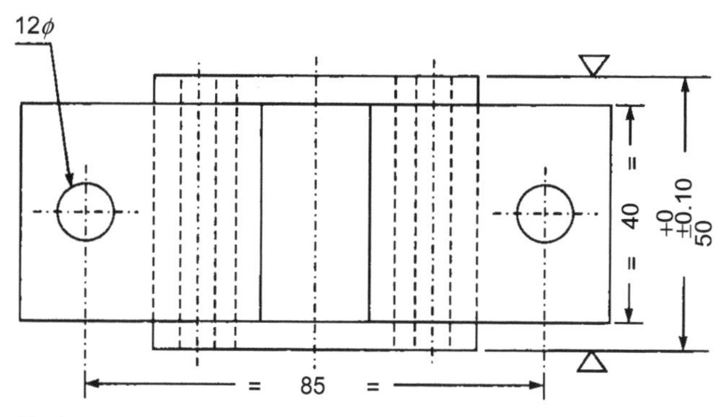

Design:

1. Milling fixtures (a) 110 × 40 base (b) 20 × 6 slot (c) 60φ bosses
2. Turning fixture bore 30φ
3. Drill jig (a) 12φ holes (b) 6φ holes

Fig. 16.7 *Workpieces for jigs and fixtures design practice*

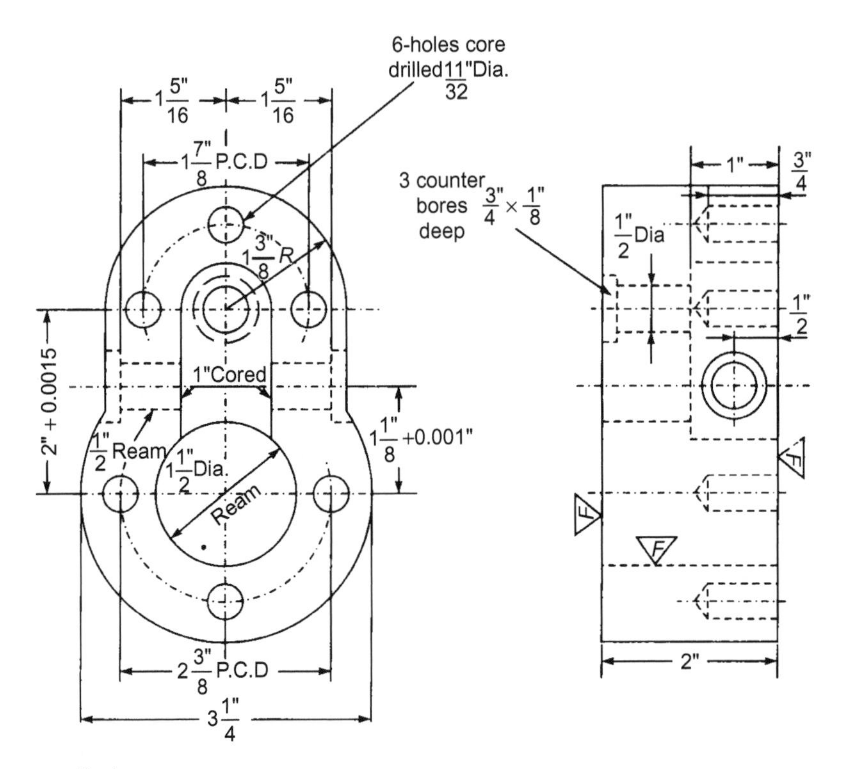

Design:

1. Turning fixture for $1^1/_2$" dia ream and one end facing
2. Milling fixture for other end face
3. Drill jigs (a) 11/32" holes

   (b) 1/2" ream, 3/4" C, bore

Fig. 16.8 *Workpieces for jigs and fixtures design practice*

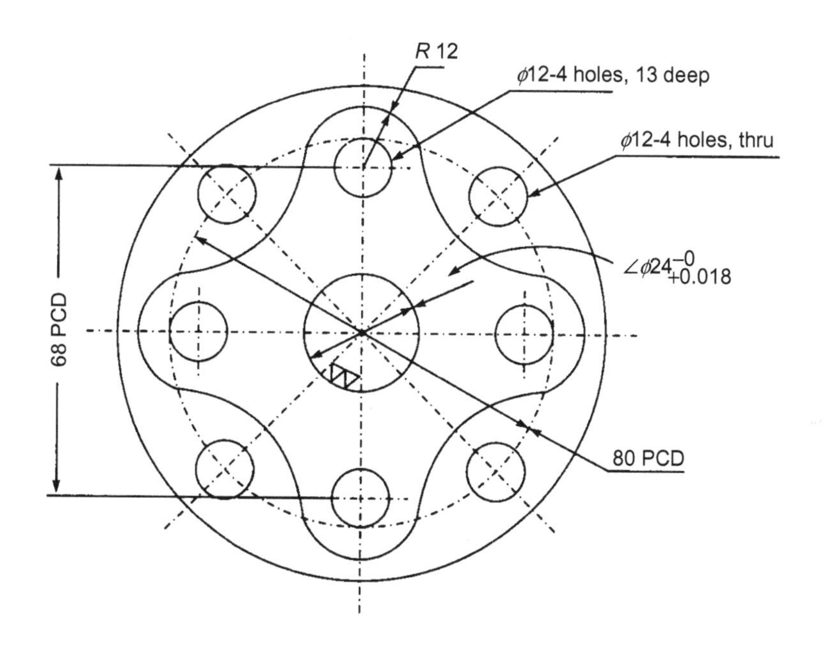

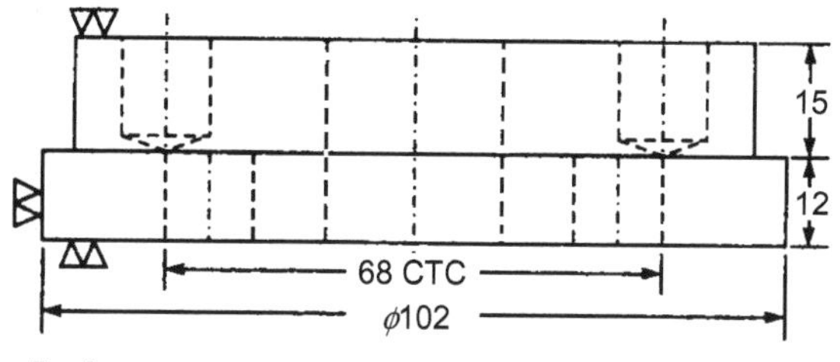

Design:

1. Turning chuck jaws for 24ϕ bore, 102ϕ turn, face
2. Drill jig for 12ϕ holes

Fig. 16.9 *Workpieces for jigs and fixtures design practice*

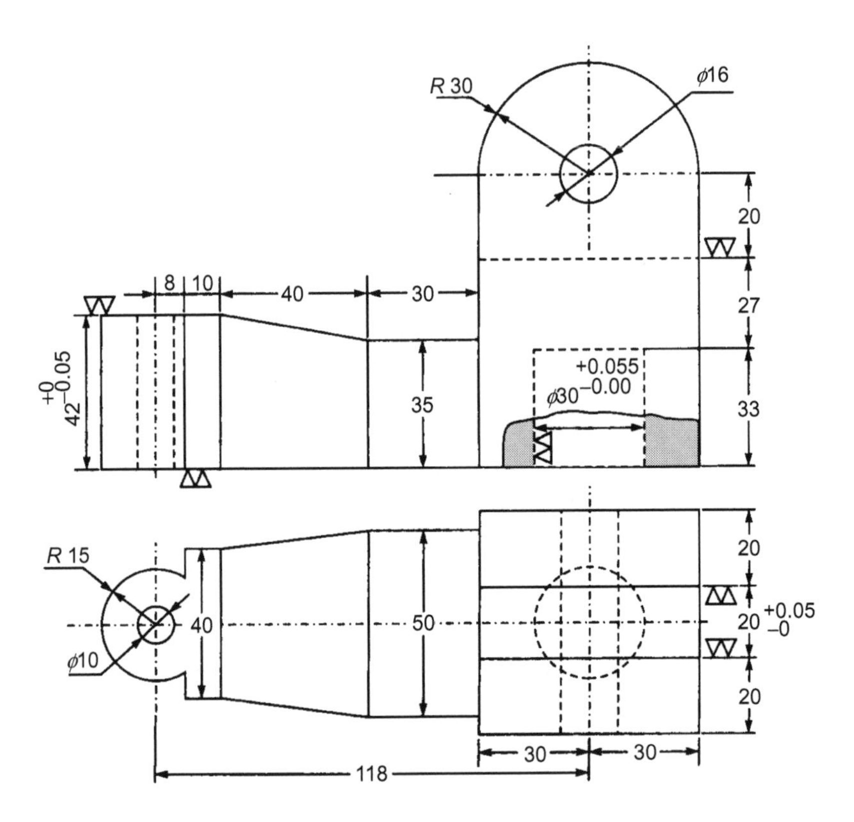

Design:

1. Turning fixture: bore 30ϕ and face base
2. Milling fixtures (a) 20 wide slot (b) 42 THK boss
3. Drill jig 10ϕ, 16ϕ holes

Fig. 16.10 *Workpieces for jigs and fixtures design practice*

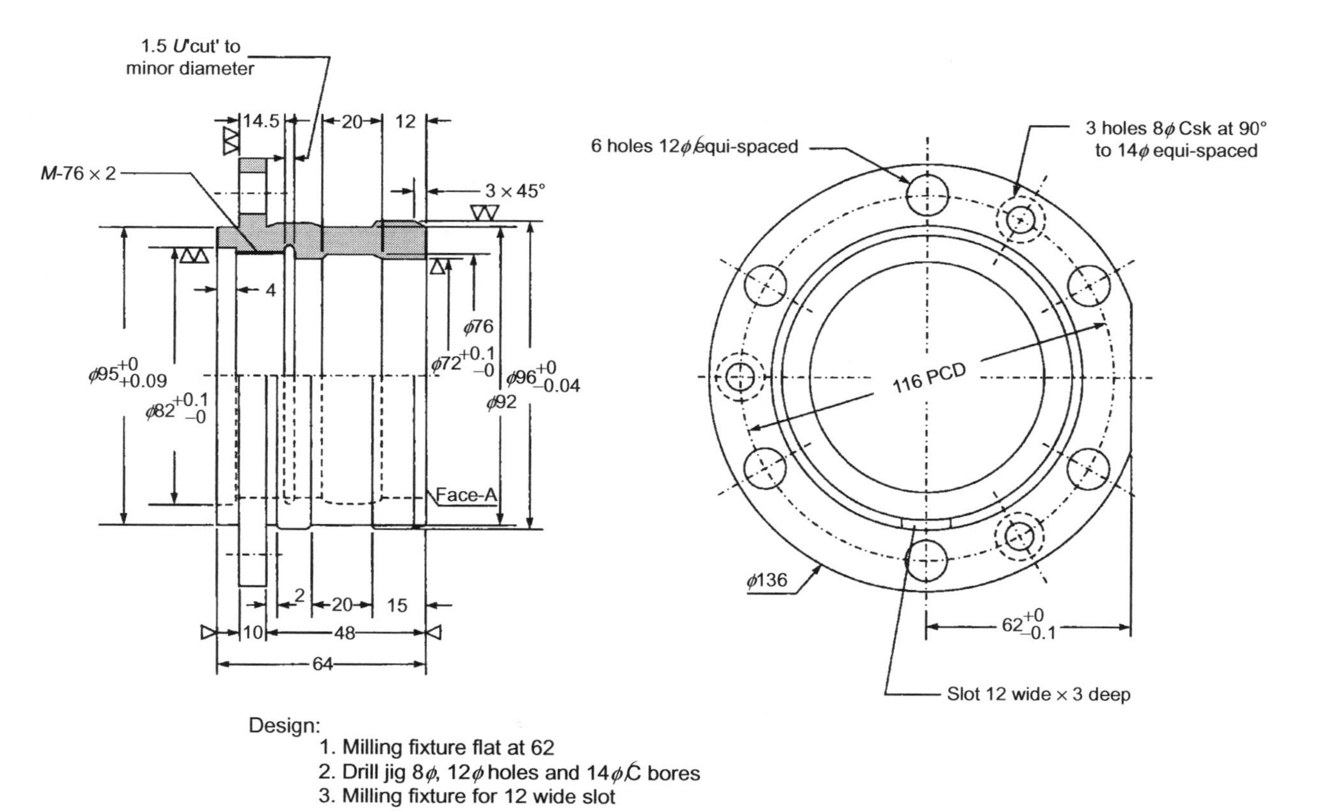

Design:

1. Milling fixture flat at 62
2. Drill jig 8φ, 12φ holes and 14φ C̸ bores
3. Milling fixture for 12 wide slot

Fig. 16.11 *Workpieces for jigs and fixtures design practice*

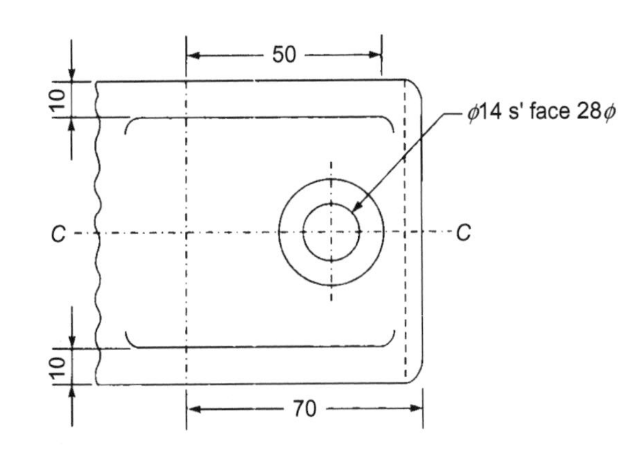

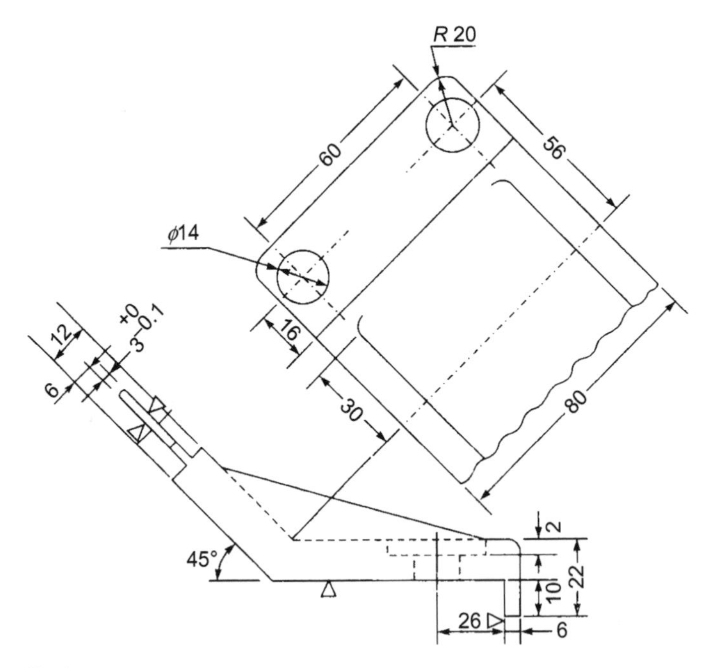

Design:

1. Milling fixture 6 THK flats
2. Drill jig 14ϕ holes
3. Projection 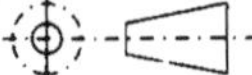

Fig. 16.12 *Workpieces for jigs and fixtures design practice*

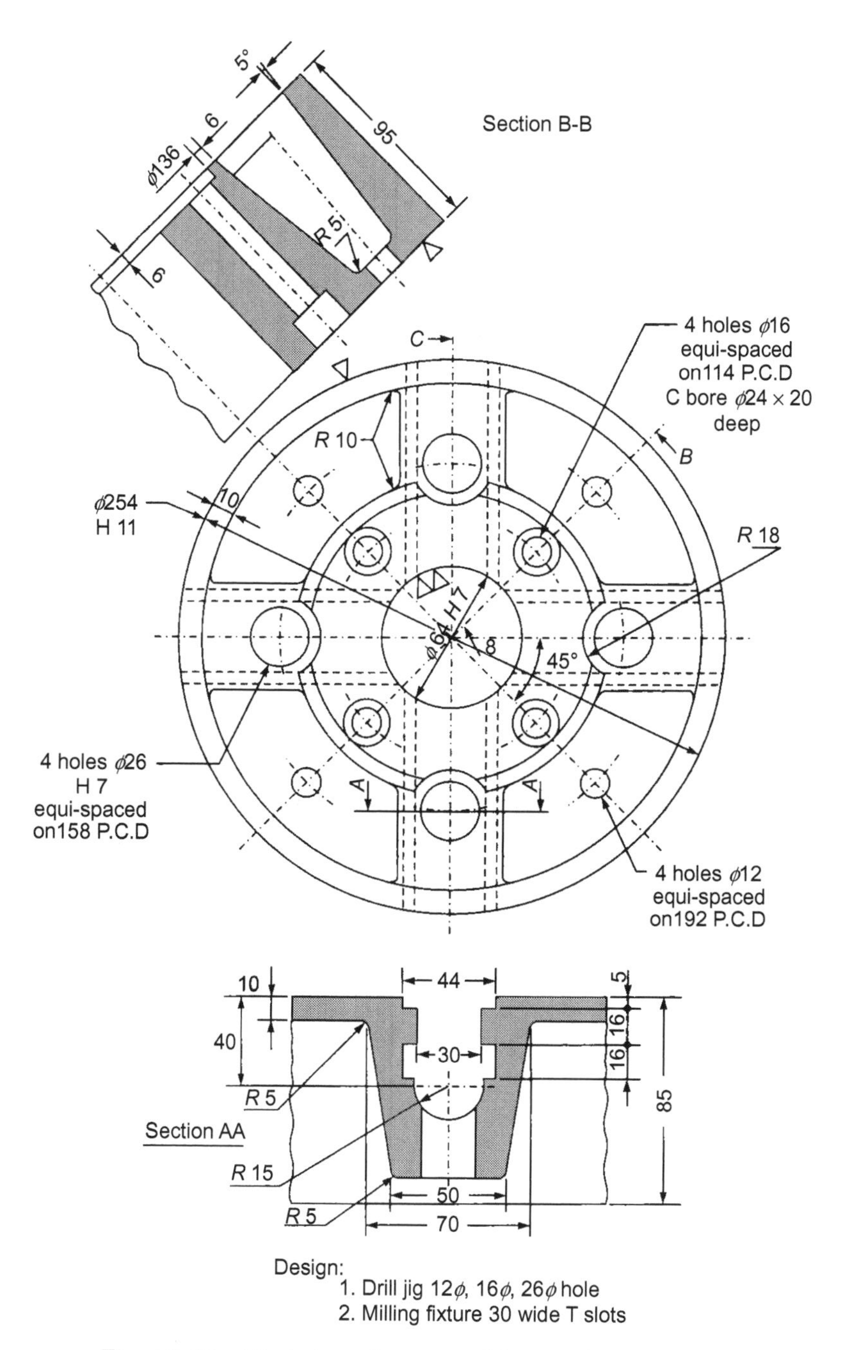

Design:

1. Drill jig 12φ, 16φ, 26φ hole
2. Milling fixture 30 wide T slots

Fig. 16.13 *Workpieces for jigs and fixtures design practice*

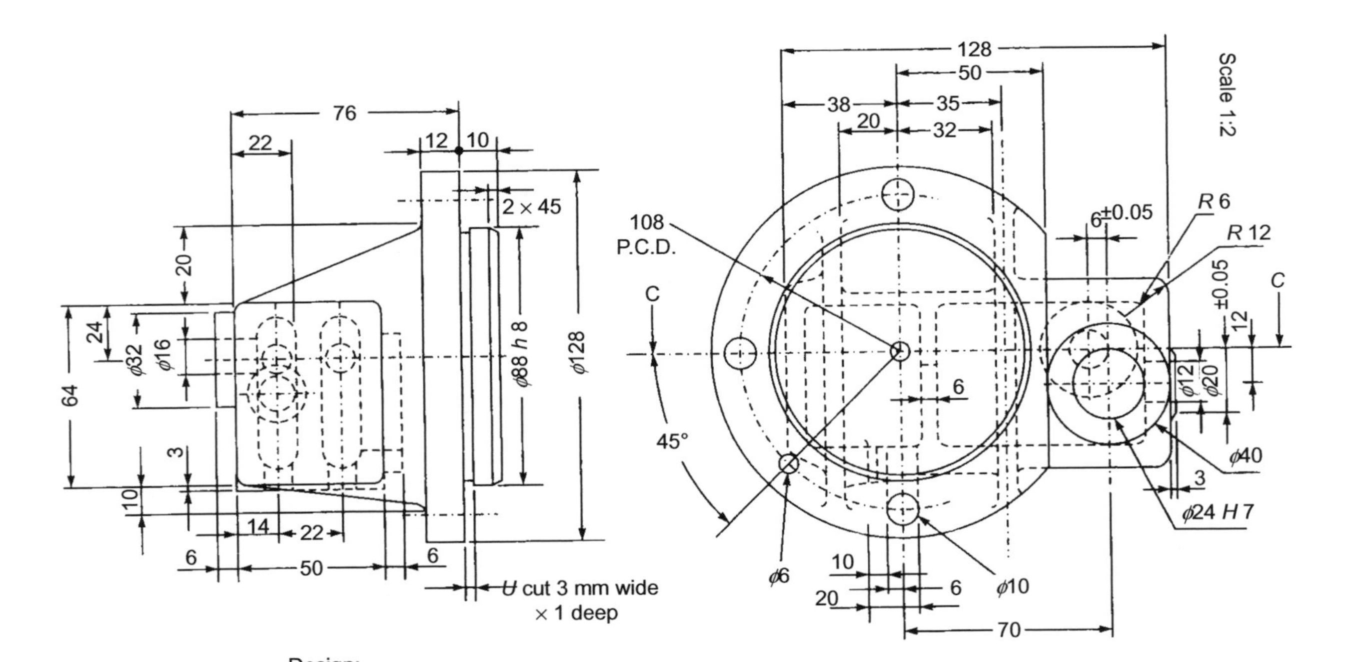

Design:
1. Turning fixture 24φ bore
2. Drill jigs (a) 6φ,10φ holes (b) 12φ, 16φ, holes

Fig. 16.14 *Workpieces for jigs and fixtures design practice*

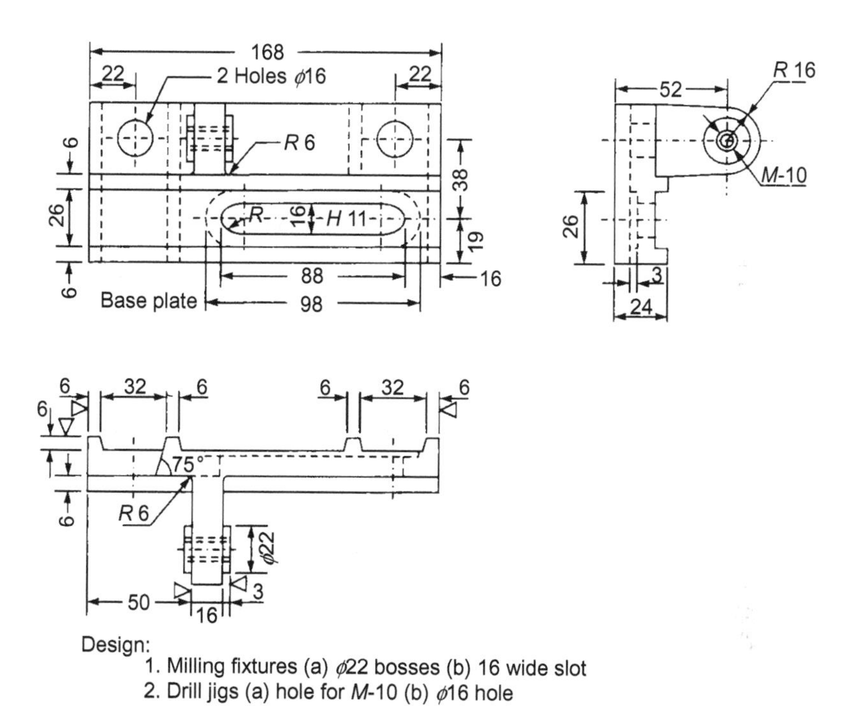

Fig. 16.15 *Workpieces for jigs and fixtures design practice*

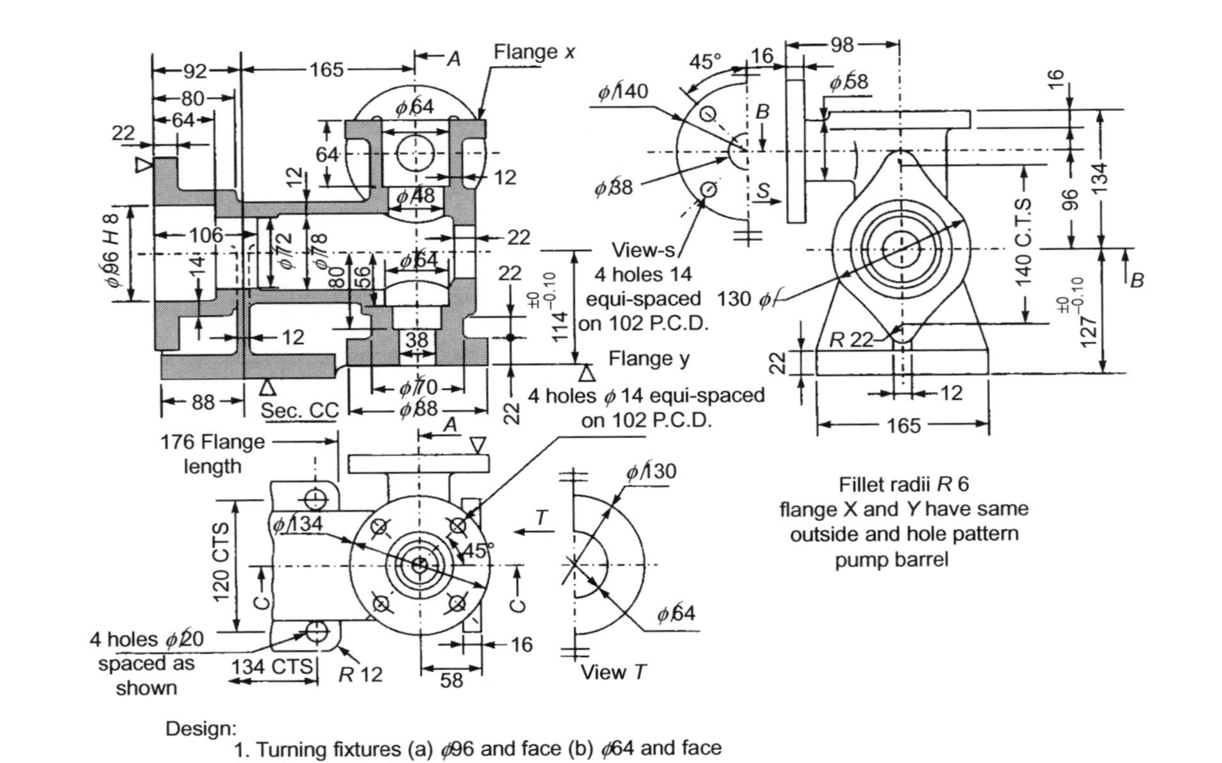

Fig. 16.16 *Workpieces for jigs and fixtures design practice*

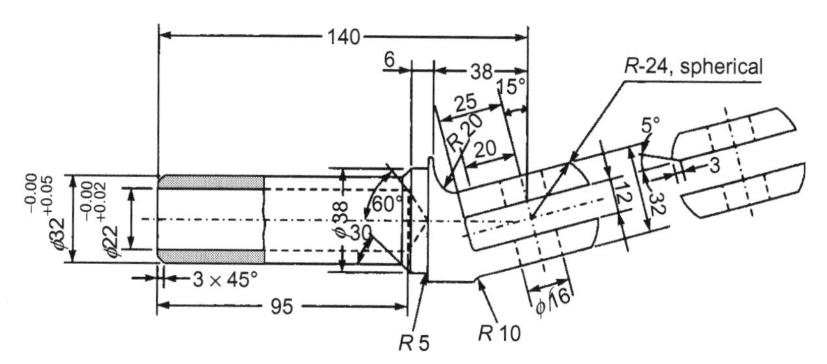

Design:

1. Milling fixtures (a) 12 slot and 32 flats (b) 3 × 5° angle
2. Drill jig 16ϕ hole
3. Turning fixture ϕ 32 and ϕ 22 bore

Fig. 16.17 *Workpieces for jigs and fixtures design practice*

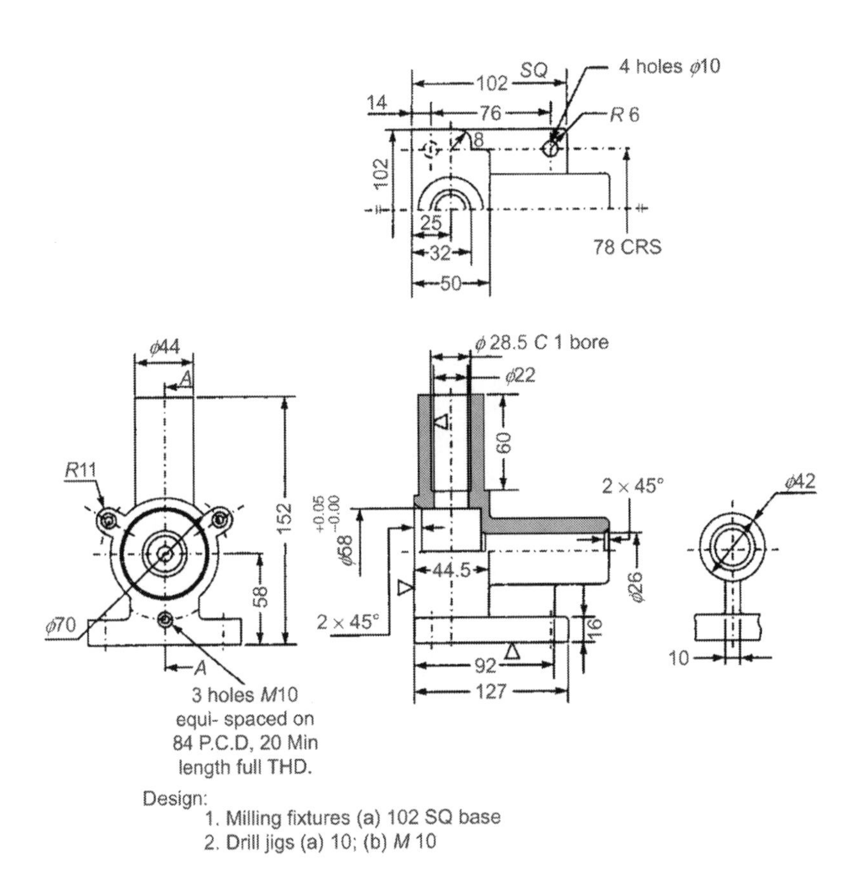

Fig. 16.18 *Workpieces for jigs and fixtures design practice*

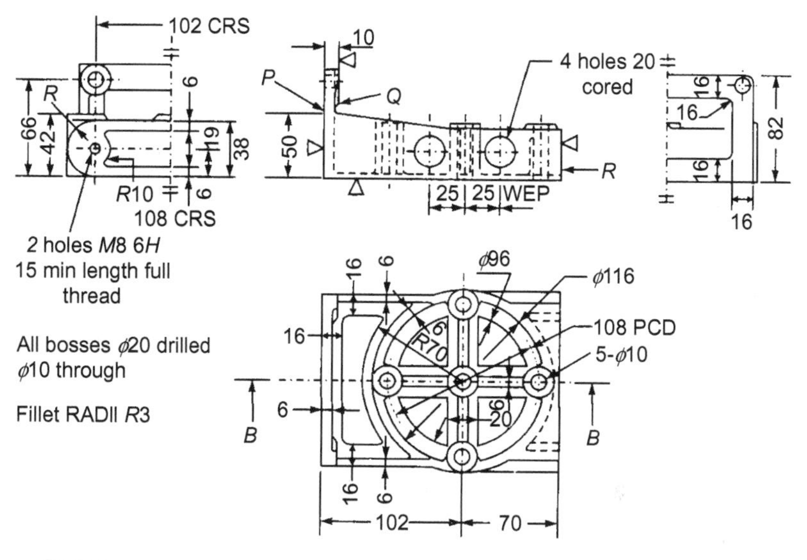

Design:

1. Milling fixtures for faces P Q R
2. Drill jigs (a) 10ϕ holes (b) hole for M8

Fig. 16.19 *Workpieces for jigs and fixtures design practice*

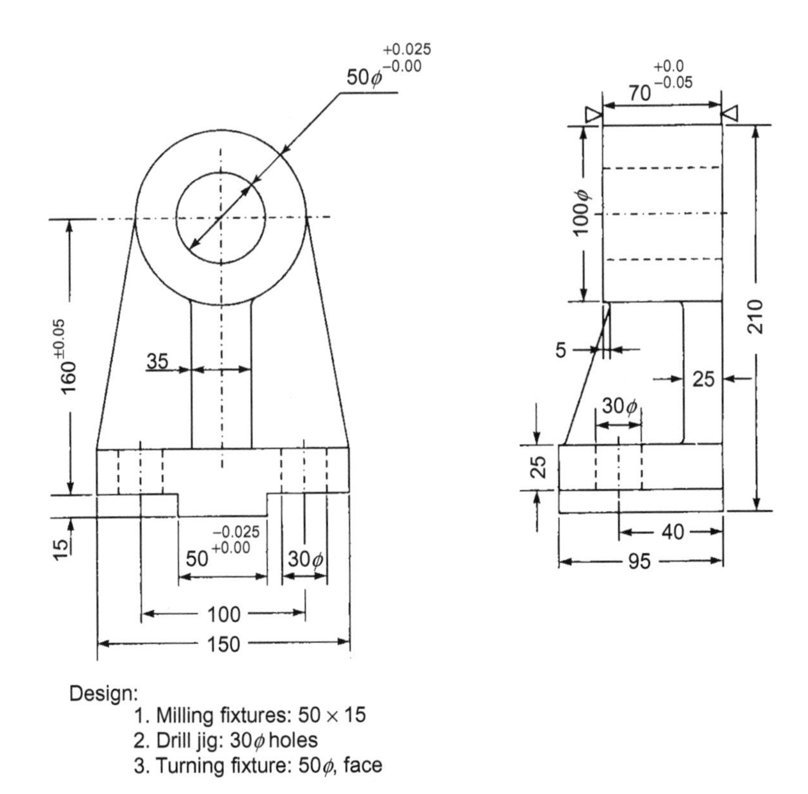

Fig. 16.20 *Workpieces for jigs and fixtures design practice*

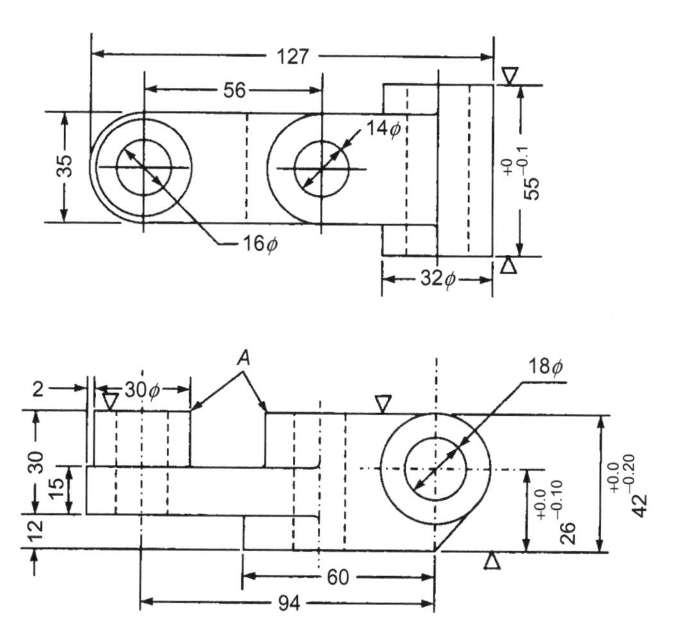

Design:

1. Milling fixtures (a) face (b) dim 55
2. Drill jigs (a) 14ϕ, 16ϕ (b) 18ϕ

Fig. 16.21 *Workpieces for jigs and fixtures design practice*

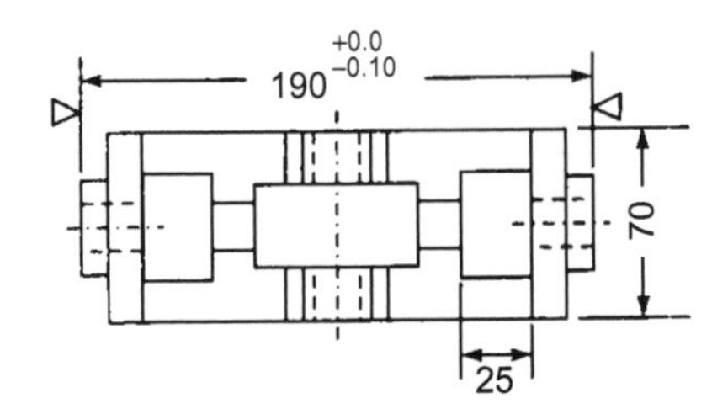

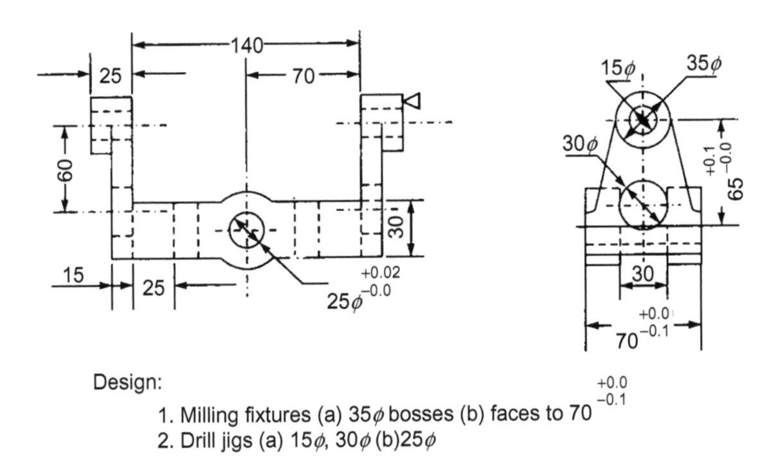

Fig. 16.22 *Workpieces for jigs and fixtures design practice*

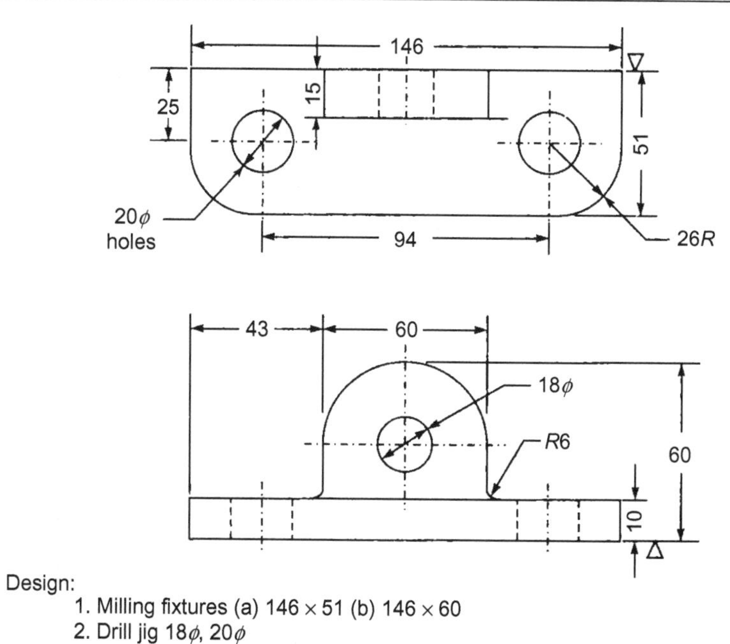

Design:

1. Milling fixtures (a) 146 × 51 (b) 146 × 60
2. Drill jig 18φ, 20φ

Fig. 16.23 *Workpieces for jigs and fixtures design practice*

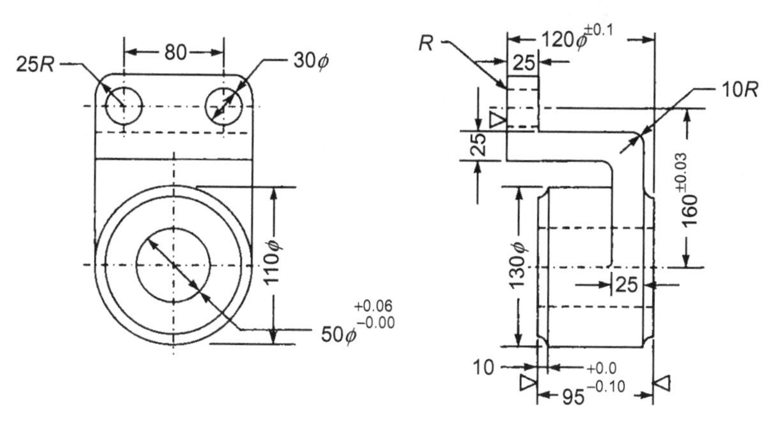

Design:

1. Milling fixtures face R
2. Drill jig 30φ holes
3. Turning fixture 130φ face, 50φ bore

Fig. 16.24 *Workpieces for jigs and fixtures design practice*

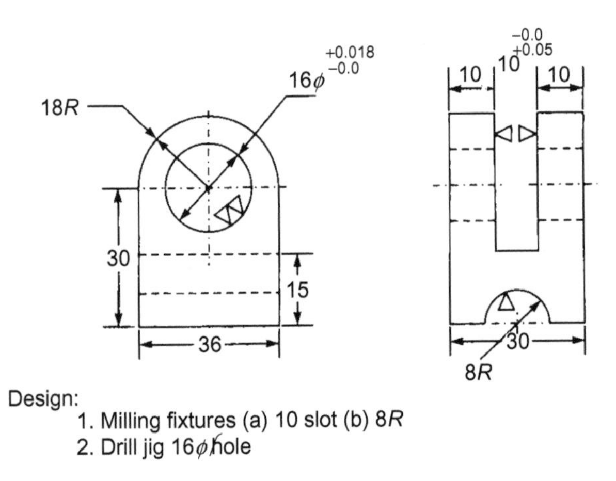

Fig. 16.25 *Workpieces for jigs and fixtures design practice*

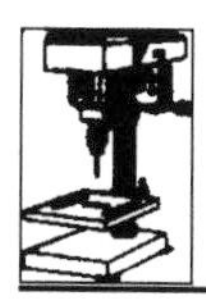

Bibliography

American Society of Tool and Manufacturing Engineers., *Fundamentals of Tool Design,* Prentice-Hall of India Pvt. Ltd., 1971.

Chapman, W. A. J., *Workshop Technology,* Edward Arnold, 1975.

Cole, C. B., *Tool Design,* American Technical Society & D. B. Taraporewala and Sons Co. Pvt. Ltd., 1969.

Colvin, F. H. and L. L. Hass, *Jigs & Fixtures*, Tata McGraw-Hill Publ. Co. Ltd., 1978.

Gates, P., *Jigs, Fixtures, Tools, and gauges,* 6th Edition, Technical Press, 1973.

Goroshkin, A. K., *Jigs and Fixtures Handbook,* Mir Publishers, 1983.

The Industrial Press, *Jigs and Fixtures Design,* Allied Publishers Pvt. Ltd., 1972.

Kempster, M. H. A., *An Introduction to Jig and Fixture Design,* 3rd Edition, Hodder & Stroughton Ltd. 1978.

Kempster, M. H. A., *Principles of Jig and Tool and Design*, English Universities Press,1968.

Jones Newnes, E. J. H., *Production Engineering Jig and Tool Design,* 8th Edition, Butterworth, 1972.

Pollack Herman, W., *Tool Design,* Reston Publishing Co. Inc., D. B. Taraporewala and Sons Co. Pvt. Ltd., 1978.

Town, H. C., *Manufacturing Technology,* Batsford H., 1980.

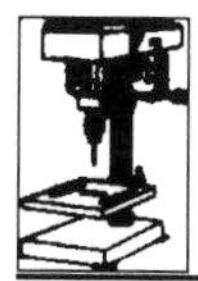

Index

Author's Profile

Prakash Hiralal Joshi, DME, AMIE (India), has heterogeneous industrial and academic experience. His industrial experience includes—design, production and tool-room supervision, planning and time and motion studies and method improvements in industries manufacturing drafting machines, diesel engines, automobile steering gears, hydraulic presses and textile and packaging machinery.

Mr Joshi has been the Chief Designer and Methods Officer in Crompton Greaves (Mumbai) and Design Manager in Acro Whitney (Pune) and ZF Steering Gears (Pune). During his career of over four decades, he has designed hundreds of jigs and fixtures and scores of press tools.

Mr Joshi's academic experience includes teaching jigs and fixtures, machine tools and machine design in Fr Angel Technical College (Mumbai) and Bharat Forge (Pune). He was also the first principal of the first ITI in Goa. Also, he has conducted courses on jigs and fixtures for National Productivity Council, Pune branch.

Since 1992, Mr Joshi has been designing tooling and special-purpose machines as a consultant in Pune and, of course, penning technical treatises to pass on the essence of his varied experience to future generations.

Made in the USA
Middletown, DE
29 August 2019